Management Problems in the Acquisition
of Special Automatic Equipment

MANAGEMENT PROBLEMS
in the ACQUISITION *of*
SPECIAL AUTOMATIC EQUIPMENT

Powell Niland

Professor of Management, Washington University

*Formerly Assistant Professor of Business Administration,
Harvard University*

~~~~~~~~~~~~~~~~~~~~~~~~~~~~~~

~~~~~~~~~~~~~~~~~~~~~~~~~~~~~~

DIVISION OF RESEARCH
GRADUATE SCHOOL OF BUSINESS ADMINISTRATION
HARVARD UNIVERSITY   BOSTON, 1961

HD
45
N5

Published by DIVISION OF RESEARCH, HARVARD BUSINESS SCHOOL,
BOSTON 63, MASS.
Printed at The Colonial Press Inc., Clinton, Mass., U.S.A.

Foreword

THIS volume is the second publication of the Division of Research which analyzes the management implications of advanced technological developments in production. The first study, *Automation and Management* by Professor James R. Bright, published in 1958, covered the broad span of problems relating to automation in production. This study deals with the first step in the automation process — the acquisition of nonstandard, nonconventional automatic equipment.

The study has two objectives. The first is to provide a detailed description of the process of acquiring special automatic equipment. This includes the key steps in the process, important organizational relationships between the equipment group and other units, both inside and outside the company, and the common types of problems likely to be encountered in projects for acquiring this type of tailor-made equipment. The second is to analyze the commonly encountered trouble spots in the process which emerge as being particularly important. These include debugging, working with equipment vendors, coordinating product design and the automatic equipment, and the analysis of project proposals.

As Professor Niland indicates, his focal concern is on administrative rather than technical or engineering matters. His study draws on the experience of both "old hands" and novices in acquiring this type of automation equipment as revealed in a series of detailed field studies. It will be of interest to other companies about to embark on automating a production process, either again or for the first time.

The financial support for this study came in part from a broad grant for research made to the School by the Ford Foundation, and in part from an allocation of research funds made available by The Associates of the Harvard Business School.

BERTRAND FOX
Director of Research

April 1961

Preface

CERTAINLY one of the outstanding industrial trends of the past decade has been the rapid increase of the use of special automatic equipment (popularly referred to as "automation"). Although this development has had many implications, some of which we may not even clearly perceive as yet, it seemed to the writer that one of the key areas of interest from a manager's point of view was the process of acquiring special automatic equipment.

This study was undertaken with the aim of giving managers a better understanding of the key problems involved in this acquisition process. It is management-oriented, not engineering-oriented, although a great deal of the topics covered might well be considered to involve a kind of engineering administration.

The author is indebted to many persons who provided invaluable assistance in completing this study. Some of the major contributors, unfortunately, cannot be mentioned by name because of the need to keep company experiences anonymous. The contributions of these business managers nevertheless were major ones, and the author is grateful not only for their cooperation but also for their universal interest and encouragement.

The idea for the study grew out of discussions with Professor James R. Bright of the Harvard Business School, who has pioneered research on the topic of automation. His initial and continuing criticism and encouragement have been a vital aid. The author is also grateful to another former colleague, Professor Franklin F. Folts, who introduced him to the organization in which the initial field research was done. These initial studies plus the discussions with Professor Bright provided the catalysts which generated this study.

Dean Stanley F. Teele, who provided a year completely free of teaching duties while I was on the faculty of the Harvard

Business School, made it possible for me to undertake the study. I am also grateful for the guidance and assistance given to me by Professor Bertrand Fox, Director of Research, under whose sponsorship the project was begun. During the latter stages of the study Professor Lewis B. Ward provided timely encouragement and aid. Miss Ruth Norton, Executive Secretary of the Division of Research, arranged for much needed editorial assistance and shepherded the manuscript through the process of producing this volume. A special word of thanks is required to acknowledge the skillful editorial aid of Mrs. Dorothy Rowland. Finally, I cannot forbear mentioning the contributions of my wife, Juel, who has not only provided much of the secretarial assistance but has also managed our family's affairs so as to relieve me of many details and to guard me from many distractions.

This study would not have been possible without the help of all of these individuals. While they are responsible for much of any merit it may have, the author alone must be responsible for any deficiencies which the reader may observe.

POWELL NILAND

Washington University
St. Louis, Missouri
February 1961

Contents

List of Exhibits

Management Problems in the Acquisition
of Special Automatic Equipment

CHAPTER I

Introduction

ONE OF THE prominent characteristics of the United States economy — indeed of the whole of Western society — has been our productive capacity. And one of the most critical elements in that productive capacity has been the machine. As early as 1829 the realistic Carlyle observed, "It is the Age of Machinery, in every outward and inward sense of that word."

Carlyle's words are particularly applicable to what has been happening in the United States during the past two decades, for machinery and equipment have emerged as increasingly important factors of production in our economy. From 1940 to 1958 the number of our production workers increased by 33%; but our annual expenditures on equipment (measured in constant dollars to offset the effects of price inflation) increased by 93%, or at a rate nearly three times faster.[1] In other words, machinery and equipment have become progressively more and more important as a supplement to the labor of our factory workers. Equipment expenditures have also become relatively more important than buildings in the recent growth of our industrial plant. In the 1920's annual expenditures for buildings typically exceeded those for equipment. In more recent years, however, this pattern has changed radically, and the annual expenditures for equipment typically have been at least twice as large as the expenditures for buildings.[2] This change has persisted throughout the economic expansion following World War II. In em-

---

[1] U. S. Department of Commerce, *U. S. Income and Output* (1929–1957 data), and *Survey of Current Business* (1958 data).

[2] Donald G. Wooden and Robert C. Wasson, "Manufacturing Investment Since 1929," *Survey of Current Business*, November 1956, p. 10.

ploying the factors of production to expand its output, the typical factory has required relatively little additional labor and relatively little additional "housing," but it has required a great deal more machinery and equipment.

Not only has there been a rise in the importance of equipment generally; at the same time an important change has also taken place in the character of some of the equipment acquired. Since World War II a particular class of equipment, special automatic equipment, has become the object of great interest everywhere. Popularly, and somewhat loosely, referred to as "automation" equipment, its primary characteristic has been its ability (after either mechanical or manual loading) to perform repeatedly one or more operations without human intervention, that is, automatically. Such special automatic equipment is being used more and more, and the imagination of all segments of society has been stimulated by the vision of the "automatic factory."

There are no quantitative data definitively showing the national expenditures for special automatic equipment, but there is evidence indicating a growing use of this particular type of machinery. A recent survey of all industries by the trade magazine, *Automation*,[3] for instance, found that of 1,675 plants replying, some 800 (48%) reported that they were already using "automation" in connection with one or more handling, conveying, and transferring applications. The same survey also reported that 435 (26%) of the plants replying were using some automatic assembly equipment.

Additional evidence of the increased use of this type of equipment can be found in the rapid postwar growth of three publicly held special automatic equipment builders serving the important metalworking segment of industry: Cross Company, Snyder Corporation, and Baush Machine Tool Company. The combined annual sales of these three companies from 1949 (the year of the postwar low in machine-tool equipment) to 1957 (the year of the postwar high) increased 8.7 times. This rate of growth was substantially greater than the rise of 3.4 times for all machine tool shipments over the same period.

There is little doubt that special automatic equipment can

---

[3] *Automation*, January 1959, pp. 20–26.

yield large dividends by reducing manufacturing costs. Two illustrations from companies visited during the field work for this project demonstrate the benefits that can, but need not necessarily, flow from a persistent long-range program of this sort.

Hallman Company. Hallman Company[4] had been making one product in its plant for more than ten years, but after three years of a mechanization program had reduced the total direct and indirect labor cost of the item from $31.72 to about $16.27. Completion of the last stage of this program was expected to take about two and a half years more and promised to lower these costs to only $6.79. Several hundred thousand dollars were needed to achieve these results, but the product was made in large quantities annually and the outlay was fully justified by the savings Hallman realized.

Patterson Company. This company, too, had been making one of its products, a consumer nondurable item, for many years. Then, over a ten-year period, 1947–1956, it spent over $17 million for new equipment. The magnitude of this program can be gauged by the fact that it was nearly seven times as great as the whole book value of Patterson's equipment ($2.5 million before depreciation) in 1947.

As a result, direct labor costs per item declined more than 50%, from $1.05 per unit in 1947 to $0.46 in 1956, despite the fact that labor rates increased about 60% over the decade. If we assume that the level of production was constant, departmental burden costs, which incorporated the increased equipment costs, would have risen by only about $0.15 per unit, an amount well below the reduction in costs achieved. (Actually they were less because of a higher volume of production.)

It should be noted that Patterson's cost of materials over this period just about doubled, rising from $0.73 to $1.36 per unit, although the characteristics of the parts purchased from vendors during this period changed only slightly. In other words, the program of equipment acquisition, in large part special automatic equipment, helped not merely to contain but to reduce sig-

---

[4] All plants from which data were collected have been given fictitious names.

nificantly the costs it could affect (labor and spoilage) despite
the onslaught of inflation, whereas material costs, unaffected by
the company's equipment program, climbed quite significantly.[5]

Stimulated by the strong general interest that developed,
numerous firms not previously engaged in acquiring special
machinery and equipment have undertaken programs to acquire
this type of equipment. As so often happens when a firm embarks on an undertaking about which neither it nor industry
generally has much knowledge, many costly mistakes have been
made. The acquisition of this type of equipment affects not
only the plant organization but the whole firm, including its sales
staff and general management.[6] Failure to perceive these effects
frequently lies at the root of many of the mistakes made.

These firms often encounter major difficulties in acquiring
specific items of equipment. Sometimes projects bog down
unexpectedly; sometimes they cost more than had been anticipated; and sometimes the finished equipment does not meet the
requirements of the factory situation for which it was designed.
As Professor Bright's study, *Automation and Management*, makes
clear, other equally important issues arise that are related to the
effective integration of special automatic equipment into the
factory. For one thing, how does a firm go about deciding
how big a program, if any, to plan in the field of special automatic
equipment? How does a firm arrange for the effective maintenance of this type of equipment, each piece of which may be
a complex and partly unique mechanism? Because the costs
associated with downtime on such equipment are usually so
burdensome, the need to increase the effectiveness of maintenance is usually urgent. How is this type of equipment to be
integrated into factory operations? This function includes knotty
questions of training, worker displacement, and preparation of

[5] For a similar illustration of the results of a sustained cost-reduction
program involving incandescent lamps, see James R. Bright, *Automation
and Management* (Boston, Harvard Business School, Division of Research,
1958), p. 30.

[6] The nature of many of these basic effects has been reported in the pio-
neering study by Bright cited above. In particular, see Chapter 15, "An
Interpretation of Automation, Its Effect on the Factory, and Its Impact on
Management," pp. 222–235.

factory personnel for drastic changes in conducting factory operations once the equipment is in operation. In my field research, however, I was particularly impressed with the difficulties that arise during the first step in automating a firm, that is, the acquisition of the equipment. The acquisition of this type of equipment was found to be markedly different from the acquisition of conventional equipment. The events taking place during the acquisition of special automatic equipment not only were limiting factors in the solutions available to many of the problems that arose later, but often gave rise to those problems.

The acquisition of special automatic equipment is, by its nature, expensive, risky, and time consuming, much more so than the acquisition of conventional equipment. As a result, mistakes are likely to be correspondingly much more costly. Although such mistakes may in the long run be considered a kind of learning charge, they constitute an unnecessarily expensive way to learn. In addition, one project is likely to be so different from another that it takes a long while and a variety of applications before a group organized to procure special automatic equipment can acquire the basic skills and knowledge for a general understanding of the problems that will probably be encountered. Finally, because the time span of this kind of project is so long and the experience of individuals is accumulated so slowly, turnover of personnel will tend to rob the remaining personnel of some of the potential benefits of experience.

It seemed likely, therefore, that a detailed investigation of the acquisition process, drawing on the experience of both seasoned and relatively inexperienced companies, would prove useful to other companies about to consider, or about to begin, such acquisitions. The following study was thus undertaken. It is a systematic presentation of key steps in the acquisition process, as well as a description of and suggested solutions for commonly encountered trouble spots. This information should provide a useful background for deciding which projects a company should undertake, or perhaps even whether it should undertake any at all, as well as being an aid in deciding how to proceed. It therefore should make the novice's initial projects more profitable, both financially and educationally.

My preliminary investigations suggested that top management

in particular needed a more comprehensive, general grasp of the acquisition process for special automatic equipment. As the study progressed, this need was often found even in companies which had been acquiring special automatic equipment for several years. In part this state of affairs arises as the result of turnover at top management levels and also in part because of the technical nature of much of the activity connected with special automatic equipment. In several ways the nature of the problems at the top management levels is reminiscent of the frustrating problems associated with giving direction to product research and development. The top management level also must initiate or at least approve the basic organization and policies of the special automatic equipment program very much as it must for product research. Likewise, top management must evaluate the performance achieved by the program undertaken. Perhaps the clearest parallel can be found in the task of allocating funds: How much shall we spend for product research? How much shall we spend for special automatic equipment? As in the case of product research, the issues are frequently presented not in general, but as a composite of project proposals, each of which or any combination of which may be undertaken or rejected. The parallel holds, too, in another respect. Such decisions cannot be made solely on the basis of the formal studies submitted as justification — instead, proposals must be analyzed and compared against a background of what will be involved in bringing the project to completion, and what pitfalls will likely be encountered. Without such knowledge as background, serious mistakes are easily made.

Responsibility for decisions affecting special automatic equipment programs cannot be assumed or avoided at will. Given the current growing emphasis on equipment, the increasingly important role of special automatic equipment, and the greater difficulties encountered in acquiring it, it follows that the skill with which a company acquires all types of equipment, and particularly special automatic equipment, will be even more important to general management in the future. When special automatic equipment rather than standard equipment is involved, the cycle for planning increases in time span and complexity, and the nice judging of risks demands greater care and skill. These are tasks which top management must prepare for and cannot avoid, for ever in the background is the threat that once a company falls behind its major competitors, it will be faced with the need for refurbishing a plant with large amounts of special automatic equipment in a hurry, a truly heroic, if not impossible, task.[7] Top management must therefore gauge its prospects realistically, avoiding unwise risks, yet not waiting too late to do too little. It must guard against unjustifiably abandoning all special automatic equipment efforts because of one unfortunate experience, an experience rooted in part perhaps in its own uncritical enthusiasm a year or two earlier.

Vitally concerned also in the administrative problems related to acquisition of special automatic equipment are the managers primarily responsible for supervising such activities: the supervisors of project engineers and project managers, the master mechanics and production managers to whom the supervisors are generally responsible, and the project leaders themselves, even when the project group consists of but one engineer responsible for one or more projects. Part of so-called middle management, these men are much more intimately in touch with the technical aspects of special automatic equipment but frequently have limited administrative experience and training. "Planning," "organization," and "control" are unfamiliar concepts to many of them, as are the concepts of coordination with other functional groups and taking a company-wide point of view. A broad understanding of the significance of their relationships to other organizational units and a systematic way of looking at the *administrative* aspects of the special automatic equipment ac-

---

[7] At least one company has faced up to just such a situation. In announcing the sale of Avco Manufacturing Corporation's Crosley and Bendix home appliance divisions in 1956, and Avco's withdrawal from the appliance manufacturing business, Chairman and President Victor Emmanuel stated in part: "The decision by Avco to discontinue Crosley and Bendix consumer products is the outgrowth of an industry-wide situation. Since 1953, competition in the major home appliance and radio-television set business has become increasingly severe. . . . Your management has given the closest attention to this situation. It has carefully weighed whether future possibilities would warrant the large expenditure of capital funds necessary to meet competition by investing in very large new plants with a high degree of automation. The decision has been not to do so. . . ." Quoted from a letter to stockholders of Avco Manufacturing Corporation dated October 30, 1956.

quisition process should therefore have value for this group of managers, too.

For the experienced firm, pursuing a continuing program over several years, this study may prove of value for repairing inroads made by personnel turnover. Men with intimate knowledge of special automatic equipment, either at the technical or at the administrative level, are in short supply and alternative opportunities are bound to be frequent. In addition, the kinds of experience that these men accumulate often train them in a way which makes them in great demand elsewhere in the organization, particularly in the factory hierarchy.

Objectives of This Study

This study has two objectives. The first is a description of the process of acquiring special automatic equipment. This description includes the key steps in the acquisition process, important organizational relationships between the special automatic equipment group and other organizational units, both inside and outside the company, and the common types of problems likely to be encountered in projects for acquiring this type of equipment. These matters are the subject of Chapter II.

The second objective is to describe in detail selected problem areas which emerged as particularly important:

Debugging. After every piece of special equipment was assembled, the companies visited typically went through a long and costly period of trying to make it operate satisfactorily. The term commonly used for this phase was "debugging." Debugging is described in detail (Chapter III) because it does not take place in standard equipment acquisition, and because so many of the difficulties encountered during debugging had important implications for preceding steps in the acquisition cycle.

Working with Equipment Vendors. Much of the special automatic equipment being acquired by the firms visited was purchased from vendors. As a result many critical problems of communications arose. This topic (including the policy question of "make or buy") has therefore been given detailed treatment in Chapters IV, V, and VI.

Coordinating Product Design and Special Automatic Equipment. The design of a product affects not only the operations which have to be performed by special automatic equipment but also the ease or difficulty with which they may be performed. Also, the rate at which changes in design are made and the nature of these changes vitally affect the economic life of this kind of equipment. Because the relationship between these two business functions is so fundamental, it was selected as the subject of Chapter VII.

Analysis of Proposals. Since appropriation approval of a special automatic equipment project was usually the "point of no return" in committing relatively large sums of money, all levels of management, from top management down to the project leaders, were found to be greatly interested in the task of appraising project proposals. Earlier in this chapter the basic role of wise project selection was mentioned. In the appraisal of special automatic equipment, there were critical factors not encountered in dealing with standard equipment proposals, factors of which management was unaware or with which management found it especially frustrating to deal. The subject of effective evaluation of proposals was therefore made the last special topic to be treated, in Chapter VIII.

In dealing with each of the four areas chosen, the ultimate objective has been to suggest, whenever practicable, such policies, procedures, or organizational structures as might facilitate the efficient acquisition of special automatic equipment. As the next chapter demonstrates, there are additional problem areas which are also worthy of further investigation, but some selection was required to permit research in depth to be accomplished. The early results of the field work clearly indicated the importance of the four areas listed above.

It should be borne in mind that the point of view here is that of the business manager rather than the technician. Administrative, not technical, matters are the focal concern although technical problems will be raised and considered, at least in a general way, as they bear on particular issues and functions. But our major concern is that of the general management of a business: the economic application of technology to the manufacturing job in a particular plant.

The conclusions drawn in this study must be qualified by the fact that it concentrates on the metalworking industries. I have broadly defined metalworking to include: fabricated metal products, machinery and equipment (except electrical), electrical equipment (including electronics), transportation equipment, instruments, and miscellaneous metal products. Primary metal producers were specifically excluded. Although I can make no claim that my findings apply outside of the general areas of these metalworking industries, it seems likely that close parallels may be found in other industries.

The basic reason for selecting a single group of industries was to permit some development in depth. Choice of the metalworking industries rather than others enabled me to capitalize on my existing familiarity with typical metalworking processes, thus expediting field studies and making for a better grasp of the problems uncovered. This choice also seemed appropriate on other grounds. The metalworking group comprises so large and important a sector of total manufacturing that any notable developments are practically certain to be meaningful to the whole of the economy. The metalworking industries accounted for 41% of the value added by manufacture in the census year 1954 and employed 40% of all persons working in manufacturing. In addition, these industries have been growing at a faster rate than have manufacturers as a whole. From 1947 to 1954, value added in manufacturing grew by about 57% while the value added by the metalworking groups increased by about 87%.[8]

Not only do the metalworking industries comprise a major segment of manufacturing, growing more rapidly than the remainder, but they face more difficult problems in mechanizing than do, say, the process industries, for metalworking plants typically deal with discrete parts rather than with the more homogeneous materials commonly found in the process industries. For the latter, standard bulk handling devices exist; moreover, they pose no problems of orientation or nice spatial relationships. In brief, the problems of special automatic equipment (especially for assembly) in the metalworking industries seemed intrinsically more challenging.

The Research Data

The primary source of material for this study has been field investigations. Aside from the notable exception of Professor

---

[8] All figures upon which these calculations were based were published in the 1954 *Census of Manufactures*.

Bright's study, the literature in the field consists primarily of periodical articles, mainly in trade magazines. Sometimes these articles have provided substantiating evidence, and sometimes they provided useful examples of types of problems not encountered in my field work. In some instances published data have been used in lieu of my own data to avoid the risk of disclosing confidential information. The field work indicated, however, that many periodical reports are misleading: they frequently disclose only the favorable results achieved — give a one-sided analysis, if you will — rather than disclose any deficiencies. One can hardly expect businessmen, or anyone else, for that matter, to publicize the projects which were written off as a total loss, or policies or procedures which proved to have great drawbacks. But the reports of success in the absence of reports of failures are misleading to anyone not familiar with the field.

The data were gathered from eighteen plant organizations (representing fifteen different corporations), four headquarters organizations for multiplant companies, and nine vendors of special automatic equipment. An industrial breakdown of the eighteen plants is as follows:

Automobiles and Parts	4
Office Machinery	2
Electrical and Electronic	8
Fabricated Metal Products	2
Other (machinery)	2

Eight of these plants manufactured industrial products and ten manufactured consumer products (some durables and some nondurables). The users were selected primarily because they were active in acquiring special automatic equipment, although traveling convenience imposed some geographical bias: nearly one-half of the users interviewed were located in the New England and the Middle Atlantic states.

None of the organizations was small — the smallest employed over 1,200 persons. Trade magazine surveys have found that plants with more than 1,000 employees have shown the greatest interest in this type of equipment.[9] Plants of this size are of

---

[9] See *American Machinist* surveys conducted in 1955 and 1957; August 29, 1955, pp. 145–160, and October 21, 1957, pp. 165–180.

great importance in metalworking, although many of these industries have large numbers of small establishments. In 1954 the thousand-odd metalworking plants employing 1,000 persons or more constituted less than 13% of all plants in the metalworking group, but they employed 48% of all metalworking employees and accounted for just slightly more than 50% of the total value added by manufacture in this segment. Thus large plants were not only the ones most interested but were also the means by which the greatest economic impact might be made.

All but one of the vendors had fewer than 500 employees, and even that one had fewer than 1,000. Just as large size was typical for users, so small size was typical for vendors.

During the field studies four types of data were gathered:

1. General information on methods of organization, policies and procedures, and problems.
2. Questionnaire replies specifically identifying trouble spots in the acquisition process and in relations with other organizations.
3. Machine histories of the major events and problems encountered in the acquisition cycle of specific pieces of special automatic equipment.
4. Selected statistical data relating to costs and elapsed time for a limited sample of individual projects.

A large proportion of interviewing time was spent with personnel at the operating level, for example, managers of manufacturing engineering, supervisors of special equipment activities, and project engineers working on this type of equipment. The interviews also included a few persons at the top management level and, as previously noted, in four cases, representatives of the headquarters staff organizations of multiproduct, multiplant corporations. In addition to supplying general information on the organization, policies, and procedures in every case, company personnel were asked to identify and discuss the most important general problem areas. The questionnaire replies, the nature of which will be more fully related in Chapter II, were drawn from the same sources.

One or more "machine histories" were obtained from 14 of the users. Each history dealt with the origin and chronology of, and the problems encountered in, the acquisition of a specific piece of equipment. Five of the histories covered several inter-related equipment units, a type of equipment which will be termed a "system" to denote its greater complexity. None of these systems was so large as to comprise a whole plant. Of the 47 histories obtained, 19 were from one organization. The precision and completeness of the data varied from one history to another, depending principally upon the procedures a company employed, the existence of records, and the memories of the personnel involved. Most of the projects had been completed in the span from 1954 through 1956.

The typical project called for expenditures of from $7,500 to $50,000 in total and, after the planning stages had been completed, took from 6 to 24 months to finish. Exhibit 1 shows data on elapsed time and expenditures for six projects, selected to show a variety of characteristics. The total time to complete these projects ranged from 13 months to 42 months. As it happened, both the longest and the shortest of these projects required about the same total expenditures. The Carlson project, however, involved a much more "tailored" machine, and by far the major portion of its designing and building cycle of 35 months was devoted to development work, using a partially assembled machine to prove out parts as they were designed. Indeed, if we assume that the development work of a pilot project is more of a design cost than a construction cost, the figures shown understate the design costs for Carlson's project.

The Fisher #3 and the Walsh projects were assembly equipment; the Carlson project combined assembly and other types of operations; and the Fisher #7, Mason, and Warren-King projects were machining equipment. The Mason project was one which relied heavily on standard machine tools, fed, linked, and controlled by special equipment designed mostly by Mason personnel (an approach sometimes referred to as "Detroit automation"). Two of these five cases involved the automobile industry, three the electrical manufacturing industry, and one was miscellaneous.

Although there were relatively complete data available on these projects compared with the typical case, in some instances the standard accounting procedures failed to charge to the project all or part of the project engineering costs in the planning stage and all or part of the costs of the services of project engineers

EXHIBIT 1

ELAPSED TIME AND EXPENDITURES DATA FOR SELECTED SPECIAL AUTOMATIC EQUIPMENT PROJECTS

	Fisher Co. Proj. #7	Fisher Co. Proj. #3	Mason Co.	Walsh Co.	Carlson Co.	Warren-King Co. (Fairchild Proj.)
Elapsed Time:						
Planning	Unknown	Unknown	11 mos.	4 mos.	*	3 mos.
Designing	6 mos.	1 mo.	12 mos.	1 mo.	35 mos.	9 mos.
Building	2 mos.	6 mos.	9 mos.	10 mos.	7 mos.	1 mo.†
Debugging	7 mos.	7 mos.		7 mos.		
Elapsed Time, Planning omitted	15 mos.	14 mos.	21 mos.	17 mos.	42 mos.	10 mos.
Total Elapsed Time (available data)	15 mos.	14 mos.	32 mos.	22 mos.	42 mos.	13 mos.
Expenditures:						
Design	$3,600	$10,200	$874,000	$ 6,300	$10,100	$64,000
Build				35,100	50,000	
Debug	500	1,800	100,000	2,300	9,500	—
Total Expenditures	$4,100	$12,000	$974,000	$43,700	$69,600‡	$64,000
Procurement Method	Make	Buy	Mainly Buy	Buy	Make	Buy

* Separate and earlier pilot study, over a period of 17 months.

† Debugging stopped before machine achieved production rate originally specified.

‡ Earlier pilot project cost about $25,000 additional.

NOTE: Figures rounded to nearest hundred or, in the case of larger figures, to nearest thousand.

and technicians during the debugging phase. Although we must guard against interpreting these statistical data too nicely, they nevertheless accurately indicate the range of the elapsed time and expenditures required to acquire special automatic equipment.

Some of the data available in the 47 machine histories were supplemented from additional projects in the same companies, making limited statistical data available for 85 projects in all. Forty-one of the projects in this statistical sample came from one organization and 19 from another. Tables showing data on the total expenditures involved and on the time required to complete this sample of 85 projects are contained in Appendix B.

The experience of one company in particular provided not only a wealth of data but even more important, an opportunity to observe developments during several projects as they occurred. In this case, I was fortunate enough to be present when a substantial special automatic equipment program was begun, and more fortunate still to be able to observe subsequent events over the following two and a half years. These events have provided an invaluable background against which to compare the approaches and problems of other companies.

Definitions

Before going further it is necessary to define in detail the key terms of this study, "acquisition process" and "special automatic equipment." I have used "acquisition process" in a broad sense to comprise the steps which take place from the time an idea for a piece of special equipment is generated, through analysis of project proposals, equipment design, construction, and debugging up to the point of acceptance by the line production organization. The term is also used to include the decision on whether to buy or to build as a method of procurement. (Others might select different cut-off points for a definition of acquisition process; depending upon their purpose and upon their accustomed way of thinking, they might make it either more restrictive or, conceivably, broader still.)

The term "special automatic equipment" in this study means a piece of equipment that has been "tailored" in large part to the requirements of one customer, and that performs more than one operation without operator intervention. So-called semiautomatic equipment which is manually loaded and unloaded falls within our definition because more than one operation is usually performed automatically after loading. By including "special" in describing the equipment surveyed, however, we exclude such standard automatic equipment as now exists in metalworking; for example, the automatic screw machine, which is certainly fully automatic, but which is, save for the cutting tools, and in some instances the holding fixtures and the cam, a quite standard, not special piece of equipment. On substantially the same basis, punched-tape controlled standard equipment (such as programmed milling machines) did not fall within our definition. The term "automation" is not used in the following chapters because of its ambiguity.

Although the metalworking industries utilize many processes, the largest part of the special automatic equipment studied performed two broad classes of operation: metalworking (mainly cutting and forming) and assembly. The remainder included a wide variety of other types of processes; for example, plastic molding, forming glass parts, packaging, and even inspection.

Having made these somewhat unglamorous statements about objectives, methods, and definitions, I will turn now to reporting my research results, begining with the topic of key steps and major trouble spots in Chapter II. Those readers who have not had much experience with special automatic equipment may find it profitable to read Appendix A first; there a detailed account is given of the events of a special automatic equipment acquisition by the Warren-King Company. In effect, this appendix is an elaborated machine history plus an analysis of some of the results of a typical project. Even the experienced manager may find it profitable to review this project's record to discover similarities to and contrasts with his own experiences.

CHAPTER II

Problem Areas and Key Organizational Relationships in the Acquisition Process

IN ANY organization, the activities of a functional unit have two important dimensions: first, the nature of the process for which it is primarily responsible, and second, the relationship of that function, in operation, to other functional units within the total organization. This chapter attempts to analyze the function of acquiring special automatic equipment as it took place in the companies studied, treating each of these dimensions in turn.

Defining the Scope and Content of the Acquisition Process

Each project, of course, had its own individual problems. But were there any general tendencies toward particular types of problems, or were there any recurrent clusters of problems? In order to probe this question, it was first necessary to break down the acquisition process for a typical piece of special automatic equipment into elements which could be evaluated. This study used the following nine operations.[1]

> Getting Ideas, Developing Project Proposal
> Appraising Project Proposal
> Determining Method, Equipment Specifications
> Justifying Appropriation Request
> Finding a Qualified Vendor (if the decision is to buy)

---

[1] A similar set of elements can be deduced from Robert L. Kessler "How Special Machinery Is Developed," *Automotive Industries,* April 15, 1953, pp. 50–53ff. See also James J. Lahm, "Organizing for Developing Automation Equipment," *Automation,* April 1957, Chart 2, p. 38, and Joseph G. Adiletta, "Comparing Machine Cost and Time Factors," *Automation,* May 1958, p. 57. See also Bright, *Automation and Management,* p. 88.

Design of Equipment
Building Equipment
Debugging Equipment
Getting Production to Accept Equipment

Deciding whether to make or buy is omitted from the list because in many instances such decisions were part of the basic policy underlying a company's whole program rather than part of the cycle for each piece of equipment. It is as a policy decision, then, rather than as an operational step that the make or buy decision is analyzed in Chapter IV.

While the steps listed are roughly in order of time, in practice there is considerable variation in sequence, some steps occurring at about the same time as others, or partly overlapping, and some steps occurring more than once in a project cycle. The first three operations listed are involved in what can be called a period of project gestation, during which one or more of the three steps may be repeated, perhaps several times. The act of appraising a project, for instance, took place, or should have taken place, not once but recurrently at various stages during the process of project development. Appraisals were rough at first, to be sure, but they became progressively more refined and in most cases became most detailed and most critical when the decision was made to request an appropriation. Likewise, the consideration of alternative methods began, or should have begun, early in the whole cycle, usually becoming the subject of early appraisals and leading to the selection of one general approach to machine processing. In some cases in the field work, notably those involving machine operations, the users often fixed basic performance specifications (for example, "85 pieces per hour") and also chose the basic processing methods (for example, drilling, reaming, and milling) but left development of the broad approach to equipment design (number of stations, sequence of operations, and rate of metal removal) to the vendors who were asked to bid on designing and building the equipment. In other words, part of the task of method development was shifted to the vendors. When the vendors' proposals were returned, the project appraisal followed in order that a choice might be made among the alternatives submitted.

The First Questionnaire — Steps in the Process as Problem Areas

After establishing these nine operations as the major elements of the acquisition process, the next step was to find some way of roughly measuring the importance of each step as a source of problems. As one means of doing this, the list of these operations was used in a questionnaire which was submitted to twelve management representatives who had primary responsibility for the acquisition of this type of equipment in twelve different plants.[2] Each supervisor was requested to classify the degree of difficulty encountered in each operation as "Large," "Small," or "Negligible or None." The filling out of the questionnaire was always accompanied or preceded by a personal interview, giving an oportunity for the airing of any problems related to the definition of the terms used.[3] Exhibit 2 shows the sum of the replies obtained by these procedures, arranged in order of the general consensus of the degree of difficulty, from the most difficult to the least difficult.

The consensus was overwhelming that the debugging operation was a major source of difficulties; three-quarters of the respondents classified it as a stage in which they encountered a large number of difficulties. The debugging step is one in which frustrating problems are unavoidable. Although a company management that is beginning to acquire special automatic equipment for the first time may expect major problems in working out the broad approach to a particular piece of equipment and in developing its detailed design, the magnitude of the debugging task often seems to be overlooked. Those who have carried spe-

---

[2] This questionnaire was not used in connection with every company contacted in the field work for this project. It was used only in plants which had acquired a number of pieces of special automatic equipment over several years.

[3] In most cases, the person filling out this questionnaire was the supervisor of project leaders in the plant, but in two cases, the questionnaire was filled out by a higher echelon of management because the organization primarily responsible for special automatic equipment projects was large enough to embrace more than two organizational levels. The individual's title varied widely, but included such terms as "supervisor," "director," and "manager" of activities variously described as "Manufacturing Engineering," "Advanced Equipment Development," or "Process Development."

EXHIBIT 2

DEGREE OF DIFFICULTY GENERALLY ENCOUNTERED IN EXECUTING
SELECTED STEPS IN ACQUIRING SPECIAL AUTOMATIC EQUIPMENT
(12 Respondents)

	Number of Times Respondents Classified Step's Degree of Difficulty as:		
	Large	*Small*	*Negligible or None*
Debugging Equipment	9	3	0
Design of Equipment	5	5	2
Appraising Project Proposal	5	5	2
Determining Methods and Equipment Specifications	4	7	1
Justifying Appropriation Request	3	7	2
Finding Qualified Vendors	3	7	2
Getting Ideas, Developing Project Proposal	3	6	3
Getting Production to Accept Equipment	3	4	5
Building Equipment	1	7	4

cial automatic equipment through this stage, however, appear to have a healthy respect for this step as a major problem area.

Two operations scored equally as secondary sources of difficulty: "Design of Equipment" and "Appraising Project Proposal." Since equipment design usually embraces a very broad, involved technical area, it is not surprising to find it of major concern. The design of special automatic equipment by definition means dealing with new and difficult problems of mechanism design and application. Furthermore, for many elements of equipment design there may be a choice of several approaches, each resting on a quite different technology. Electronic, hydraulic, and pneumatic control devices, for instance, all are often alternatives to mechanical cams and levers, and making the best choice calls for a high order of knowledge and skill.

Because economics as well as technology is at the heart of the acquisition of this type (or almost any other type) of equipment, it is appropriate to find appraisal ranked as a matter of major concern. The uncertainties likely to be connected with estimates of such fundamentals as technical feasibilty, project expenditures required, savings to be realized, and primary service life all contribute to the difficulty of this step.

Not far behind as a source of difficulty was the operation, "Determining Methods and Equipment Specifications." Once a project has been earmarked for serious consideration, the working out of basic specifications and the broad (as distinct from the detailed) design is of first-rank importance. Currently, this task seems to be more of an art based on skill and experience than it is a routine matter yielding to a well-defined body of rules and principles. It is my impression, based upon the individual machine acquisition histories compiled, that the importance of this step may be even greater than this ranking indicates because shortcomings at this stage often underlay difficulties which came to the surface only later, say in the debugging operation.

Both of the firms answering "Negligible or None" on the step, "Finding Qualified Vendors" were making 90% or more of their special automatic equipment. Thus, of the ten firms which had made any important use of vendors, three found this step a major source of problems and the seven others found it at least a minor source of difficulties.

Although it lacked the urgency, in general, of the other steps, "Getting Production to Accept Equipment" sometimes constituted a major problem area, especially when little or no preparation for this stage had been undertaken. Special automatic equipment, unlike most standard machinery, invariably requires no small amount of special operator training and a certain amount of actual operating experience on the equipment. It is often several weeks or even several months before operating personnel are able to achieve standard output and quality. Problems of machine adjustment sometimes develop into tasks requiring broader skills than operators typically possess; therefore, getting successful performance usually involves the maintenance group as well.

The questionnaire results are also of some significance in what they did not show. For one thing, the consensus did not show any step to be *un*important — some one among the twelve respondents found every step a major source of difficulty and most found each step either a major or a minor source of difficulty. Another negative result, which is perhaps a little surprising, is the very clear opinion that the building stage proper for special automatic equipment was seldom a major source of difficulty, despite the fact that this step almost always involved the largest share of total cost.

Some Limitations to the First Questionnaire Results

Manifestly these data are an imperfect device for identifying the trouble spots in acquiring special automatic equipment. For one thing, the decision as to whether a step was a "large" or a "small" source of difficulty was highly subjective. Furthermore, to a very considerable degree, the importance assigned to a particular step as a source of trouble was determined not only by the particular projects undertaken by a respondent but also by his general approach to his job and by the policies of his company. In addition, general tendencies would by no means hold for each project. In several instances respondents noted that while one step might most often be a major source of problems, they had completed projects in which only minor problems had emerged during this stage. Likewise, they reported that on occasion an operation usually presenting only minor problems sometimes encountered important, even critical, difficulties.

We must also recognize the possibilities of bias in the replies. Most of the respondents, although supervisors, were primarily technically oriented in their day-to-day activities. This orientation may have resulted in a tendency to place undue emphasis upon problems they encountered in their daily activities and in a failure to perceive, let alone objectively evaluate, problems related to nontechnical activities. For example, most of the supervisors reported that there was no shortage of ideas upon which to work. A representative statement of their views appeared in a recent article by an equipment development engineer who wrote:

> The selection of projects is seldom a problem. [Operations] characterized by high costs, excessive worker fatigue, or a high rejection rate, are usually worthy of consideration. The foremen, the industrial engineers, and the quality control people can all help in this matter.[4]

---

[4] Lahm, "Organizing for Developing Automation Equipment," pp. 36–40.

If a supervisor sees it as his job to work on those ideas presented to him and his men, plus obvious ones encountered at random, he may feel that he has encountered few, if any, major problems in this stage of the process. On the other hand, the responsibilities of a special automatic equipment group may be conceived in much broader terms, and as a result may affect the number of problems he perceives. Specifically, the supervisor of the organization may be responsible for systematically discovering and selecting those opportunities for using special automatic equipment which promise to yield not just an acceptable return but the best return for the time and money expended. One of the supervisors interviewed, and one, incidentally, whose organization seemed to be rendering a distinctly superior performance, said that getting ideas, good ideas, for possible projects and doing a good job of analysis on them was the most important part of his job.

The Cost of Process Steps

Rather meager cost data were available on most of the steps in the acquisition process as we have defined them. Only occasionally, for instance, was any record found of the amount of effort devoted to the step of determining methods and working out equipment specifications. The rare case in which such a record was found was always one in which the operation was so large that a special pilot project had been set up to work out the general approach to the project or to test the technical feasibility of certain processes or mechanisms. For steps such as "Finding Qualified Vendors," one would not expect to find cost data being regularly accumulated. Some expenditures data, however, were available on the two important steps of design and of debugging.

Exhibit 3 compares actual design costs with the total costs for 13 projects, starting from the time of the approval of the appropriation request. Records were not available to permit separating design costs from the total in the other cases in the statistical sample; a major cause lay in the fact that a large number of the projects in this sample were cases in which the equipment was bought, rather than made, and this kind of breakdown of the vendor's price was not readily available. The data which were available, however, are probably sufficient to indicate the im-

EXHIBIT 3

DESIGN COSTS OF 13 SELECTED SPECIAL AUTOMATIC EQUIPMENT PROJECTS

		Design Cost	Total Project Cost	Design Cost as % of Total Cost
Make Projects		$ 2,200	$ 14,000	16%
		3,600	13,700	26
		10,000	69,600	14
		80,000	250,000	36
		253,000	3,205,000	8
	Subtotal	$348,800	$3,552,300	10%
Buy Projects		$ 500	$ 2,700	19%
		1,100	5,300	21
		6,300	43,700	14
		7,800	25,400	30
		15,000	256,000	6
		95,000	146,000	65
	Subtotal	$125,700	$479,100	26%
Combination Make and Buy Projects		$15,300	$ 70,100	22%
		27,000	294,000	9

Summary

Below 5%	6% to 10%	11% to 15%	16% to 20%	21% to 25%	26% to 30%	31% to 35%	36% to 40%	Over 40%
—	3	2	2	2	2	—	1	1

Median 19%

NOTES: (1) Dollar figures rounded to nearest hundred, and larger dollar figures rounded to nearest thousand.
(2) "Make" means designed and built by the using company.

portance of the design step. The range of the middle half of the cases, between 14% and 22%, and the median, 19%, are representative of the general proportion of design expenditures to the total in acquiring this class of equipment.

The relative importance of the design stage was not, of course, necessarily a function of the total cost of the proect. Instead, it varied with the number of machines of this design which were to be built, with the degree to which standard major subassemblies were used, and with whether a particular piece of equipment was the first of its type or was basically a revision, albeit a major revision, of an earlier model. The design cost also varied with the technical difficulty of the project, broadly speaking, which was a compound of many aspects, including the nature of the process, the characteristics of the workpiece(s) involved, the knowledge possessed about its proposed application, and the number of operations included. Thus we found instances of a relatively large design cost for a small project and, on the other hand, other instances of relatively small design costs for some very large projects. In any event, the design step was typically a major element of cost, usually about 20% of the total, as well as being a very fundamental and critical step in each project.

More data are available on the magnitude of debugging costs (Exhibit 4) than on design costs. Even so, figures could not be obtained in a great many instances, mainly because no record was kept of them on a project basis; instead, they were frequently just charged somewhere in the accounting system to an overhead account. The data which were available, however, indicate the range of the middle half to be from 6% to 17% of total cost, with a median (middle) figure of 12% of the total project cost. One might expect that debugging costs would comprise a smaller portion of the total when a vendor designed and built the equipment than when the user designed and built it because the vendor typically undertook a fairly large amount of debugging, presumably leaving less as a result for the user to do. The data on Exhibit 4, however, do not furnish support for such a view.

The debugging skill among companies also varied greatly. (Fisher, whose cases dominate the buy group in number, but not in amount, was relatively inexperienced at the time.) Therefore, the amount of debugging actually obtained per dollar of expenditure probably varied greatly from company to company. Furthermore, a careful and skillful design operation tends to hold the debugging required to a minimum, while a deficient performance in the design stage is likely to result in proportionately more problems in the debugging stage. The most important factor of all affecting the debugging cost, however, is the variation in the

EXHIBIT 4

DEBUGGING COSTS OF 29 SELECTED SPECIAL AUTOMATIC EQUIPMENT PROJECTS

	Debugging Cost	Total Project Cost	Debugging Cost as % of Total Cost
Make Projects	$ 200	$ 2,300	9%
	300	13,700	2
	500	4,100	12
	900	14,000	6
	1,000	8,600	12
	1,800	5,300	34
	9,500	69,600	14
	75,000	250,000	30
	130,000	3,205,000	4
Subtotal	$219,200	$3,572,600	6%
Buy Projects	$ 100	$ 2,000	5%
	400	2,300	17
	500	5,200	10
	500	3,500	14
	1,000	25,400	4
	1,400	6,300	22
	1,500	30,700	5
	1,700	10,200	17
	1,800	12,000	15
	1,900	16,000	12
	2,100	19,300	11
	2,300	43,700	5
	2,800	29,100	10
	3,000	12,500	24
	3,300	12,700	26
	4,900	13,900	35
	18,000	256,000	7
	126,000	188,000	67
Subtotal	$173,200	$688,800	25%
Combination Make and Buy Projects	$ 3,000	$294,000	1%
	12,000	70,000	17

Summary

Below 5%	6% to 10%	11% to 15%	16% to 20%	21% to 25%	26% to 30%	31% to 35%	36% to 40%	Over 40%
7	5	7	3	2	2	2	—	1

NOTE: Dollar figures rounded to nearest hundred and larger dollar figures rounded to nearest thousand.

technical complexity of the project. The greater the advances attempted, and the more complex the equipment or system, the more costly it is likely to be to debug.

The financial data on debugging need to be interpreted liberally because of the ease with which costs appropriately chargeable to a project may in fact be charged elsewhere. Some of the items are easily lost by charges to other accounts, especially the time spent by mechanics, electricians, and project engineers, which often are charged, intentionally or not, against a general overhead account. One must therefore assume fairly wide margins of error, more probably in the direction of understating rather than overstating total costs of debugging.

In spite of the limitations inherent in the data on debugging expenditures, their general magnitudes are in accord with the supervisors' opinions, recorded on the questionnaire, that debugging is a very important operation.

The Second Questionnaire — Problems Involving Other Organizational Units

The pilot study not only indicated a need for identifying the key operations in the acquisition process and locating the major trouble spots therein, but it also suggested that important problem areas might lie in the relations between special automatic equipment groups and other organizational units. A second questionnaire was therefore used to inquire about relationships with other organizational units generally.

Exhibits 5, 6, and 7 show the results of the survey using the second questionnaire. The special automatic equipment group typically had its most frequent relations with the company's machine design group, machine shop, and purchasing department. The relations adjudged most important and most likely to be major sources of problems, however, were those with the product design department and equipment contractors.

The main usefulness of the data in Exhibit 5 lies in the picture they paint of the activities of the typical special automatic equipment group and its supervisor. As we have already noted, their principal relations were with the machine design, machine construction, and purchasing departments. (In perhaps two or three cases the term "machine designers" was apparently inter-

EXHIBIT 5

FREQUENCY WITH WHICH SPECIAL AUTOMATIC EQUIPMENT GROUPS
HAD RELATIONS WITH OTHER ORGANIZATIONAL UNITS
(12 respondents)

	Number of Times Classified as:			
Organizational Unit	*Very Frequent*	*Often*	*Sometimes*	*No Relations*
Company Machine Shops	6	3	2	1
Company Machine Designers*	6	2	3	1
Purchasing	5	5	2	—
Product Design	4	5	3	—
Quality Control-Inspection	4	4	3	1
Top Management	4	1	7	—
Equipment Contractors	3	6	2	1
Financial and Cost	3	2	7	—
Production	3	2	7	—
Maintenance	3	2	6	1
Industrial Engineering	2	6	3	1
Other Departments†	1	—	7	4
Consultants	—	2	4	6
Sales	—	—	6	6

* Special automatic equipment group's own responsibility in two cases.

† Those filled in by respondents included legal (patents), field engineering, production control and central staff groups.

preted to include tool designers who worked on holding fixtures for special automatic equipment.) Less frequently, the special automatic equipment group's activities involved the departments concerned with product design and quality control. Perhaps most striking of all is the breadth of the relations developed in acquiring special automatic equipment. Relatively frequent contacts are indicated with almost every one of the eleven "internal" organizational units listed, with even the sales department being involved "sometimes" in half the cases.

In several companies the line production supervisors were in frequent contact with the special automatic equipment programs, but in others the production department was not much involved until equipment was ready to be put on the production floor. The latter condition seemed to obtain especially in those plants in which the major emphasis of the special automatic equipment

EXHIBIT 6

IMPORTANCE OF RELATIONSHIPS BETWEEN SPECIAL AUTOMATIC
EQUIPMENT GROUPS AND OTHER ORGANIZATIONAL UNITS
(12 respondents)

	Number of Times Classified as:		
Relationship with: (*organizational unit*)	*Large*	*Small*	*Negligible* *or None*
Product Design	11	1	0
Equipment Contractors	10	1	1
Top Management	9	0	3
Company Machine Designers*	8	3	1
Quality Control-Inspection	8	2	2
Company Machine Shops	7	3	2
Purchasing	7	3	2
Production	6	4	2
Financial and Cost	6	3	3
Industrial Engineering	5	7	0
Maintenance	5	4	3
Other Departments	3	5	4
Sales	2	4	6
Consultants	—	4	8

* Special automatic equipment group's own responsibility in two cases.

group was on equipment for new products or new models of old products. When the equipment replaced machines currently in use on the production floor, the communications between these two organizational units seemed to be much more frequent, and a higher rating was assigned to production as a source of problems. It is quite possible that some increase in the frequency of contacts, especially during the initial stages of project development, might help to minimize problems involving the production group.

One of the many similarities shown by Exhibits 6 and 7 was the high rating accorded relations with the product design group. Other evidence collected during the field work and elsewhere also pointed up the great importance of these relations. They seemed to be among the most fundamental relations as well as among those most difficult to establish and maintain efficiently. The spatial and dimensional characteristics of the workpiece, the material of which it was made, and the functional purpose to

EXHIBIT 7

DEGREE TO WHICH OTHER ORGANIZATIONAL UNITS WERE SOURCES
OF PROBLEMS FOR SPECIAL AUTOMATIC EQUIPMENT GROUPS
(12 respondents)

	Number of Times Classified as:		
Organizational Unit	*Large*	*Small*	*Negligible or None*
Equipment Contractors	6	4	2
Product Design	4	7	1
Company Machine Designers*	4	6	2
Production Department	4	5	3
Purchasing	4	3	5
Company Machine Shops	2	6	4
Quality Control-Inspection	2	6	4
Industrial Engineering	2	5	5
Top Management	2	3	7
Sales	2	2	8
Financial and Cost	1	7	4
Maintenance	1	6	5
Consultants	—	4	8
Other Departments	—	1	11

* Special automatic equipment group's own responsibility in two cases.

which it was put in very large part determined the kind and complexity of problems for the project engineer working on a special automatic equipment project. The shape (or "geometry") of the workpieces, for instance, is crucial in determining the ease or difficulty with which they may be fed by rotating or vibratory hoppers. The nature of the reference surfaces[5] provided and the tolerances demanded in the finished piece limit the kind of device which might be used to hold it while necessary operations are being performed, and may even affect the number of work stations required on the equipment. In assembly work, the simplicity or complexity of the relationship between two parts and the method by which they are to be fastened together are all important. Since in a great many cases one or more aspects of the design of a part are chosen arbitrarily, some of the problems of equipment design can be simplified by making minor, or in some cases major, changes in the design of one or more of the workpieces involved. In practically every one of the machinery

---

[5] The surfaces from which all critical dimensions must be measured.

histories obtained, several changes of this kind had been made. For these reasons coordination of product design and production engineering became the object of special inquiries early in the field work.

The relation with contractors who design and build special automatic equipment also emerged as an important one in questionnaire replies, and it, too, gained even greater significance as individual machine acquisition histories were compiled. In all but two of the plants visited, vendors responsible for both design and construction steps were important sources of equipment and provided 40% or more of the volume of equipment being acquired. Even in the two companies where this was not true, and in which over the long run 90% to 95% of expenditures went to design and build special automatic equipment within their own organizations, there were occasional but important projects which involved purchases from outside builders.

The importance of top management backing was very often stressed in field interviews as well as in questionnaire replies. The large expenditures involved, the significant risks assumed, and the substantial time lag between promise and realization — ranging from 6 months to 24 months or more — were so great that the enthusiasm of top management for any such undertaking was essential.

Although in a very few instances the production department played a large role (including, incidentally, two companies whose departmental superintendents were responsible for the special automatic equipment project budgets), as a rule the production department seemed to be involved in only two ways. First, foremen, general foremen, and departmental superintendents comprised an important source of suggestions for special automatic equipment projects. The more typical line supervisor was willing to suggest possible projects but regarded a project once undertaken as primarily someone else's responsibility (that is, the responsibility of the project engineer and his supervisor) until it materialized as equipment installed on the production floor.

We have already mentioned a second and more important aspect of the relationship with the production department in reporting on the first questionnaire. This was the necessity for the production organization to accept the equipment as part of the normal production routine. Sympathetic cooperation was usually a critical factor in the transition to regular production. One supervisor of special equipment development said that in his experience special automatic equipment installed in a particular department was likely to prove to be anything from a complete failure to an outstanding success, depending upon the attitude of the foreman involved. The necessity for the production group to accept the equipment sometimes worked to create pressure on the special automatic equipment group to complete projects. The production organization may press for acceptance of special automatic equipment before it has been debugged properly, particularly if the equipment is not a replacement but is essential to start production of a new or redesigned product. Alternative production methods being used temporarily may be so clumsy and costly that rather than delay acceptance of equipment, the production group would accept it even though considerable debugging was still obviously required.

The importance assigned to the purchasing department was often justified on the basis of its responsibility for the procurement of parts when the company was building its own equipment. Its importance was also considered great in other instances; even when complete machines were being procured under the direction of a project engineer, the paper work of procurement was invariably handled by someone in the purchasing department. Sometimes the purchasing department included a specialist who assisted the project supervisor in locating sources of supply and in bringing new sources of potential value to the attention of the special automatic equipment group. Quite often, too, the purchasing department was an active expediter when the equipment was being procured from a vendor. In all plants visited, however, the decision on where to place the order invariably rested wholly with the personnel of the special automatic equipment group.

The importance of the maintenance department arose in most cases because it was the source of technicians who assisted in installing the completed equipment and who, probably more importantly, in most cases helped in debugging. In companies which had several years of experience in operating special automatic equipment, this group was sometimes a source of suggestions when a replacement machine was being designed. In any event, the maintenance group was ranked low as a source of problems. The sales department was rarely involved; in some instances, however, it was adding pressure to complete a project as quickly as possible, was concerned with design characteristics from the standpoint of customer reaction, and was concerned with the forecast of demand for the product involved.[6]

The "other" departments mentioned by respondents included legal (patents), field engineering, production control, and central staff groups. The patent aspects of special automatic equipment seemed to be important only in the electrical industry, parts of which had a history in which patents were important. Consultants were used rarely and only for research and development of a mechanical or electrical engineering nature to develop a process application or to perfect a particular mechanism. Such instances could be termed preliminary investigations designed to evaluate the technical feasibility of key steps or operations which were considered in perfecting a particular piece of special automatic equipment.

Summary

On the basis of the evidence gathered, it seemed quite clear that acquiring special automatic equipment was a complex type of activity requiring a great deal of technical knowledge plus sound administrative policies, procedures, and organizational arrangements to implement the knowledge. As far as internal activities were concerned, we found that a major cluster of problems centered about debugging. While there was fairly great variation from firm to firm in the appraisal of critical problem areas in the process of acquisition, all persons interviewed classified debugging as either a large or a small source of problems; this was the only process step which no respondent classified as a negligible source of problems. Other major clusters of problems were found to exist in the process steps, "Appraising Project Proposal" and "Determining Methods and Equipment Specifications." So far as relations with other organizational units were concerned, the two major sources of concern were relations with product design and relations with equipment contractors. The relationships which at one time or another had been important problem areas covered an impressively wide range.

---

[6] For an elaboration of the relationship to sales, see Bright, *Automation and Management,* pp. 212–221.

CHAPTER III

Debugging: Distinguishing Characteristic of the Acquisition Process

PERHAPS the most distinguishing characteristic of the acquisition process of special automatic equipment is the debugging (also called bugging, grooming, running, and development). Making the equipment perform satisfactorily after it has been completely assembled is usually a major operation in the process of acquiring special automatic equipment. The kinds of problems that arise are not limited to errors in machine design (although these are by far the most common ones), but embrace many other types of problems, too. These problems are intimately related to what has or has not been done in the preceding steps. Indeed, it is probably not an exaggeration to say that the chief object of debugging is to correct mistakes made earlier but not discovered until an attempt is made to operate the fully assembled equipment for the first time.

Although the essential task of training the regular operators for the equipment often takes place during the latter stages of debugging, this task has been considered as a distinct one, and therefore is not included in this analysis.

The Importance of the Debugging Phase

Debugging creates substantial costs both direct and indirect. Data presented in Chapter II showed that direct costs might range from 6% to 25% of the total costs of designing, building, and debugging. In a few instances debugging costs have been as high

as the cost of building.[1] Debugging costs are not only significant but also uncertain and difficult to predict.

In addition to the cost yardstick, the number of calendar days
which elapse during the debugging period must also be considered. Elapsed time, of course, is likely to be closely related to
cost and especially to the cost of time devoted to the equipment
by the project engineer and the technicians doing debugging.
But the time factor is also a measure of indirect costs which are
likely to be proportional to the elapsed time. Even though they
are not likely to be recognized in the accounting department's
charges to the project account, these costs may be considerable.
For one thing, the accumulated total of project expenditures up
to the point at which debugging begins represents a capital investment on which no return is being earned during the time
taken for debugging. Then, too, savings which might be realized
by operating the equipment are foregone; in many instances
these may not merely be deferred but forever lost. If the primary service life of the machine will be only three, four, or five
years, the savings for even six months is a significant fraction of
the total.[2] If the equipment is to manufacture a new or redesigned product, no profits will be foregone if debugging has been
completed by the production deadline set. Any unforeseen delay, however, may create a need for finding temporary sources of
supply. In this event, there are not only the capital costs of the
unproductive equipment being debugged, but also the added
expenditures associated with higher cost production temporarily
needed to meet production deadlines.

The data shown in Exhibit 8 indicate that the elapsed time required for debugging is likely to be of significant magnitude.
For all the projects shown there the typical (median) debugging
span was between six and seven months. This time also comprised a significant proportion of the total acquisition cycle time,
measured from the time an appropriation request was authorized

---

[1] Our own field research and see R. L. Kessler, "How Special Machinery
Is Developed," p. 53; Herman Melzer, "Developing Special Automatic
Equipment," *Tool Engineer*, September 1956, p. 210; James J. Lahm,
"Organizing for Developing Automation Equipment," p. 39.

[2] Anticipating our discussion in Chapter VIII, a project which promises a
rate of return after taxes of 20% on the basis of a five-year life will yield
only about 14% if its service life is reduced to four and a half years.

until the equipment reached the production level in operation. The typical debugging period was equivalent to 40% of the acquisition cycle time, and the debugging cycle for slightly more than half of the projects tabulated fell in the range of 30% to 49% of the total cycle time.

The number of make projects is manifestly too small to justify much statistical analysis, but one might still expect that usually the time spent in debugging would be a smaller portion of the total acquisition cycle when the equipment was bought than when it was made by the user. The data fail to support this expectation and some of the reasons for this failure are revealing. One reason is that each of the four make projects in Group A which shows a total acquisition cycle of more than 40 months had been preceded by a pilot project of several months' duration to test the feasibility of some of the key mechanisms involved. Thus, while the wider scopes of these projects increased the

EXHIBIT 8

Elapsed Debugging Time as a Percentage of Acquisition Cycle Time, Selected Projects

| | *Group A (all from different plants)* | | |
	Total Cycle Time (mos.)	*Time Spent in Debugging (mos.)*	*Debugging Time as % of Total Cycle Time**
Make Projects†	43	17	40%
	42	17	42
	44	15	35
	48	22	46
	18	6	33
All Make Projects	195	77	40%
Buy Projects	22	9	41%
	15	9	60
	11	1	9
	17	7	41
	27	8	30
	14	2	14
	18	6	33
	18	10	56
All Buy Projects	142	52	37%
Group A	337	129	38%

EXHIBIT 8 (Continued)

	Group B (all from Fisher Company's plant)		
	Total Cycle Time (mos.)	Time Spent in Debugging (mos.)	Debugging Time as % of Total Cycle Time*
Make Projects†	18	2	11%
	15	7	41
	13	5	38
	7	2	29
All Make Projects	53	16	30%
Buy Projects	14	6	43%
	14	11	79
	14	9	64
	17	13	76
	15	8	53
	14	8	57
	6	1	17
	12	6	50
	7	3	43
	17	7	41
	10	3	30
	6	1	17
	13	4	31
	13	1	8
	2	½	25
All Buy Projects	174	81½	47%
Group B	227	97½	43%
Groups A and B Combined	564	226½	40%

Summary, Groups A and B Combined								
Below 10%	10% to 19%	20% to 29%	30% to 39%	40% to 49%	50% to 59%	60% to 69%	70% or more	Median
2	4	2	7	10	3	2	2	40%

* Acquisition cycle time excludes any time spent on prior pilot study.
† "Make" means designed and built by the using company.

likelihood of a lengthy debugging period, the pilot projects reduced it. Then, too, all these make cases involved veteran organizations. Fisher's typical experiences (Group B) are in direct opposition to the expectation we stated above, but these data cannot be weighed heavily because of the effect of Fisher's inexperience. Inexperience probably hampered the firm in a major portion of the buy projects, but it had less effect on its few make projects, both because the latter were undertaken mainly after Fisher had acquired considerable experience, and because they were not as complex as many of the buy projects.

Whatever the deficiencies of these data, however, it must be recognized that proportionally more time would be required for buy projects simply for the project engineers and technicians to become acquainted with the details of the equipment and with the problems involved in its operation after the builder had made delivery. Likewise, a vendor's personnel are unlikely to recognize as many problems during the design and construction stages. These will then have to be dealt with by the users in debugging.

One would also expect that if an operation were as much a source of problems as we have suggested this one to be, actual performance would often fall short of what had been estimated in advance. This was true almost without exception, as is shown by Exhibit 9, which presents the data available on the degree to which the actual elapsed time exceeded the time estimated before

EXHIBIT 9

ACTUAL COMPARED WITH ESTIMATED ELAPSED TIME FOR DESIGN AND BUILD AND DEBUGGING OPERATIONS, SELECTED PROJECTS

| | Group A (all from different plants) | | | | | |
| | Design & Build Elapsed Time | | | Debugging Elapsed Time | | |
	Estimated (mos.)	Actual (mos.)	Excess of Actual (% of Estimated)	Estimated (mos.)	Actual (mos.)	Excess of Actual (% of Estimated)
Make Projects	15	29	93%	10	15	50%
	19	26	37	3	17	513
Buy Projects	3	10	234	5	7	40
	5	6	20	3	9	200
	6	10	67	1	1	0
	8	19	137	6	8	33
	9	13	44	7	9	29
Group A	65	113	81%	35	66	89%

EXHIBIT 9 (Continued)

| | *Group B (all from Fisher Company)* | | | | | |
| | *Design & Build Elapsed Time* | | | *Debugging Elapsed Time* | | |
	Estimated (mos.)	*Actual (mos.)*	*Excess of Actual (% of Estimated)*	*Estimated (mos.)*	*Actual (mos.)*	*Excess of Actual (% of Estimated)*
Make Projects	1	5	400%	1	2	100%
	2	8	300	1	7	600
	3	15	400	1	2	100
	4	8	100	1	5	500
Buy Projects	2	9	350	1	4	300
	2	2	0	(less than one month)		
	2	3	50	1	11	1000
	2	5	150	1	1	0
	3	10	233	2	1	−50
	3	4	33	1	13	1200
	3	6	100	2	8	300
	3	3	0	(less than one month)		
	3	3	0	1	3	200
	3	10	233	2	7	250
	4	5	25	1	9	800
	4	7	75	2	3	50
	5	5	0	2	8	300
	5	6	20	2	6	200
	7	8	14	3	6	100
Group B	59	122	107%	25	96	284%
Group A and B Combined	124	235	90%	60	162	170%

Summary, Groups A and B Combined

	Under 26%	26% to 50%	51% to 75%	76% to 100%	101% to 200%	201% to 300%	Over 300%	Not Calculated	Median
Design & Build	8	4	2	3	2	4	3	—	71%
Debugging	3	5	—	3	3	4	6	2	100%

the project was begun.[3]   Data are given for both the combined operations, Design and Build and the operation Debugging, so that some perspective may be obtained.   In comparing the two sets of data, however, it should be remembered that in the buy

---

[3] The number of projects for which these data were available was smaller than the number included in Exhibit 8.

cases, the vendors invariably had a backlog of work for other customers which might be the source of unexpected delays.

While the median amount by which the actual schedule exceeded the original estimates is 71% for designing and building combined in Exhibit 9, it is 100% for debugging. We are dealing with elapsed time and not with quantities of labor or cost, but the fact that debugging for the middle half of these cases took between 50% and 300% more time than was planned is an unmistakable indication that serious and unexpected problems developed here, even after discounting these results somewhat because Fisher's special automatic equipment group was inexperienced in the beginning and encountered such an unexpected workload that it built up a backlog of equipment awaiting debugging.

To summarize, debugging is characterized not only by substantial direct costs but also by significant delays as the result of unexpected problems and other difficulties. The indirect costs which arise when there is delay in getting special automatic equipment into production can be even more costly than the direct cost of the additional debugging effort which may be required. Indeed, delay in the debugging stage may be said to be costly not once but twice. Before we discuss policies and procedure that may aid in minimizing the time spent in debugging, however, we will describe the general types of problems that arise during this period, in the belief that the more that is known about the sources of debugging problems, the better are the chances of either avoiding them or solving them efficiently.

Kinds of Problems Encountered in Debugging

A sample of the kinds of problems encountered in debugging is set forth in Exhibit 10. The data cover 32 separate pieces of equipment acquired by 13 plants on which the author gathered project histories. The tabulation is based on the answers the author received in each case to the question, "What were the principal problems you had in debugging this equipment?" (In more than half the cases, the equipment had been purchased, and in each of these cases the vendor who built it undoubtedly discovered and remedied additional defects.) Some problems were of greater magnitude than others. In the case of B Company, for

EXHIBIT 10

TYPES OF DEBUGGING PROBLEMS
32 EQUIPMENT PROJECTS

Type of Problem	Fisher Co.	A Co.	B Co.*	C Co.*	D Co.*†	E Co.*†	Seven Other Plants‡	Total All Plants
Feeding	7	1	1				6	15
Handling				2			8	10
Holding	2		1				1	4
Quality of Parts	6	1			1		1	9
Other Machine Design	10	4		7	1	1	14	37
Processes or Materials	4	3	2	2		1	5	17
Holding Tight Tolerances	5	1	1			1	1	9
Chip Disposal	1						2	3
Maintenance	1						3	4
Inadequate Auxiliary Services	2		1				1	4
Production Needs Interference	1					1	2	4
Lack of Debugging Manpower	2							2
Miscellaneous	2	1		1	2		1	7
Total	43	11	6	12	4	4	45	125

* Experience tabulated related to only one machine.
† Hand loaded (no automatic feeding).
‡ Data cover ten pieces of equipment.
NOTE: A, D and E cover buy projects; B and C, make projects.

instance, a satisfactory solution to the feeding problem required the expenditure of one man-year of engineering time, whereas none of the other feeding problems tallied required the expenditure of more than perhaps one-sixth of this amount of effort.

Because most of these equipment projects involved automatic rather than hand feeding of parts and workpieces, feeding problems were frequent. Developing feeding devices generally entails a large element of "cut and try," and the difficulties of perfecting such mechanisms have frequently been noted in the literature.[4] Some of the parts feeding problems encountered in

[4] See Kenneth R. Treer, "Automated Assembly — 3," *Automation,* December 1956, p. 59, and George H. DeGroat, "Automatic Assembly," *American Machinist,* September 10, 1956, p. 141.

the field work were related to the fragility or other quality of the workpieces handled, but most of the time they were related to the shape or "geometry" of the part. The same characteristics created similar problems in handling and positioning the parts, subsequent to the feeding operation. Some shapes were easy to feed and handle, and some were very difficult. In the case of C Company's equipment in Exhibit 10, for instance, the shape and center of gravity of the part were such that even after much experimentation with the hopper design, parts were sometimes being oriented so they faced in exactly the reverse direction required. The parts had to be oriented not only in terms of "front" and "back" but also in terms of the proper surface of one being "up" and another being "down." This company's solution was to use a series of electrical inspection devices in the chute connecting the vibratory hopper with the rotary work table. These devices checked each part as it slid down the chute, to determine whether or not it was properly oriented. Parts not properly oriented "frontwards" were shunted off into a tote-box, from which they were periodically fed again into the vibratory hopper by an operator. Parts which were simply upside down were shunted into a special piece of track which rotated them 180° and delivered them right-side up at the machine. Parts properly oriented — "front" end foremost and "up" side uppermost — were fed directly into the processing equipment.

Another major class of problems arose because parts deviated from their specifications. These deviations were likely to increase the complexity of the problems related to feeding, handling, and holding.[5] Various circumstances might allow some or many parts to be "off spec." Inspection might be lax; or sampling inspection might be designed to catch only flagrant violations of the specified limits; or, most likely of all, there may have been no inspection procedures established to check this particular dimen-

---

[5] Other sources confirm the importance of this type of problem; for instance, the principals of one firm building assembly machines have asserted, "Experience has proved many times that 75% to 95% of downtime on assembly machines can be traced to off-tolerance parts." See Kendall, Host, and Kendall of Kenhos Corporation, "What's Holding Back The Automatic Assembly Machine?", *American Machinist*, May 6, 1957, p. 137. This problem was frequently mentioned, too, by the vendors interviewed as another phase of this research.

sion. Such conditions were often encountered, for instance, when the tolerance involved was not important either from the standpoint of easy hand processing or for satisfactory functional performance when incorporated into a subassembly or an end item. The drafting practice of many companies included using a standard footnote on all drawings stating "all tolerances unless otherwise noted are .010," or some other arbitrary tolerance figure. If such a perfunctory or blanket specification has been incorporated in the drawing of a part but is not important with respect to some dimensions, it is not likely that an inspection operation wil be set up to check it. Nor would setting up such procedures be advisable — until the special automatic equipment designer depends on this specification in providing a holding fixture or a feeding track.

Another problem arose when the specification was silent with respect to some quality, usually other than size, and this omission became significant for the first time because of automatic processing. In one case, for instance, the amount of burr allowed on a stamped part became critical for satisfactory operation of feeding and handling devices. Under the earlier methods of hand assembly, a considerable burr had had no effect on the efficiency of hand assembly or on product performance. For the satisfactory performance of newly acquired special automatic equipment, however, it was necessary to grind (or sharpen) the stamping dies after every 50,000 pieces had been stamped out instead of every 250,000 pieces, as in the original operation. Tumbling was tested as a way of removing burrs, but sufficient tumbling to remove the burr also rounded corners on the part and created a new feeding problem even more difficult to remedy.

A third problem did not actually involve the part at all, but only foreign matter present in the supply of parts being fed into the machine. For instance, an automatic screw machine may automatically eject into a tote box not only the finished parts which it makes but also the "short end" of the bar stock remaining. Chips of metal from the machining operation also may be deposited in the tote box. Under subsequent manual processing, operators will not pick up short ends or chips, but when special automatic equipment processing replaces such manual processing, the whole contents of the tote box — workpieces, short ends, and chips — are likely to be dumped into the hopper feed. Then, when the foreign matter enters the flow of parts through the process, the equipment is likely to jam. Obviously, sampling inspection procedures cannot prevent foreign matter of this type from entering the machine; on the other hand, 100% inspection or sorting may be prohibitively expensive as a solution. The same kind of problem occurs when stamped parts are involved — a malformed part, or part of a part (resulting from less than the required area of metal being in the die at the instant of forming), is likely to jam a special automatic machine.

Other less frequently encountered quality problems were caused by parts which were adequately inspected after a primary operation but were bent or otherwise damaged when they were transported. Even dumping a tote box of parts into a hopper may damage several fragile parts enough to cause harassing problems.

If we add the 29 instances of problems in feeding, handling, and holding parts to the 9 additional cases in which the quality of parts created other types of important debugging problems, we find that the physical characteristics of the part were intimately involved in nearly one-third of the major problems we have tabulated.

The measure of difficulties caused by feeding into the machine parts which do not conform to specifications is the amount of downtime caused by jamming. One supervisor of special machine development pointed out that if a machine operates at the rate of 1,000 pieces per hour, the presence of even 2% defective parts, any of which could interfere with the machine's operation, would be likely to create jams at an average rate of about 20 times an hour. If it took an operator an average of only one minute to locate and clear each such jam, production output would not be 1,000 pieces per hour but only about 667. When assembly machines are involved and two or more parts are being processed, these effects are magnified. If the supply of each of only two parts contained just 2% defective items, and the designed operating rate and time to clear jams were as assumed above, the expected production rate would be reduced to around 333 per hour on the average, since under most circumstances a machine would not be able to operate when either part jammed. Simultaneous jamming of both parts would probably be negligible. Under many circumstances, the situation is not quite so discouraging as the example implies, for some types of defects and some degrees of deviation are not likely to cause jamming. Furthermore, for those characteristics which are inspected, many quality control procedures nominally designed to assure meeting a quality specification of 2% defectives are in fact likely to assure a much higher quality level, sometimes as little as 0.5% defectives, for example.

Machine design problems tallied under the heading of "Other Machine Design" were for the most part simply errors made in designing one of the mechanisms incorporated in the machine. They included problems of trap doors which failed to open, of operations which had to be done simultaneously but had not been synchronized. Mistaken assumptions about the conditions of use resulted in employing bases which were too light, electrical equipment which had too small capacities, and components which lacked sufficient ruggedness.[6] Some were more flagrant, such as improperly locating a shear pin, the intended function of which was to shear off and protect the main gear train of the equipment when an overload occurred. When an overload did occur, the shear pin failed to function and the whole gear box had to be replaced. Another example involved simply failing to allow sufficient clearance, which caused a rotating table to jam against the cap on a stationary center post. The frequency of these errors of oversight simply attests to the impracticability, if not the actual impossibility, of designing a new and complete piece of equipment without making any mistakes.

Another major class of debugging problems is shown in Exhibit 3 under the heading "Processes or Materials." For the most part, they represent the kinds of difficulties that are often associated with adopting a new process or a new material, regardless

---

[6] L. S. Thomas, a chief electrician with the Pontiac Division of General Motors Corporation, found that while limit switches (a component frequently used many times in a single piece of special automatic equipment) gave 3,500,000 operations before failure under laboratory (ideal) conditions, in operation on machine tools in the plant they gave only 650,000 operations. The difference was attributed to the effect of dirt, oil, coolant, and misapplications present in actual use but not under laboratory conditions. See James C. Keebler, "Wired for Automation," *Automation,* December 1958, p. 32.

of whether the changes are connected with special automatic equipment. One instance encountered in the field work for this study was that of a company that faced several problems in trying to mechanize a precious-metal plating operation which was one step in a series otherwise composed of metalworking and assembly processes. The problems in this one step were mainly chemical and were therefore less familiar to the engineers responsible for the project. In other cases, process problems encountered were in the engineer's general field, such as metalworking, but fell in a complex and highly developed subarea, such as the grinding wheel composition and cutting action problems in the Warren-King Company case (Appendix A). Likewise, a radical change of raw material, such as from steel to plastic, or even in one case simply a change to a new and quite different type of steel, was responsible for some important debugging problems.

Sometimes a change in a process has more far-reaching effects than have been predicted. Only after the equipment has been built are these effects realized. Consider the following example of the problems which developed after a change was made from hand-soldering of electronic component terminals, one at a time, to dip-soldering a whole circuit assembly composed of many electronic components:

> One of the big problems at present is the characteristic changes [i.e., changes in the electrical characteristics] which take place when an electronic part or assembly is exposed to soldering temperature for a long time. This isn't likely to happen with hand soldering but (is) under the extreme conditions used for soldering under an automated setup. In some cases, the changes can be so severe as to shift the characteristics of the part beyond their specified limit.
>
> . . . In shifting from hand soldering, which involves a second or two, the dip period in an automatic setup may extend to 30 seconds with the solder at a temperature of 450 degress to 650 degrees F. In that time as many as 200 to 300 parts [terminal connections] can be completed, but the temperature effect is considerably greater.[7]

These process-materials problems will further complicate the task of debugging. Sometimes such changes cannot be avoided;

---

[7] H. J. McGarvey and G. P. McKnight, "Soldering: Automation Breeds New Problems," *Iron Age,* August 15, 1957, pp. 104–105.

indeed, the main value of some pieces of equipment was derived from their ability to use a new but potentially more efficient process, or cheaper materials, or both.

The type of debugging problems classified in Exhibit 10 as difficulty in holding tight tolerances on some operations is not unique to processing by special automatic equipment — failure to hold tight tolerances lies at the root of many hand operation difficulties, too. Cases were encountered in which tool wear was rapid, or difficult to adjust for, and in which it was difficult to hold one dimension in relation to another with the precision demanded. Lack of precision in the basic workpieces frequently affected the ease with which close tolerances could be achieved in subsequent processing.

The remaining types of problems suggest the variety of causes, many of them resulting from simple oversights, which can create major, costly delays during debugging. Perhaps the most significant of these is failure to provide adequate auxiliary services. In all such instances noted in Exhibit 10, auxiliary services already existed, but they had not been checked against the particular equipment to be installed, and their inadequacy was not discovered until the equipment was well into the debugging period. In two of these cases, electrical elements in the special automatic equipment functioned imperfectly because of voltage variations in the existing electrical current supply lines, but it took each of these firms several weeks to discover this fact.

The problem of chip removal, to avoid injury to the part during subsequent operations and interference with the clamping or machining of the next piece at the same station, is one of which vendors are fully aware at the time equipment is designed. It is also the type of problem which is likely to be identified quickly and remedied during debugging at the builder's plant, before the user takes delivery. Nevertheless, the full implications of a problem sometimes are not apparent until the equipment has been running for a time. In one case, for example, a mixture of coolant and abrasive found its way into the main bearings of a machine and damaged the equipment badly before it was discovered.

The maintenance problems referred to include only those which appeared during the debugging period, and included instances in which routine adjustments were too time-consuming, repairs of replacements were required too frequently, or clearing a jam of parts took too long, because of the way in which the machine had been constructed. To avoid excessive downtime in production operation, the equipment was modified to expedite maintenance operations, or to reduce the frequency with which they were required, or to accomplish both of these results.

The fact that debugging activities may be put under pressure by production schedule needs, and the fact that a shortage of debugging manpower may occur, may be the result of poor initial planning. On the other hand, some of these instances simply demonstrated that it is unrealistic to expect to be able to think of everything.

Of the miscellaneous group of difficulties, only one will be mentioned. This was a major problem of production scheduling which had to be solved in order to permit a newly acquired piece of special automatic equipment to process several parts. This machine had to be set up differently for each part, and, as the time needed to change machine setups was eight hours or more, only long runs were economical. There were preceding operations on the parts, however, and the flow of these parts throughout the plant had to be rescheduled to provide for the accumulation of a large lot of each part just before it was scheduled to run on the special automatic equipment. Whenever a piece of special automatic equipment produces at a materially different hourly rate from either preceding or subsequent operations, this kind of problem arises.

Although these major debugging problems typically took many man-weeks of effort to diagnose and solve, in most of the projects a very large part of the time and effort was actually expended on problems other than those tallied. These were problems no one of which was major but which in total had a large impact. For instance, one supervisor described how in the latter stages of debugging some bolts would not hold tight but would gradually become loose from vibration after a short period of operation. It was simply, but not quickly, solved: "We finally learned that dipping the bolt in glyptol before we ran it home solved the problem." None of the problems like this one was very important but each project had dozens of them; and in sum their solution constituted a large share of the debugging effort. And sometimes the simplest problems — simplest in retrospect, that is — were among the most frustrating.[8]

To summarize briefly, our data indicated that a wide variety of problems is typical of debugging. Many problems involve the nature of the parts being processed rather than the machine elements alone. Both the physical characteristics and the degree of control over the quality of parts flowing through equipment had an important bearing on the kinds of problems arising. Machine elements in themselves were also an important source of trouble for users even though in most cases in our sample the equipment had presumably been debugged earlier by the vendor who had built it. In the event that a company designs and builds its own equipment, these kinds of problems are likely to comprise a large portion of the total. When new processes or material were involved, additional problems were almost inevitably added. The bulk of the debugging, however, was usually composed of a great many small problems which gradually yielded to systematic but tedious study and experiment. Since special automatic equipment by definition is made up of new mechanisms and new combinations of tested mechanisms, there are bound to be some errors of both commission and omission in planning, designing, and building them.

Policies and Procedures to Avoid or Minimize Debugging Problems

Efforts to minimize the time and money expended on debugging can take the form of, first, steps to avoid problems or reduce their magnitude and, second, steps to bring completed machines to a state of satisfactory production performance as efficiently as possible. The first type of action, to prevent or minimize problems, calls mainly for steps to be taken in planning before the

---

[8] Sometimes they were so simple that they were amusing, as in the case of some newly installed equipment which suddenly developed a habit of stopping in the middle of an operation for no apparent reason. After several days of frustration, a vendor's representative happened to observe that the machine stopped as a workman took a short cut to a nearby drinking fountain. It developed that his clothing had brushed against the buttons of the master switch, and the "bug" was remedied by making a simple sheet metal hood to protect the switch button. See R. S. Alexander, Letters to the Editor, *American Machinist*, July 15, 1957, pp. 223ff.

equipment is built, while the second type of action takes place after the equipment has been partially or wholly assembled and focuses on the operating aspects of debugging *per se*.

The foundation for any policies or procedures designed to minimize debugging problems must be a general awareness among special automatic equipment project leaders and their supervisors of the kinds of problems which are likely to develop in debugging operations. Ideally, an awareness of the same kind among product designers, production supervision, and top management is also desirable because it will help in obtaining the cooperation required from these groups. In a company which has acquired a few pieces of special automatic equipment, such knowledge will already exist, at least among several if not all of the persons involved. In a company which has not, however, there is a problem of getting this background. Perhaps the preceding section's recitation of major types of problems will stimulate responsible personnel to undertake plant visits to companies known to have such experience, or to vendors, or to both. The author was unsuccessful in locating much of value in the literature on this topic. On the other hand, his field work convinced him that experienced project leaders and supervisors were quite willing to identify and discuss the problems encountered in their projects if they were asked to do so. Three or four plant visits, planned to develop such information, are likely to create the awareness desired and give the optimum return for the time spent. Subsequent experience can be depended upon to provide a basis upon which to broaden and deepen their appreciation.

Whether a company's personnel are experienced or inexperienced, their supervisor will be remiss if he fails to continue their training by reviewing the experience gained during the projects they undertake. Periodic conferences should be held to review the debugging and other problems encountered during projects recently completed and the ways in which they were handled. Moreover, after some appropriate interval — at the end of a piece of equipment's first year of production operation, for example — another type of conference should be held, with appropriate maintenance and production personnel present, to review the general performance of the piece of equipment and the operating and maintenance problems which have been encountered. All project leaders, machine designers, and technicians would probably have something to contribute to, and also something to gain from, both types of session.

Given this kind of foundation, one area in which action may be effective in avoiding some debugging problems lies in coordinating the product design organization with the equipment acquisition group. A conscious effort by product designers when a part is first designed (or is redesigned) to adopt shapes which are easy to orient, feed, or locate, can help to reduce the burden of debugging. Product design-production engineering coordination is a topic which covers a broad field, and all of Chapter VII is devoted to the topic because of its importance.

Another step of first-rate importance for avoiding debugging problems is using pilot projects and mock-ups to test the feasibility of a doubtful mechanism, new processes, or feeding and handling devices. In the Knight Company, for instance, the standard procedures allowed a supervisor to authorize expenditures of up to $1,000 for the purpose of investigating such problems. If the idea emerging seemed to be a good one, the appropriation could subsequently be increased, by vote of Knight's cost reduction committee, up to $10,000. Often sums up to this amount were expended for further investigation and mock-ups before any equipment was finally designed or ordered from a vendor. Similar policies were followed in a few of the companies visited, but it was far from being a general practice in those cases in which it might have been useful.

Tests need not be elaborate. For some types of investigations vendors are sometimes prepared to give limited help. One special machine tool builder, for instance, maintained a test facility to which an engineering specialist was assigned, and a small lot of a particular part could be run at different speeds and feeds or with special tools to observe the effect of such changes on tool wear, surface finish, or other characteristics.

Predesign testing of feeding devices in particular seems to be a desirable yet relatively inexpensive way of avoiding some of the many problems in this area. No equipment user was found to be doing this, but one vendor reported that such testing was a standard step in its routine for estimating the cost of feeding devices. At least one of the vendors specializing in the design of feeding devices was reported to maintain several commonly used devices of different sizes for the purpose of making test runs before designing a feeding mechanism.

Providing facilities for predesign testing and building of mock-up mechanisms, for the common use of personnel from several plants, might well be an appropriate function for a central process development organization in large multiplant corporations.

A third practice is likely to be equally productive in minimizing the debugging efforts required for a particular project. A careful investigation should be carried out to discover any discrepancies between the production specifications (usually the blueprint) for a part and its actual condition as it is currently being processed in the plant. Whether a particular part specification should be relaxed to agree with existing conditions, or whether production procedures and processes should be changed to bring conditions into agreement with existing specifications, is a question to be decided in each instance of a discrepancy or conflict. Such questions cannot (or should not) be decided by the project engineer, even though in many cases he may have a thoroughly legitimate basis for advocating one particular course of action. The general objective of this investigation should be to make sure that the parts that come from the production process are identical with the parts that were specified when the proposed equipment was designed.

This step should take place some time in the early stages of developing a project proposal, probably before full-dress economic justification is attempted and undoubtedly before even preliminary equipment design is attempted. It should utilize a valid sample of parts, taken, if possible, over a period of time so as to assure that significant variations are not overlooked. Using appropriate assistance available from the quality control or inspection department the project leader can develop quality control charts showing the variation in outside dimensions and locating surfaces, for instance, along with data on variations in other relevant quality attributes, such as the hardness and irregularities in outline when the workpiece is a casting. Part of the useful data may already have been compiled under existing routines; for example, control charts may already be kept in the screw machine department which produces the part to be processed by the contemplated special automatic equipment. Supplementary investigation, however, needs to be made to fix the quality characteristics of these parts as they would be when fed into the proposed machine. The project leader must constantly be aware of the possibilities that parts damaged in transit, short ends, and foreign matter may be present in tote boxes feeding the machine.

As a safeguard, the special automatic machine designer (whether the user's or a vendor's employee) should be furnished with a list of specifications the project leader has checked, plus a summary of the observed variations relating thereto. The machine designer should also be instructed to notify the project engineer of any specification he proposes to assume or to read from the workpiece blueprint. And as a further safeguard, as soon as the detail equipment drawings become available, they should be checked to establish the important relationships between the part and the equipment, including such things as surfaces grasped by holding fixtures, locating surfaces employed, and feeding tracks; and it should again be determined whether the implied dimensions of the workpiece are in accord with the actual condition of parts in current production.

If the special automatic equipment is to machine or assemble a part of a new design and this new design is not currently in production, the kind of procedure just described cannot be fully implemented. A supply of sample parts, however, may still be of some help even if they are produced on a pilot run basis, rather than under actual production conditions. To be sure, sometimes even this step is not possible. But whether it is or not, the machine designer can list the surfaces and dimensions he has used as a basis for designing the special automatic equipment, and the product designer can verify these and insure that they will be considered in the event that last minute changes in the part are proposed. Such a list can also be used by the plant's quality control supervisor to assure that the parts as produced or purchased agree with the specifications for the items listed. There is no denying, however, that there are more likely to be difficulties when the parts to be processed by proposed special automatic equipment are not in current production.

In a very broad sense, an investigation of the condition and quality of the parts supply is actually a step toward a clearer definition of the job to be done by the proposed equipment. The proportion of defective parts and foreign matter which must be accepted is a fundamental factor underlying the over-all equipment design. It may determine the very feasibility of designing technically satisfactory equipment, and if the project is technically feasible it materially affects the nature of suitable performance specifications, especially with respect to feeding methods and capacity. The 100% automatic inspection of parts fed into a piece of equipment may sometimes be necessary and feasible, but this solution is likely to be so difficult and costly as to threaten the justification for the project. In any event, the necessity for 100% inspection should be established before the equipment is built rather than at the time it is being debugged.

Finally, standardization of common components and the adoption of common construction practices for special automatic equipment will make it much easier to locate the causes of trouble in many cases and will increase the speed with which many changes can be made. When equipment is purchased, standardization should help the project leader and debugging technicians to learn more quickly, and perhaps learn more that is useful, about the equipment from the vendor's personnel. The Joint Industry Conference (JIC) standards program,[9] in which the automotive firms are strongly represented, has been an attempt to coordinate the setting of standards on an industry-wide basis, but some large buyers of equipment have also developed standards of their own for both purchased and user-built equipment. The module (or so-called building-block) design policy for special automatic equipment, of which we shall say more in Chapter VII, likewise has a similar advantage in facilitating debugging. While very little standardization may be justified on the grounds

---

[9] For an interesting history of the JIC standards and the methods by which they are established, see J. Q. Holmes, "Conception and Development of JIC Standards," Paper No. 42, *Collected Papers, 1957 Silver Anniversary Edition* (Detroit, American Society of Tool Engineers, 1957). For a review of the various sources for equipment and tool standards, the types of items covered thereby, and some additional standards now being developed, see the same author, "Standards for Manufacturing: What We Need," *American Machinist*, December 14, 1959, pp. 115–117.

of facilitating debugging alone, these benefits are supplemented by others. Standardization also facilitates the over-all maintenance function over the whole life of the equipment[10] and serves, too, to achieve a measure of control over the quality of the equipment acquired. Furthermore, as will be discussed in Chapter VII, module construction results in substantial economies under some circumstances by making it possible to re-use basic machine elements in later projects. Just how far it will pay to go in standardization will depend upon the individual circumstances of each plant, that is, it will depend in part on how many of these opportunities are available and how willing and able its management is to exploit them.

Several other steps which may be taken to minimize debugging problems will be noted briefly.

1. As a matter of routine, the project engineers should verify that the kinds of auxiliary services required by the proposed equipment would in fact be available in the quantities needed. The earlier specifications for such auxiliary services can be spelled out the better, as they may have a bearing as well on the economic advisability of the project.

The prospective demands on the central supply of electricity, compressed air, steam, water, and so on probably needs to be reviewed frequently in many plants because it is likely to be more economical to expand capacity for each of these services in fairly large steps rather than in small ones and on a planned rather than emergency basis. This kind of planning and reviewing probably would be done by a different unit, such as the maintenance group. Individual project checks by the project engineer would still be worth while, as the particular location at which the equipment will be installed may affect the distribution systems of the services.

2. The step of determining the general approach to the equipment, usually termed the preliminary layout, can usually benefit from criticism of others in addition to the project engineer or machine designer responsible for the project. A group meeting of other project engineers engaged in acquiring similar special automatic equipment has proved to be a useful source of criti-

---

[10] On this point, see Bright, pp. 153–154.

cism and helpful suggestions for improvement in some companies. Foremen and, at least under some circumstances, specialized maintenance personnel may also contribute valuable suggestions at this time.[11]

3. The detailed drawings for a piece of special automatic equipment should be checked by someone other than the person who drew them. If the equipment is being designed and built by the user, routine checking generally is the responsibility of the drafting group, which may or may not be part of the equipment acquisition group; if the equipment is being purchased, checking is the responsibility of the vendor. The basic features of the equipment, however, and especially the basic features of the tooling and handling elements, should be subjected to a special, detailed, and independent review by competent technical personnel, preferably the project engineer when he has not played a major role in design work, and by someone else competent to do so in other cases.

4. The ability and experience of the project engineers and their supervisors are almost certain to have a significant effect on the amount of debugging which will have to be done. This comment is even more applicable to the machine designer. One who has seen several pieces of special equipment he designed go through the entire development cycle is likely to design another piece of such equipment with fewer bugs than a man who has not. Even years of experience with closely related design work, such as laboratory-type equipment or jig and fixture design, is not equivalent.[12] Until such men are recruited or trained the charges for debugging are likely to be inflated.

---

[11] Kessler of the Delco-Remy Division of General Motors notes the utility of such a procedure. See "How Special Machinery Is Developed," p. 144. One of the companies among those included in the writer's field work was also found to be following this procedure and reported valuable results.

[12] One company interviewed during the field work reported a very unhappy experience with equipment designed as a first attempt by tool designers from their own organization. Similarly, a case was encountered in which a vendor with considerable experience in building laboratory-type equipment seriously underestimated the strain of factory operations and delivered "underbuilt" equipment which could not withstand the continuous pounding of daily operations.

Policies and Procedures That Expedite Debugging Once It Has Begun

Although the actions we reviewed in the preceding section will reduce the burden of debugging which will have to be done, they will by no means eliminate the debugging step for special automatic equipment. In this section, therefore, we shall focus on policies and procedures which will hasten whatever operations must be performed to get the equipment to function at normal levels of production.

The training, experience, and ability of personnel comprise a key factor in efficient, quick debugging. The general tenor of field interviews indicated that much of the burden of debugging rests upon technicians — machinists, millwrights, and electricians — who have a special knack for making mechanical and electrical devices work. They are persons skillful with their hands and tools, and they possess imagination. They also seem to enjoy solving the myriad of little mechanical (and electrical) problems, solutions to which comprise a large part of the process of debugging. Casual observation suggested that some project engineers seem to have like capabilities.

If little or no equipment like this has been acquired before, specialized technical knowledge about control devices — pneumatic, hydraulic, and especially electrical (including electronic) control devices and systems — is likely to be inadequate. Existing employees, even those already classified as electricians, for instance, may require extensive formal training to equip them to deal effectively with the electrical and electronic controls typically incorporated in special automatic equipment, and may thereby bring about some further specialization in the plant's maintenance group. If the program becomes large enough, some technicians may be permanently transferred to the special automatic equipment group.[13]

The company just starting on a program to acquire special automatic equipment will be handicapped by a lack of general background as well. Just as some understanding of the kinds of

---

[13] See Bright, pp. 160–161, on the skills required for general maintenance of this type of equipment.

problems involved in debugging may help a project engineer in avoiding problems, so such knowledge is of some help to both project engineers and technicians in speeding the solution of problems encountered. If available personnel have no experience, visits to plants with recent experience in debugging special automatic equipment will help technicians, too, and doubly benefit the project engineers.

If the equipment is being designed and built by a vendor, then the user's personnel have the problem of becoming familiar with the equipment's construction and operation during a relatively short period of time, either just before or just after it has been delivered. Vendors will usually permit inspection of the equipment before delivery and also make available some of their personnel to help; it will usually pay users to take advantage of all such opportunities. We shall return to this topic again at greater length in our chapter on dealing effectively with vendors.

Several other actions besides the basic one of selecting and training capable technicians may increase the efficiency of actual debugging operations. Again, close liaison with the product design engineering organization is desirable. During this phase good liaison may be able to accomplish two things: first, it will undoubtedly facilitate making minor design changes in parts which may simplify debugging problems, and second, especially if the product design for the part is a new one, it may help prevent, modify, or delay design changes which might create additional debugging problems. Company policy and the administrative environment should be such as to encourage the project engineer to suggest possibilities for product design changes as a means of speeding debugging operations, and to expect the product designer to be receptive to such suggestions. Such practices need not infringe on the traditional prerogatives of the design engineer if it is clearly understood that the design engineer possesses complete veto power (at least pending appeal to higher management) of any modifications suggested. This observation is made without in any way depreciating the delicate administrative problems that may be involved in implementing such a policy in the face of the traditions which seem to exist in many companies.

At the beginning of debugging, some changes which promise

to raise the rate and quality of output from a newly assembled piece of equipment will be obvious. Thereafter, however, certain quantitative data will probably be of considerable help in locating sources of trouble, in measuring the efficiency of solutions tried, and in forecasting the remaining time needed to reach ultimate performance efficiencies. A machine log should accumulate such information as:

Output speeds, yield, and quality of experimental runs.

Hours run, production rate and number of defective pieces produced.

Downtime record, including minutes (hours) down; part of machine (or other reasons) causing stoppage; and cause.

In addition, the output should be subjected to 100% inspection or, for runs too large for this, to sampling inspection so that control charts can be plotted for important specifications.

An example is shown in Exhibit 11, which is a reproduction of a weekly report made on a project in the Wheeler Company. Shortly after the week covered by this report, the equipment was started running on a regular production basis, with monthly results, both shrinkage and average hourly production rate, as shown in Exhibit 12. When this piece of equipment had its first test run in February 1954 with 243 items, it had produced a little more than 25% defectives. It took four months of debugging to reduce the defectives from 25% to 5%, and then eight months more to approximate its rated hourly production capacity. Much of the slow growth in this latter period was related not to bugs in this particular piece of equipment but rather to the downtime of other pieces of equipment which performed preceding and subsequent operations on the product, and to the problems of coordinating their performance. The growth curves in Exhibit 12 — rapid at first but progressively slowing down, for both the quality and rate of output — were typical of several projects for which comparable data were available.[14]

An example of a tabulation of downtime on equipment which was running on a semiproduction basis, with debugging con-

---

[14] For an interesting exposition on a similar phenomenon, the growth in reliability of missile and electronic systems, see H. K. Weiss, "Estimation of Reliability Growth in a Complex System With a Poisson-Type Failure," *Operations Research*, October 1956, pp. 532–545.

EXHIBIT 11

SAMPLE PROGRESS REPORT, WHEELER COMPANY

Subject: Special Automatic Equipment Project 7A
Date: May 6, 1954
To: Robert Roberts (Special Automatic Equipment Group Supervisor)

During the test that was run Tuesday, April 27, 1954, progress was made, but in our opinion it was not satisfactory.   Herewith results:

Gross — 222   Net — 207   Shrinkage — 6.8%

The following is a breakdown of the above figures:

Defect Code		No.
27	—	5
34	—	4
36	—	2
51	—	4
	Total	15

These were more or less general and will have to be traced individually. Another test was run also.   Following is the summary:

Gross — 393   Net — 369   Shrinkage — 6.1%

The following is a breakdown of the above figures:

Defect Code		No.
27	—	14
34	—	6
36	—	1
51	—	2
55	—	1
	Total	24

You will note the greatest factor responsible for the above shrinkage are the 27's.   These 27's are different to the extent that they do not occur at the edge of the joint.

Analysis of the joints of both the broken products and good products from our machine, shows a bad weld in the flange, which so happens to be the weakest part.

We have tried several methods to rectify this situation but it still remains elusive.   As soon as this deficiency has been corrected we will run further tests.

                                                                                  E. L. Gerard

EXHIBIT 12

PER CENT SHRINKAGE AND AVERAGE HOURLY PRODUCTION
DURING DEBUGGING, WHEELER COMPANY

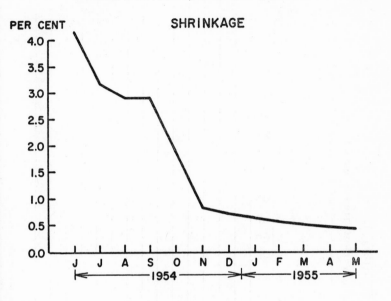

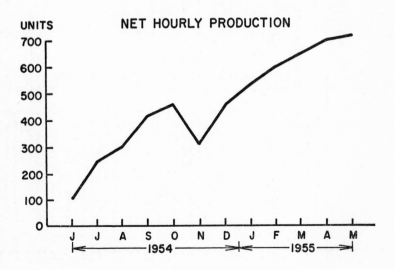

EXHIBIT 13

EXAMPLE OF DAILY DOWNTIME SUMMARY

Descriptive Analysis of Downtime
Dept. No. 67 Automated Line
Oper. No. 1   Machine Grinder

Period of Time: 5–6 thru 6–1

Daily Downtime Hours

Item	Cause of Downtime	5–6	7	8	9	10	11	13	14	15	16	17	18	20	21	22	23	24	25	27	28	29	30	Total
1	Wheel Change	(5) 1.4	(3) .5	(3) .9	(3) 1.0	(3) .4	(3) .5	(3) .6	(3) .8	(2) .3	(1) .3	(2) .4			(2) .3	(4) .7	(1) .2	(1) .2		(3) .5	(3) .5	(3) .5	(3) .7	10.9
2	Repair Water Line		.7																					.7
3	Repair or Adjust Clamp		1.0																					1.0
4	Replace Belt on Reducer Unit						.3																	0.3
5	Replace Hangers in Conveyor						.4																	0.4
6	Replace Shear Pin in Conv. Motor						.3				.6							.3			.2	.2		1.6
7	Clean Discharge Chute							.1						.3										0.4
8	Replace Bulb in Panel							.1																0.1
9	Plumbing Repair										.5													8.5
10	Replace Conveyor Flights														.1	.5				.2	.3	.1	.3	1.5
11	Short in Machine (Water)															1.5								1.5
12	Jam in Hopper																.5							0.5
13	Check Electrical Cycle																.3	1.5						1.8
14	Replace Spindle Bearings																9.0							9.0
15	Replace or Adjust Locators																	2.5		.3				2.8
																								41.0

NOTES: Did not operate every day.
Figures in parentheses on "Wheel Change" line show number of wheel changes each day.

tinuing, is shown in Exhibit 13. This tabulation refers to the downtime of one grinding unit which was the first machine in a series. Therefore the problems include those of initially feeding the part, processing it at this machine, and conveying it to the next. The figures in parentheses above the first item indicate the number of times the equipment was down during the two-shift period involved. At this stage of debugging the most frequent cause of downtime was simply the routine replacement of the abrasive wheel; these occasions accounted for about one-quarter of the total downtime. The coolant (water) system was directly and indirectly a major cause of downtime, requiring repairs to itself and being responsible for an electrical short and (through leakage of coolant with abrasive grains) damage to the spindle bearing. The feeding and handling systems were a third major source of downtime even though this was near the end and not the beginning of the debugging period. Supplementing this report was another giving the daily total of number of units produced.

It is likely to be worth while to continue to accumulate at least some of these data, probably on a sampling basis, after debugging is terminated and for as long as a piece of special automatic equipment is in operation because of its value in other ways. These data can be used to determine the size of in-process inventories which it will be economical to carry for the purpose of absorbing the effect of unavoidable downtime; to identify likely areas for later cost reduction projects; to identify problem areas which may be alleviated by performing frequent preventative maintenance, say on weekends, to avoid downtime during scheduled hours of operation; and to provide a basis for curing weaknesses in machine design in the event a project is undertaken either to design a new model of the equipment or to make major modifications to the existing machine. Analysis of these data can also comprise the central focus of review sessions, such as we suggested earlier, say one year after debugging has been terminated, for the purpose of training project leaders and equipment designers.

During initial debugging it should also be useful to maintain a record identifying the lots of raw material processed and to accumulate the findings of a sampling inspection of each lot before it is processed. Again, care needs to be taken to select samples at the location from which they are being fed into the machine, and to inspect for foreign matter.

At one or more times during debugging a process capability test or a statistically designed experiment may be a helpful technique. The first kind of test will indicate whether the process is "in control" — that is to say, whether the machine is doing about as well as can be expected, given its present capabilities, or whether the current variations in performance probably can be reduced by identifying some one or more factors which are acting in other than a random fashion. A piece of equipment may be performing about as well as expected, given the existing state of its physical condition, the nature of the process involved, and the kind of parts being fed into it. In this event a basic change in some one of these variables (such as tighter tolerances on incoming parts) is likely to be necessary to get improved levels of quality in the output. On the other hand, a malfunctioning mechanism, an occasional lot of over- or under-sized parts, or a change in any other controllable factor will affect the data plotted on the control charts.[15]

---

[15] Detailed consideration of control charts and statistical quality control procedures is beyond the scope of this work. For a basic description of the control chart, see American Standards Association, *Control Chart Method of Controlling Quality During Production,* standard Z 1.3–1942 (New York, The Association, 1942); or Edward H. Bowman and Robert B. Fetter, *Analysis for Production Management,* Chapter 6, "Statistical Control" pp. 147–179 (Homewood, Irwin, 1957). The classic treatment of the topic is W. A. Shewhart, *Economic Control of Quality of Manufactured Product* (New York, Van Nostrand, 1931).

For a short description and a simple example of a machine capability study see William G. Ireson and Eugene L. Grant (Editors), *Handbook of Industrial Engineering and Management* (Englewood Cliffs, Prentice-Hall, 1955), pp. 1009–1011. Further description and comment on its use may be found in J. M. Juran (Editor), *Quality Control Handbook* (New York, McGraw-Hill, 1951). Basic concepts are discussed by Juran in pp. 257–266, and he makes a useful distinction between process capability charts and control charts on pp. 278–279. On p. 265 he suggests the possibility of using machine capability studies to test machine tools. In pp. 704–716, L. A. Seder discusses the application of machine capability studies to automatic screw machines.

For a description of design of experiment and analysis of variances, see Dorian Shainin, "The Statistically Designed Experiment," *Harvard Business Review,* July–August 1957, pp. 67–73; and Bowman and Fetter, cited above, Chapter 8, "Industrial Experimentation," pp. 205–237.

An interesting approach using a control chart technique for analysis, as

Whether or not the process is "in control," it may be useful to employ a statistically designed experiment, permitting analysis of variances to identify one or more specific factors which may be linked with variations in quality. Despite their formidable sound, such statistical techniques are potentially quite useful in debugging because, utilizing other techniques, the diagnosis of the cause of the trouble often takes many more man-hours than the remedy. Among the machine histories compiled there were many problems which seemed to stump debugging personnel for as much as two or three weeks and occasionally even for six months. For these kinds of problems in particular and also as a device useful in determining the most profitable direction for further effort after obvious initial defects have been remedied, statistically designed and analyzed experiments justify the pains required for learning how and when to apply them.[16]

Process capability tests had been undertaken in two of the companies visited. In the Young Company they were employed, after considerable debugging, on several pieces of automatic equipment which essentially comprised the manufacturing facilities of three departments. A committee of manufacturing engineering, quality control, and production representatives undertook a program to raise the quality level of the finished end product of these three departments. It was anticipated that the quality of parts produced by some pieces of equipment and the quality of some purchased parts would have to be raised, and process capability tests were used to discover the best places to direct the committee's efforts.

The other firm, the Lodge Company, performed process ca-

---

well as an excellent example of the power of these techniques, is contained in Kenneth S. Stephens, "A Simplified Method of Analyzing Experimental Data," in *Western Electric Engineer*, July 1958, pp. 20–26.

[16] No systematic attempt was made to develop data on special types of instruments which might be useful in debugging, but I did encounter one case in which a firm had found it useful to measure the frequency of sounds emitted by a piece of equipment, employing a laboratory instrument, as a means of locating faulty mechanisms. A very similar approach to finding the cause of certain kinds of bugs using electronic devices to analyze the frequency of vibrations set up in operation has been briefly reported elsewhere. See *American Machinist*, March 26, 1956, pp. 106–107.

A timing and recording device and its use in debugging are described in Kirk E. Birell, "Diagnostic Tools for Automatic Equipment" (Abstract), *Tool Engineer*, August 1957, pp. 205–206.

pability tests on a single-station prototype which had been constructed to determine the feasibility of automatically performing certain basic operations. Quality attributes in this case included several electrical characteristics, and visual examination was not very successful in spotting the causes of the variations in electrical test results. As a further step, therefore, statistically designed experiments were conducted, varying selected factors in an experimental design to establish the effect, if any, that variation of each factor had on the quality of production. An analysis of the results of these experiments proved to be very helpful to the project leader in finding out how the production equipment should be designed to achieve the quality required. Although this example dealt with less than the fully assembled machine, there is no reason why the same techniques could not have been used in much the same way during the later stages of debugging.[17]

The foregoing comments imply that there should be close liaison with the quality control department during debugging operations. The project leader should not expect, however, to rely on quality control representatives to direct the debugging efforts; the most they can do is to provide him with some statistical techniques which may aid him to achieve his objective more quickly. The project leader must suggest the hypotheses to be tested by the statistically designed experiments, and the usefulness of the results are more likely to depend upon the hypotheses than upon the statistics. To use their help most efficiently he needs an understanding of at least the basic elements underlying the compilation and interpretation of control charts. Certainly this is not a formidable task. Foremen and machine operators have often been given a grasp of such fundamentals in a matter of days by means of special training programs. Having grasped these elements, in most instances the project leader probably also should be able to collaborate with company quality control engineers in the use of more advanced statistical techniques.

---

[17] Strictly speaking, Lodge's machine was a mock-up, and this illustration is one we might have included in our discussion of how to reduce the amount of debugging which had to be done, for it took place before the final equipment had been designed, let alone assembled. It seemed more appropriate, however, to include all comments on the use of statistical techniques at one place in this chapter.

Aside from their statistical skills, quality control personnel may also bring a fresh viewpoint to bear on problems and therefore be doubly valuable to the project engineer.

As a concluding suggestion, good project planning and scheduling are essential to minimize the kind of delays that occur when equipment is delivered and all qualified debugging personnel are busy on other projects. Failure to allow adequate time for debugging, including a safety margin, or failure to have an adequate amount of qualified debugging manpower available when it was needed, or both, created costly problems time and again in the plants visited. Not only do such mistakes make getting the equipment into production more costly than it ought to be, but particularly when the equipment is to be used to produce a new model product, mistakes are likely to put a strain on the special automatic equipment group.[18] In two cases in the field work, heavy pressure and overtime for project leaders and technicians were sustained for several months with great damage to morale and to the mental and physical health of the special automatic equipment group's members.

Good planning begins with careful, realistic estimates of the kinds and amounts of man-hours likely to be needed in debugging. When there are more than two or three project engineers, it is often useful to draw up a rough bar chart, similar to a machine load chart, forecasting the work load of each active project through to its completion and charting the results with respect to project leaders and types of technical assistance required. Analysis of past experience and more care will raise the quality of such estimates. As we have seen, however, the best

---

[18] When a whole plant is a new one and is being constructed to make a new product or a new model of product and many pieces of special automatic equipment are planned in conjunction therewith, the problem of planning, scheduling, and coordination can easily grow beyond the capacities of the management and the technical organization (who themselves are likely to be new). All that can be done is to recognize this possibility and take care to avoid it, perhaps postponing some special automatic equipment projects as one way of containing the quantity of changes that have to be absorbed. Coordination at this level and of this scope, however, is beyond the scope of this study. Bright's *Automation and Management* contains examples of several programs involving whole new plants. See especially his DeSanto case, pp. 116–117, and his Chapter 9, pp. 123–131. See also *Business Week*, "It Doesn't Always Pay to Put All Your Chips on Automation," August 10, 1957, pp. 58–64.

of forecasts about debugging matters are found to have wide limits of error. Therefore, there must be frequent reassessment and rescheduling of each project in the light of new conditions and new knowledge which are bound to arise after initial time schedules have been established.

The Thompson Company, for instance, found itself in a cycle which began with a period of several months in which all project engineers and technicians were overloaded with projects in the debugging stage. This was followed by a comparable period in which no equipment at all was being debugged but during which new projects were developed that would lead to a debugging overload several months later. The project engineers adapted to this kind of situation, though it seemed quite clear that it was not the most efficient way for them to work. The effects on technical personnel were more serious, for it was more difficult to meet the peak demands for able personnel, and in slack periods they had to be assigned to general maintenance work which did not require the specialized training they had received.

Such an extreme situation could have been greatly improved by initially planning in detail the manpower requirements through the completion of each project, by revising these estimates periodically in the light of subsequent developments (especially delays in equipment delivery), and by frequently reviewing the status of projects and by rescheduling, taking advantage of personnel turnover, variations in possible work assignments, and the sequence with which projects were begun. Under the best of circumstances the debugging function will no doubt continue to demand much flexibility from all personnel connected with it, but effective planning can do much to reduce the amplitude of the swings in demand, and to provide advance notice which will often facilitate making adjustments to unforeseen events.

Organizational Responsibility for Debugging

In general, a project leader should be responsible for the project from the time it is started until it is formally accepted by the day-to-day production organization. This kind of arrangement precludes many opportunities for "passing the buck." Another major advantage of such a policy is that, through the project leader, it assures a feedback of the lessons learned about machine design, general approach, and avoidable pitfalls, knowledge which is likely to benefit subsequent projects. This does not mean that the project leader personally should do all the work debugging requires; although there are always exceptional leaders who can do this, the pedestrian work of the debugging function can almost always be done more efficiently by skilled technicians with general guidance.

Terminating the responsibility of the project leader may be difficult. Unless provision is made for termination at the appropriate time, the project leader's intimate association with a particular piece of equipment may lead him to continue past the point of diminishing returns and involve him in trying to service the equipment when it is, or should be, in a production status and therefore the responsibility of others. It is also a temptation for production supervisors to call upon the project leader to help with problems which can be handled, perhaps less quickly but in the long run more efficiently, by regular maintenance personnel.

Several considerations from the standpoint of both the special automatic equipment group and the production department probably will be involved, and some may be conflicting. The precise timing can be decided on the merits of each individual case by the special automatic equipment supervisor, the plant superintendent, and the supervisor of both. Alternatively, some broad principle may be agreed upon in advance, such as production of a minimum number of good workpieces in three consecutive work days, or a minimum output over one forty-hour week. Even so, exceptions will probably arise which dictate an earlier or a later transfer date.

It will help to have a policy, clearly understood by all, that once the production department formally accepts the equipment as a means for meeting its daily production schedules, the project leader will cease to have any further responsibility, and to require a formal acceptance, say by a simple memorandum at the time of the transfer from the production department. Such a policy does not, of course, preclude the training of operators or the production of output for the use of the production department prior to the transfer, while responsibility remains with the project engineer. Probably in most cases these activities should take place concurrently and cooperatively.

The foregoing arrangement of full project leader responsibility for debugging may be less suitable when the special automatic equipment organization is quite large, say, 25 persons or more. With a large organization there may be more to gain from greater specialization by forming a debugging group to debug all equipment, although the author is not fully convinced that this is so. The skills (or the lack of skills) of the particular people available in a small organization may also make it advisable to terminate a project leader's responsibility when debugging starts and rely on production and maintenance personnel. In either of these events, it would seem only prudent to try to pass on some of the benefits of the debugging experiences, say, by holding meetings between project leaders and debugging personnel to review formally the debugging problems encountered and to discuss ways and means of minimizing them in future projects.

The value of these suggestions is not universally supported by the practices of the plants visited. In one plant with a very good record of performance extending over several years, the supervisor of the group reported that there were no formal procedures for turning equipment over to the production department. Furthermore, in this case the project leader was often relieved of responsibility before the debugging technicians were finished; the project leader was relieved when the group supervisor decided he was making no, or very minor, contributions to progress. The ability and interest of the particular individual concerned also played a major role in this supervisor's decisions, and so, at times, did the demands of other projects. The fact that the project leader stayed on the job while major defects persisted nevertheless clearly placed *de facto* responsibility on him for design, construction, and "making it work."

If the debugging responsibility does not rest with the project leader, there seem to be advantages in having it be one of the primary responsibilities of the supervisor of the special automatic equipment program rather than a responsibility of the maintenance or line production groups. This arrangement gives greater assurance of easy feedback of experience and it avoids divided responsibility. Any other arrangement runs the risk that the feeling of responsibility for a completed job would be lost or, if not, that it would have its impact at too high an organizational level to be very effective.

Whether the technicians who do the debugging are permanently assigned as part of the special automatic equipment group depends primarily upon the size of the program and the skills required. Potentially, permanent assignments make possible greater control over both job assignments and training, but they must be balanced with the necessity for full utilization of personnel in the face of a variable demand for a variety of skills. The talents of particular individuals and the nature and history of the rest of the plant's organization may also be important factors in some instances.

Summary

The central body of problems encountered in debugging reflect the fact that one or more of the mechanisms involved in the equipment are new (or even unique) and/or the particular combination of mechanisms comprising the total equipment is new.

What happens in the debugging phase is a reflection of what was and was not done in earlier steps, especially in the definition of the problem, the consideration of alternative approaches, and the development of equipment specifications.

Several steps, to be taken before equipment is built, have been suggested which should reduce the dimensions of problems and delays posed during the debugging phase. Product design coordination, including the awareness by the product designer of the part played by "geometry," is of great value in reducing problems in feeding, handling, and positioning by automatic equipment. Pilot projects, including construction of mock-ups of equipment elements, before the equipment design is made final may often be a means, too, of cutting down on debugging difficulties. A careful sampling of parts to be processed, to determine their dimensions and qualities, and a check of the results with the parts' specifications were suggested as a routine for discovering discrepancies early. Procedures were also suggested to control dimensions and other qualities which may be fundamental to the proper functioning of the equipment. Still other routines were suggested to insure adequate auxiliary services, to catch flaws in the basic equipment design at the layout stage, and to minimize errors in the detailed drawings for the equipment, all of which should reduce the debugging load.

On the other hand, it is possible to overemphasize the goal of minimizing the amount of debugging which has to be done. After some point it is certainly not economical and probably not even feasible to try to reduce any further the debugging which will be required. Instead, the cheaper and quicker solution is to organize to execute such operations efficiently. Based upon the sample of companies visited, it seems advantageous to adopt a somewhat more systematic approach than most companies followed. Elements of such a systematic approach include closer liaison with product designers to expedite changes in parts and the early, continuous collection of data for the purpose of more effectively guiding the application of debugging efforts. Somewhat greater general use of statistical techniques in this respect also seems to be well advised.

The availability or nonavailability of talented personnel seemed pretty clearly to make a great difference in debugging efficiency. Experience appeared to be of considerable value, especially at the technician level, because such an important part of day-to-day activity evidently rests on personal skill rather than on conventional routines. But a systematic approach, including training through periodic reviews of project experiences, is likely to be of great help to either experienced or inexperienced personnel in making the most of their capabilities.

Even under optimum conditions, debugging is likely to remain a significant cost element in acquiring special automatic equipment. As such, it must simply be endured — with as much philosophic calm as is possible. Some solace may be derived from the following comments of Kessler, who has been quoted earlier in this chapter because of Delco-Remy's extensive experience, embracing more than 1,000 units of this type of equipment:

> Special machines are not built by pessimists and they seldom justify the optimism of their builders when first tried out. . . . To one who is not in close daily contact with the machine, it would seem that the machine builder does not know what he is doing. Today he knows just what is wrong and tomorrow it is

something different.   He is always apparently just on the verge
of getting it into operation.   When "bugging" a complicated
special machine this may extend over a considerable period, but
it is truly remarkable how seldom a skilled development organization will have a complete failure.[19]

---

[19] "How Special Machinery Is Developed," p. 147.

CHAPTER IV

Make or Buy Special Automatic Equipment?

ONE OF THE principal objectives of this research project was to
try to find out when a user would be better off making his own
equipment from start to finish and when he would find that relying on vendors to do the job was the better policy. What
factors determine whether making or buying is the more appropriate course of action?

Before attempting to present an analysis of these alternative
methods of procuring special automatic equipment, it will be
useful to lay some groundwork. First of all, we shall concern
ourselves only with the first acquisition of a particular design of
equipment. In many instances, perhaps even in most, observed
in the field work, only one of each kind of special automatic
equipment was procured because one unit met the production requirements. Even in instances in which one or more duplicates
of a particular kind of equipment were acquired, the first one (or
prototype) was the critical undertaking. Once a piece of equipment has been constructed which performs satisfactorily, the
problems involved in obtaining one or more duplicates undoubtedly will be fewer and considerably less difficult.

The second preliminary point concerns the scope of assistance
rendered by vendors. If we concern ourselves with the three
broad operations of design, construction, and debugging, it is
conceivable that a vendor could be found to provide assistance
with respect to any one, or two, or all three of these elements.
It is the author's opinion that the critical issues of procurement
policy, however, revolve around the question of who should perform the design work, the user or a vendor. It is possible, of

course, for the user to design a piece of equipment and to contract with a vendor to fabricate and buy parts and to assemble the completed machine. As a practical matter, in such a case the responsibility for making the finished equipment work must lie almost wholly with the user. When the machine has been assembled, the user's personnel must take the initiative in debugging it. If after all practicable steps have been taken the equipment performs poorly (or, sometimes, not at all), it will be hard to lay any blame on the outside builder in this case. In other words, except as to shop capacity and load, the implications are still substantially the same as those in which the user not only designs the equipment but constructs it as well.

Conversely, if a vendor is employed to design the special automatic equipment, the question of who makes or buys the parts and assembles the machine is likely to be of secondary importance from the standpoint of general policy. As a practical matter the unknowns in each case of special automatic equipment usually make it unwise to assign only the design responsibility to vendors. (Exceptions include a specialized subassembly mechanism, such as a feeding device, and preliminary experimental work, such as testing or developing a unique mechanism. Even in these cases, however, a final product should be a working model of the mechanism involved.) In most instances the results of a policy of buying are much more likely to be satisfactory if the vendor, in addition to having the design responsibility, is required by contract to construct the equipment and to prove its successful performance by a test run before the prospective user takes delivery. Then there can be no question of divided responsibility if the test run is unsatisfactory or if the equipment proves to be a complete failure. Again, in the instances examined in the field work, the vendors were almost without exception required to do the whole job — to design, construct, and debug the equipment, at least to the degree of substantially proving out the basic design.

Therefore, for the purpose of our analysis of special equipment procurement policy, the subsequent discussion will be focused on comparing a policy of designing, constructing, and debugging by the user's own organization with a policy of relying on vendors to perform all three of these steps (even though a portion of debugging will inevitably fall to the lot of the user when a vendor is employed).

With these preliminary comments out of the way, let us address ourselves to the question of the actual policies of the field sample companies.

Make or Buy Policies of Field Sample Companies

The field work for this project included eighteen establishments acquiring special automatic equipment. Four of them made most of their special automatic equipment, five made and bought about equally, and nine bought most of their special automatic equipment.

Some firms were dissatisfied with their current policy but followed it because it was expedient. Three of the ten "mostly buy" establishments had quite new programs and had been engaged in acquiring this type of equipment for only three years or less. Each, therefore, had no pre-existing staff with the specialized skills required to build its own equipment. Furthermore, such skilled personnel (machine designers, "automation specialists," etc.) were in short supply nation-wide. To accomplish the program these companies planned, therefore, they relied completely on contractors. Even if we grant that buying may be justified as a short-run expedient, it does not follow that buying would be a sound policy to continue in the long run.

A company was more likely to make its own special automatic equipment, rather than to buy it from contractors, if assembly equipment constituted an important part of its program. All four of the establishments making most of their special automatic equipment were heavily engaged in programs to acquire assembly equipment. The acquisition of assembly equipment was a major element in only two of the ten firms buying most of their special automatic equipment. In both these companies, the decision to buy was based on expediency, to get a new, large program started in the face of a shortage of trained special equipment designers and builders.

Arguments Favoring Buying

Eight arguments[1] were usually made in favor of buying special automatic equipment.

---

[1] See also Bright, p. 107, for a list of considerations.

1. By building many different kinds of equipment for a variety of applications and customers, vendors have learned the most efficient ways to go about developing special automatic equipment.

If a company is acquiring this type of equipment for the first time, this is a good argument for a temporary policy of buying while the equipment group, both as individuals and as a team, are gaining experience and skill.   In the event that a company's requirements over the years for special automatic equipment are small and sporadic (say, $50,000 or less every two or three years), the vendor's experience probably makes buying the only practicable policy.

2. Vendors have a more extensive technical knowledge of the process involved, of machine design, and of the task of debugging special automatic equipment.

Here the alleged advantage of the vendor depends on the circumstances; sometimes it is real and important, and sometimes it is not.   Some vendors have broad and deep knowledge of processes having wide industrial application, for example, die casting, welding, milling, and grinding.   But in some instances using companies have as great or greater knowledge of relevant processes (usually other than machining) for a particular type of application than the equipment vendors.

A qualified vendor is, however, likely to have superior technical knowledge of machine design.   As many companies learn too late, knowledge beyond that of most tool designers is needed.

Finally, debugging skill is likely to depend heavily on the knowledge and ingenuity of the particular technicians involved rather than whether they work for a builder or a user.   A contractor's personnel will benefit from repeated experience and from having encountered a wider range of problems than most users' personnel, but knowledge of the product, of preceding operations, and of operating conditions aid in the debugging and (given technicians of equal capabilities) are likely to give a user's personnel some significant advantages over outsiders.

On the whole, then, the weight of this argument in favor of buying varies from "zero" to "very significant," depending on the particular processes and applications in the user's plant.   For

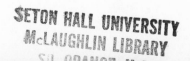

relatively cut-and-dried applications, the qualified vendor seems to have a significant but not overwhelming advantage. Given time and a continuing program large enough to warrant the cost, a typical user can probably provide equal competence in these technical areas for a majority of its projects by adding to its organization a qualified machine designer and one or perhaps two process specialists. Some companies already have process specialists whose skills and knowledge can be tapped. From time to time in a continuing program, however, it seems very likely that there will be some projects developed which involve technical skills for which vendors are better and more economically qualified than the user's organization. For example, a plant using very little welding probably would find it more profitable to use a vendor under most circumstances when a welding equipment project was undertaken, even though in most other cases it designed and built its own equipment.

3. Vendors, aside from their general skill and technical knowledge, bring to bear on a project a new point of view and new ideas.

When three or four vendors bid competitively for a project, several outside points of view are assured. It is also true that a new point of view may not produce a practicable and novel idea. Indeed, there is the possibility that a novel approach may be pursued in ignorance of certain important background data and may lead the project to trouble or even disaster rather than to glory. Many points of view can be obtained in another way. If a company's continuing procurement effort is large enough to afford, say, half a dozen or more qualified project leaders, it can hold a design conference in which these men analyze the suggested design and offer alternatives for each proposed machine. This procedure would probably develop the feasible alternative approaches even more effectively than would the review of several vendors.

4. Vendors employ standard subassemblies which reduce the amount of debugging involved, lower the construction cost, and increase the over-all reliability of the equipment.

The use of standard subassemblies, such as bases, indexing mechanisms, drill heads, and control mechanisms, is a widespread practice among vendors, although the proportion of a machine which may be assembled from a builder's standard components naturally depends upon the job to be done and the compromises in equipment design which may be made to permit use of standard elements in lieu of specially designed elements. It must be pointed out that the advantages of standard subassemblies by no means need be given up by a firm that follows a policy of making its equipment. Standards can be developed for frequently used elements, just as vendors developed theirs. Moreover, many vendors offer their standard subassemblies for sale, as separate units, as well as building them into equipment. Finally, vendors striving for maximum use of their standard components may overlook or disregard other, more promising approaches to the basic design.

5. Using a vendor virtually insures a double check on the basic ideas of a project. The basic approach proposed will be thoroughly scrutinized by both the vendor's designer and the user's project leader. In dealing with such a complex and uncertain task as acquiring a special automatic machine, this double check is highly desirable.

A double check will be obtained only if the buyer's project leader is competent to do the checking and takes the time to do it thoroughly. In other words, there is a cost involved in getting the double check, even though it is not always recognized. For an additional cost, the company following a make policy can also obtain a double check. For one thing, a design conference of several project leaders within the company will automatically do a good job of criticizing and perfecting the alternative approaches that are suggested.

6. Purchased equipment is cheaper.

Although this argument was advanced by several of the persons interviewed, there is no conclusive evidence of its truth or falsity. An example drawn from the field work will serve to emphasize the practical difficulties of trying to compare cost figures.

The executives of the Young Company decided that they would attempt to answer the question of relative costs for their company by conducting an experiment. Young's own designers were given a layout sketch (no detailed design data at all) for a piece of special automatic equipment being considered and were asked to prepare a quotation to construct the equipment. The Young Company already had a firm quotation from a vendor based on the same layout to build the same equipment, but this information was withheld from Young's designers. When the two quotations were compared, it was found that Young's own shop was about 40% higher than the vendor. Ignoring the probable differences in detailed design (which, if significant, not only affected the initial cost but also the potential performance and operating costs), there were two circumstances which invalidated any comparison between the two figures. The first was the matter of the overhead rate applied — the Young Company's figure was quite radically affected by the nature of its primary manufacturing organization, of which the design group and its machine shop were minor elements; whereas the vendor's sole activity was special automatic equipment, and its overhead rate, although unknown to Young's executives, was different because its organization had been developed solely for manufacturing special automatic equipment. The second factor was the eagerness of the vendor to get a contract for that particular project. The project was one of the first of a series in a continuing program of the Young Company, and the head of its special automatic equipment group stated that he believed the vendor may have purposely shaved its bid to "get its foot in the door."

7. It may be difficult, if not impossible, for a using company to keep a design-and-build organization busy over the span of several years. This problem is likely to be most critical during the cyclical fluctuations in sales and profits of a particular firm.

Historically, capital expenditures have shown wide cyclical fluctuations. Such cyclical variations are especially important to the firm which decides to make, rather than buy, its special automatic equipment requirements, for the skilled personnel involved are not easy to hire or to train. Quick expansion of an organization making its own equipment can be very costly if, indeed, it can be done speedily at all when the skills needed are in short supply nation-wide. Such a condition suggests two methods of accommodation. The first is to plan and execute a long-range program of building special automatic equipment which will not fluctuate significantly, but will be so scheduled and managed as to become relatively stable in magnitude, in order to employ the special automatic equipment organization continuously. The second method is to adopt a policy of procuring all special equipment by buying, rather than making it. The first approach is manifestly difficult, but sharp fluctuations can probably be avoided in many companies by projecting special automatic equipment activities, say, three years ahead at all times, and keeping the work load reasonably level during this period. Periods of higher-than-average requirements may be met by a shift in part to purchasing, rather than making, appropriate kinds of equipment. Sometimes the reverse policy can be followed in periods of fewer-than-average acquisitions, making equipment which under other circumstances might be purchased. In other words, the policy being suggested is one of organizing to make most (but not all) normal requirements, and using vendors to absorb any excess, a policy frequently used in planning production operations generally.

It should be noted that a policy of buying all special automatic equipment may not only be impractical; it also does not entirely avoid the problem of expanding and contracting the special automatic equipment organization. Even when equipment is bought, project leaders and some technicians will be required, and the need for their services will fluctuate with the size of the acquisition program. The gross number of people involved will merely be less than if the organization were making its own equipment.

This analysis suggests that using vendors should have some place in almost every company's policy, even when a make approach is desirable on other counts, simply to help keep an even load on the special automatic equipment organization and to avoid the serious injuries to its efficiency which inevitably accompany attempts to increase or decrease its capacity quickly.

8. Using vendors will permit a given program to be completed faster and/or permit a larger program to be accomplished by a fixed number of personnel in the using company.

Given the shortage of the skills involved and the relatively long time span needed to integrate new personnel into a special automatic equipment organization, the only practicable method of executing a project within reasonable time limits may be to follow a policy of buying. A second and somewhat similar situation exists when a company is starting to acquire special automatic equipment for the first time and wants to build up a large program quickly but has few qualified personnel in its organization. In both situations, following a policy of buying from vendors has strong appeal, since the effect of using vendors is to buy capacity, either temporarily if the policy is temporary, or permanently if the policy is continued after the particular circumstances in which it originated have changed.

With a buy program the need for machine designers, draftsmen, machinists, toolmakers, assemblers and, to some degree, debugging specialists is eliminated. So far as the project leader himself is concerned, most of the detailed coordination and follow-up activities related to a project are not his responsibilities but are performed by the vendor's personnel. He avoids the considerable effort involved in directing the activities of the people involved (for example, designers, shopworkers, and assemblers) and avoids, too, the burden of solving the problems they are likely to bring to their supervisor.

In lieu of such duties, he has acquired other functions. He must communicate the buyer's requirements to the vendor's personnel initially and at intervals during the project. He must also review important decisions and plans submitted by the vendor and carry out a program of systematic follow-up, not on every detail, but at key times and with respect to key elements only. He may also assist, perhaps, with other personnel from the user's organization in the latter phase of debugging. The task can be said to be supervising not several workers but a single deputy. To this task of coordination and follow-up is added the effort required to discover qualified vendors in the first place and to conduct the contract negotiations as required over the duration of the project.

Whether the firm is making or buying equipment, the responsibility of the project leader for technically evaluating the over-all approach remains the same. If a vendor delivers a piece of equipment which functions but fails to meet one or more of the basic requirements of the situation, such as ability to change over quickly from one size part to another, not because of malfunction but simply because the vendor did not design it to meet this requirement, the project leader cannot escape full responsibility. First-rate vendors are likely to be aware of this kind of pitfall and will try to guard against its happening. The details of the equipment design are a different matter, for they should be the builder's clear responsibility.

Although just how much of a task and how difficult a one these administrative burdens add up to is a moot question, it seems clear that on the average their sum in man-hours required is likely to be measurably less than the sum of the make project leader's tasks. As a general impression, based on the field observation, the work load of the buy project leader might be halved over the term of the project. There is also some suggestion that the administration of a buy project may require less detailed technical competence and, rather clearly, considerably different and possibly more administrative skills than the heading of a make project of equivalent size and complexity.

In any event, even if there are some additional administrative costs involved, the use of vendors may still have a clear advantage in permitting an increase in the size of a program that can be executed by a given number of personnel in the buyer's organization.

Arguments Favoring Making

Let us turn now to the principal arguments in favor of making special automatic equipment — that is to say, having it designed and built by the user's own organization.

1. Company personnel are more likely than vendor personnel to come closer to doing the best job that can be done. Vendors, on the other hand, are likely to aim at delivering a machine of minimum performance capability.

Perhaps the most obvious counterargument to this contention is that it is quite possible that company personnel will *overdo* their efforts to get the best job that can be done, and carry expenditures beyond the economical optimum point simply because of their zeal. Another counterargument is the proposition that if company personnel know what they want and will only spell out their requirements, vendors will shape their designs and bids accordingly. It must be admitted, however, that there are bound to be limits to the ability of company personnel to spell out in advance the specifications for a particular piece of equipment. By definition, there is a certain amount of development work associated with each project involving a new piece of special automatic equipment, and all the critical specifications are not likely to be clear until after the project is well under way. Some problems will not be known until the design work has progressed quite some way, and others may not become apparent until even later, even as late as in the debugging stage. Some mechanisms (a vibratory feeding bowl is a good example) may even have to be developed in part at least by "cut and try" as the project develops. Since the vendor is presumably committed to a fixed price in many procurements of this type of equipment, his personnel cannot reasonably be expected to seek any but minimum solutions as these types of problems arise. When the user's own personnel are involved, however, the problems will obviously be apparent to the project leader and may, if desired, be more fully explored. Furthermore, after considering alternative designs, a more expensive (but more desirable) design may be adopted for a given equipment subassembly. The more important the decisions of this type which may have to be made — in other words, the greater the number of uncertainties and the more important they are in the successful design and construction of the equipment desired — the greater the weight this advantage assumes for the user.

2. Company designers are more likely than are vendor personnel to take account of maintenance requirements in designing equipment.

This argument in support of making singles out only one facet of equipment performance, albeit one which may many times be quite important. For the most part, however, the author believes this argument should carry only minor weight in deciding procurement policy. If the equipment is of an efficient but rugged design operationally, maintenance should be infrequent; if maintenance is infrequent (other than routine cleaning and lubrication), the fact that it may be difficult or costly, or both, may be irritating but can hardly be fatal. On the other hand, if there is a good deal of downtime during day-to-day operations for adjustment, tool changes, clearing "jams," cleaning, or replacement of parts, the chances are that the design would be defective operationally. That it may be easy to fix the equipment under such circumstances is a little beside the point — the point is that it needs fixing so often.

There is one way a vendor's designers can be required to make suitable provisions for facilitating maintenance. If company personnel know what provisions may make for more efficient maintenance (either generally or for a specific piece of equipment), then it should not be too difficult to incorporate these ideas into the specifications set up for the vendor to meet. Before construction is begun, the designs can be analyzed specifically to spot maintenance problems: analyzed perhaps by a maintenance supervisor or other person who is experienced in equipment maintenance and who will view the problem as one who expects to assume some responsibility for the equipment once it is in operation.

3. Company personnel will have a knowledge of:
   (a) the process as applied to a particular manufacturing operation;
   (b) the product, its quality and functional requirements; and
   (c) the operating conditions which at best can be only partially taken into account by a vendor.

The knowledge of company personnel about the process, the product, and the operating conditions can, of course, be communicated to vendors, but only at some cost and only incompletely. Vendor personnel will probably never begin to absorb all the knowledge in these areas which the using company personnel may acquire and usefully bring to bear. Even enabling the vendor's personnel to go part way on this score requires the expenditure of considerable conscious effort and skill.

It follows, then, that a make policy is favored if in the projects undertaken pertinent knowledge concerning the process application, the product, or the operating conditions, or all three, are either substantial in amount or critical in nature. In projects in which the amount of development is sizable, knowledge in these areas is likely to be highly desirable, even essential. In the field work, many automatic assembly equipment projects tended to be of this nature.

4. In buying, a substantial amount of time and money must be expended in maintaining an organization to deal with vendors. Most of this would be avoided if the user designed and built its own special automatic equipment.

5. Company personnel will have to do significant amounts of debugging even if equipment is purchased.

Both of these arguments imply that there is an overhead cost attributable to a buy policy which can and will be eliminated under a make approach. This topic was first brought up in our discussion of point 7 of the advantages of buying, namely, the ability of a project leader to procure larger amounts of equipment in, say a year, through buying rather than making. As we noted then, under a policy of buying, there is a significant amount of additional, unavoidable administrative work — notably, contract placement and administration, communication of requirements and background knowledge, and follow-up activities — which a buying approach creates. How costly this is, however, is another question. The time spent on these overhead activities is likely to be directly proportional to the complexity of the equipment and the uniqueness of its application. The greater the amount of background information needed, the greater the effort needed to find suitable contractors, to communicate the requirements for the equipment and the essential background facts, and to follow up on progress as a vendor carries through the contract. But if a continuing flow of projects can be channeled to one vendor, then the cost of effective liaison may be lessened appreciably.

6. If a firm designs and manufactures its own special automatic equipment, it can obtain a competitive advantage by keeping its advances as trade secrets. Dealing with vendors, on the other hand, means that competitors will have easy access to similar equipment.

This seems to be one of the most firmly entrenched arguments in favor of a do-it-yourself policy. There is no doubt that competition in some of the mass-production industries has taken the form of internally developing and making special automatic equipment. In most cases of mass production, of course, the competitive advantages of low-cost production are critical — a firm with the most efficient production facilities often can set its own course, even in the face of larger but less efficient competitors. Whether keeping one's competitors "in the dark" really adds to a company's competitive position, however, is debatable. Instead, it can be argued that the competitive advantage comes first and foremost from being the first plant to have the advanced equipment in operation. The lead time on simply duplicating similar equipment, given fully detailed specifications, and putting it into production may be from one to two years. But product design changes and advancing process technology stand a good chance of largely nullifying the benefits from having similar equipment in production two years after one's competitor. It is also questionable whether trying to keep competitors in the dark is a reasonable objective in today's mobile employment market for technicians and engineers.

It cannot be denied that avoiding the use of vendors certainly decreases the opportunity for competitors to learn about equipment developments. The author's field work revealed several instances in which one company's representatives discovered — and examined — a competitor's equipment under construction in a vendor's plant. Indeed, there were two cases in which a vendor deliberately sought out a client's competitor and offered to build duplicates of equipment recently designed and built in the vendor's shop. There was also evidence, however, that some builders were very diligent in preserving the benefits of equipment development for the company financing its design and development. One vendor, for instance, stated that its policy was to request the original client's permission before contracting to deliver like equipment to a competitor. In another instance, a representative of the purchaser reported that he had negotiated with the builder over the length of time a new piece of equipment would be withheld from competitors, and had settled for a three-year period.

7. A company may be able to obtain patents, which both aid its competitive position by levying royalty charges on competitors who wish to use equipment developed, and also provide a source of income that may somewhat offset the costs of supporting the organization required to design and build special automatic equipment.

For most businesses, this argument carries little weight. It is not a very common situation in which one firm pays any appreciable royalties on equipment to a competitor. For one thing, such tribute is not merely a matter of money but is also a matter of pride. Furthermore, many pieces of equipment are likely to be so tied to a unique product design that they would be of doubtful value to a competitor using a differently designed part or subassembly. There are situations in which such patents might be used in negotiating royalty-free licenses from competitors, but they do not seem likely to occur frequently. And as for the income argument, situations in which it will become important seem likely to be even rarer. Noncompeting applications are, of course, a potential source of income, but they would seem to rate low, too, in probability of occurrence for most companies.

8. It is often difficult to get qualified vendors to undertake projects which involve significant technical advances.

This argument deserves careful consideration. Even though machine tool builders (either by inclination or necessity, or both) seemed to be featuring automated equipment more and more, during the course of the field work it became evident that few of them were willing to take on projects which involved substantial expenditures on design and development. Since in many cases only one or two machines for a single customer would be the result, they stood to gain little financially, and their attitude was understandable, however regrettable from the prospective buyer's point of view. Business in the machine tool industry was then booming, skilled designers and project managers were scarce, and it made sense to spread their skills thin and give preference to orders which used little design time, or which promised to have wide application in numerous using companies. Besides, most such builders were not organized to perform custom work efficiently. There have since been indications that some builders have begun organizing to undertake such projects, and the reduction in machine tool orders in the ensuing recession may have increased the attractiveness of custom work. One trade service, in correspondence with the writer in mid-1959, indicated that some builders believe that about 40% of the dollar value of orders was composed of "specials," although the term is so loosely used that no precision can be attributed to the figure.

There are, of course, a few vendors who are specialists in this type of equipment and who have all along been willing to undertake the design and development of special automatic equipment. Very few of these, however, have the personnel and facilities to do a good job of this sort. An even smaller number are sufficiently experienced, well-financed, and confident of their abilities to accept such projects on a fixed-price basis. Finally, the field work brought out the fact that even the most experienced firms set limits to the risks which they will accept. On projects which, in their opinion, involve an excessive risk and considerable development effort, they will simply decline to bid. The more experienced and the more capable the vendor, the more careful the management seemed to be in this respect. In some cases, the approach of even special equipment builders was surprisingly cut and dried in limiting the scope of projects which were considered suitable for the organization to undertake, at least on a firm bid basis.[2]

Given these conditions, the only reasonable method of using vendors is to place a contract on a per diem or other basis for such development work as, if successfully concluded, may reduce the risks involved to the point where a design and construction contract may be placed. This greatly diminishes the attractiveness of a buy policy for a large program at least, since, whatever the legal rights of the buyer to control the results of the development contract, much of the experience and know-how gained will remain with the vendor's personnel. Second, a procedure requiring successful completion of the development phase first may under some circumstances delay completion of the total project involved. If the project is handled on a make basis, however, and the company will accept the risks involved, there will be the possibility of concurrent programming which will shorten the over-all lead time.

In conclusion, it seems likely that most projects involving significant technical advances will, almost by definition, benefit sub-

---

[2] On the reluctance of vendors to undertake some projects, see Bright, pp. 111–112.

stantially from the background of process application, product, and operating conditions which is so difficult and costly for vendor personnel to bring to bear under most such circumstances. These are also the kinds of projects which are most likely to be undertaken as part of a large, continuing program, another circumstance under which buying loses some of its appeal to a potential user.

Conclusions on Make or Buy

The foregoing analysis suggests that if a program is continuous and large the most advisable course is a compromise between the two extremes of policy, a combination of making and buying. Ideally, such a combination policy would permit the allocation of a project to a vendor when there was stress on the need for an outside viewpoint and special technical competence; while another project, in which the need for internal knowledge and coordination was paramount, could be made rather than bought. For instance, many machining operations are more efficiently executed by vendors, while much equipment for assembly operations (especially if they are complex) are more likely to benefit from manufacture by the using firm. Even part of a project, rather than the whole, may be executed by buying and the remainder by making. To illustrate, there has recently arisen a handful of specialist firms engaged in designing mechanical feeding devices (hoppers, syntron bowls, and similar devices). A user might well contract with one of these specialists to design the feeding mechanism while designing and fabricating the rest of the machine, including all processing steps, within its own special equipment organization.

Under a combination policy the work load in the shops and among project leaders and designers can be taken into account in assigning projects to vendors. Some measure of stability for the internal organization may thereby be achieved although careful planning will also certainly be needed to realize this potential. From another point of view, being prepared to either make or buy may also help on occasion to meet urgent production schedules in at least two ways. First, capacity to acquire this type of equipment may be expanded by assigning a larger proportion of projects to vendors than might otherwise be ideal. And second, company personnel may be assigned equipment projects on a make basis when a vendor will not undertake them or when a qualified vendor cannot make delivery soon enough. To some degree, of course, changing the nature of the project leader's job in this fashion is almost certain to diminish the efficient functioning of the special automatic equipment organization, but the offsetting gain to the total company in the long run may be well worth the sacrifice.

There are at least three other general types of situations in which a combination policy may not be the best choice. The first of these is one in which most of a user's special automatic equipment program is composed of highly complex special automatic equipment. As we mentioned earlier, projects of this type, which call for so much detailed knowledge of the individual process application problems, of the product design, and of the particular operating conditions, are likely to lend themselves better to a make approach.

The second general type of situation in which the combination policy is not advisable is one in which a company is first embarking on a program to acquire special automatic equipment. Because of its lack of experienced personnel, such a company will be faced with the necessity of hiring or transferring the best people available and giving them experience. To give them experience, two very different approaches may be used. One is to set to work on a single project with a small group — say of only two or three persons (the total of both engineers and technicians). The other is to use the same number of persons to undertake one or two projects using vendors. Under either approach major mistakes are so likely that the principal return from the first project or two is more likely to be the value of the experience gained than the lowering of costs effected by acquiring special automatic equipment. The policy of using vendors, however, exposes the personnel concerned to a wide variety of ideas and should force the evaluation of alternative approaches to the same project used by different vendors. It enables, even forces, the user's project leaders to observe the general procedure followed by the professional builder. It probably gives the personnel of the using company more perspective simply because so much of the detail during design and construction is eliminated. It may permit more projects to be completed in a short time, although there is little point in trying to accomplish many such projects under these conditions. Finally, it may have the further advantage of putting pressure on a manufacturing organization to change in a hurry its habitual ways of doing things. The use of a vendor may overcome any inertia present in a way that a do-it-yourself approach would be much less likely to accomplish. Beginning to acquire special automatic equipment by buying calls for the initial project to be the kind that well-qualified vendors will undertake. And care must be taken that a well-qualified vendor is actually found and awarded the contract. If the vendor to whom a contract is awarded turns out not to be well-qualified, many, if not all, of the advantages are lost and one or more problems will be created to burden the user's embryo organization.

Finally, a third exception to the advisability of using a combination policy is the company whose program is limited in size, or is periodic, rather than continuous. In this situation it is desirable, perhaps even essential, that all special automatic equipment be bought. The total acquisition cost is likely to be lower and the resulting performance of the equipment better.

A company planning a small special automatic equipment program needs to consider another element, which we have not earlier mentioned. This is the fact that more often than not the efficient choice of a basic approach to a project usually requires that more than one person be involved. A representative of one company which has designed and built a large quantity of special automatic equipment over the years had this to say in commenting on the job of working out a design for a new piece of equipment: "We got nowhere if we worked individually on a job. We had to converse with others about our problems and work out solutions from discussions." The field work revealed other ways in which this need was met, varying from organized brainstorming sessions to informal discussions over coffee between two project leaders. Both techniques for the interchange of ideas were common among special machine tool builders visited during the field work. If a company has only one project leader continuously engaged in a program of acquiring special automatic equipment, this factor should carry considerable weight in favor of buying.

Perhaps the overriding generalization which might be drawn concerning procurement policy for special automatic equipment is that it probably would be wise to review continually any decision on procurement methods in the light of changing circumstances both within the company and outside it. The combination policy, potentially at least, tends to keep this issue alive by subjecting each project to analysis before a decision is made as to whether to make or to buy the equipment involved. But more than a project-by-project review is necessary. Internal conditions are constantly in a state of flux. There will be changes, for instance, in the volume of demand for a company's product, in its financial capacity to underwrite a larger special automatic equipment program, and in the number and qualifications of available project-leader and supervisory personnel. Externally, changes are also taking place. Two recent developments seem to open up more opportunities for an economical do-it-yourself program. The first of these has already been mentioned: the emergence of several specialist firms which will contract for the design of various feeding devices, without assuming responsibility for the whole machine. The second recent development has been the availability of standard modules of equipment, for example, indexing tables, machine bases, and drill heads. The firms offering these items for sale are special equipment builders who use these same basic subassemblies in carrying out their own equipment projects. It is such developments as these, externally and internally, which need to be recognized and analyzed in periodic top-management reviews of a company's special automatic equipment program, whatever its current procurement policy for this type of equipment.

CHAPTER V

Working Effectively With Vendors

As WE HAVE SEEN, there is a place of considerable importance for vendors in most programs, with the relative prominence of buying equipment varying with the particular circumstances of the company involved. From observations of vendors and using companies, it became clear that the results various users obtained from vendors varied widely in quality. Investigation revealed that the principal variable influencing the quality of the results obtained was the effectiveness with which the using company's personnel dealt with the vendors. How effective these dealings were seemed to depend on the extent to which the buyer's representatives planned in advance. In this chapter we shall examine this relation from the point of view of the user (buyer); in the next chapter we shall examine it from the point of view of the vendor.

In many ways, the acquisition of special automatic equipment can be considered as a problem in the purchasing of services rather than the purchasing of goods. The satisfaction of the user will lie not in the appearance of the machine or in the way that it operates, but instead will depend upon how well it does the job to be done. Of course this is true of all capital equipment and is more or less true of almost all so-called industrial goods which are purchased by a firm. But in the case of special automatic equipment a major variable is the ability of the vendor's engineers to provide the professional services which will assure that the equipment as delivered operates efficiently and fulfills the needs of the user. Unlike other capital equipment, a similar model cannot be seen in operation before contracting for its purchase, and how well it will perform its intended function is questionable at the time an order is given to the vendor. Efficient purchasing of special automatic equipment involves far more than the application of policies and techniques which have been developed for a company's purchasing department. On occasion, many of these are quite likely to be useful, and several of them are recommended in the following pages. Invariably, the purchasing department may usefully perform some auxiliary functions. The purchasing of special automatic equipment constitutes a highly specialized task, however, and in the plants visited the locus of authority lay in the project leader, under the manufacturing or the engineering organization, and not in the purchasing agent.

Getting organized to achieve the optimum results from vendors may seem an obvious first step in buying special automatic equipment. Be that as it may, the deficiencies in this respect seemed to be far greater than the attainments in the cases of many of the companies visited by the author in his field work. Two factors especially accounted for haphazard efforts in this respect: the hurry with which many programs were undertaken, and a lack of comprehension of the vendor's problems in carrying out his part in producing satisfactory equipment. Problems were intensified if the user was inexperienced in acquiring special automatic equipment. A wide variety of factors, however, were important in the results of individual projects, depending on the circumstances. The subsequent sections will therefore be devoted to a step-by-step examination, in approximately chronological order, of the principal areas in which it seemed to the author a using company's personnel could establish policies and procedures which would facilitate getting the best performance from a vendor.[1]

Developing Potential Sources of Supply

Very few firms interviewed followed a systematic approach to developing potential sources of supply. This was so despite the fact that qualified vendors were often hard to find (one user in two years investigated 35 potential vendors but placed orders with only four), and despite the fact that by the time vendors were called in speed was usually of the essence. As a result, the

---

[1] Incidentally, many of the comments made about the planning steps would be just as appropriate for a make project as for a buy project.

contract to design and construct the equipment was too often given to the first qualified bidder that could be found.

To do an efficient job of selecting vendors, information on potential sources of supply must be compiled in advance of the actual need to solict bids or negotiate a contract. Three steps can help build up a file of useful data. The first is to canvass appropriate directories, such as *Thomas's Register*, and extract the information found therein, even though the coverage may be incomplete and the other data sparse. The second is to assign someone to scrutinize trade journals, both advertisements and articles, on a routine basis for leads on vendors, the kinds of equipment they are building, and (sometimes) the names of their clients for future reference. This scrutiny should include both one's own field and others — those in the electrical industry should include one or two trade journals in metalworking (perhaps one in the chemical industry, too) and vice versa. The third step is to preserve a record of one's own past experience that will prevent its being lost through personnel turnover. As each contract is completed, the project leader can be required to summarize that experience (say in half a page or less) pointing out the strengths and weaknesses of the vendor or vendors in that particular undertaking. Likewise, when a detailed survey is made of a builder to whom an award is not subsequently made, a written report on the builder's facilities and other resources, along with an appraisal of his potentialities as a source of supply and a statement of why an award was not made, should be added to this file.

If a systematic program of developing information on potential sources of supply is followed, the time required for placing a contract should be minimized and at the same time there will be greater assurance that most if not all of the sources which should be considered are in fact considered.

Pre-Award Planning

Before an award is made to a vendor, there are several steps which should be taken by the project leader to plan the procurement efficiently. The elements involved in this pre-award planning include defining requirements, developing specifications, and communicating these requirements to potential vendors.

The common method of specifying one's requirements for machining equipment (as distinct from assembly equipment) among firms visited in the field work was to furnish a potential vendor with a set of prints for machining operations and a statement of the required production of good pieces per hour. Sometimes these were all the data supplied. In some cases, however, there were additional specifications, such as the type of surface finish and the allowable scrap rate. Once in a while the specifications spelled out the inspection required and placed some restrictions on the types of some of the components (usually simply a reference to "JIC [Joint Industry Conference] standards for all electrical elements," but sometimes in greater detail). Equally rare was a statement of what would be considered "satisfactory performance" for the finished equipment. Although a judgment concerning "satisfactory performance" usually depended largely upon the results of a test run in the contractor's shop, the duration of this test run or the number of good pieces to be produced over some number of hours, or both, were infrequently established as part of the specifications. Nor were bidders informed of inspection standards and methods — in many cases, probably because the prospective purchaser's project engineers had not tried to find out what they would be. In no case did the author find the variations in the nature of the workpieces to be handled described in detail, save as they happened to be noted on a workpiece print or as they were indicated by the range of characteristics which happened to be associated with several sample workpieces furnished the vendor. It was a rare occasion, too, when more than one of a part was sent to a bidder as a sample.

Another element which was perfunctorily treated was the percentage efficiency assumed. With respect to the actual average output over the time period of say, a month, two general types of factors will affect the average hourly production, assuming no interruptions in the supply of workpieces: those relating to machine downtime for setup, adjustment, and maintenance, and those relating to allowances for the machine operator for rest periods and personal needs. The latter are clearly best estimated by the buyer and should be taken into account by his personnel in fixing the required output levels, rather than by involving the vendors directly. Factors of the first type, however, are in part a joint responsibility of the buyer and the vendor and in part the vendor's responsibility. Downtime on account of setup time is partly a function of how long a setup change takes, which usually depends upon the design of the equipment, a responsibility of the vendor. It is also partly a function of how many setup changes will be made per month, which will be determined by the number of different parts or assemblies to be made and the inventory and scheduling policies to be followed for each, decisions for which the buyer must take responsibility.

Considerably more development of specifications typically seemed to be undertaken in the equipment projects concerned with assembly operations. In great contrast to the typical practice for machining equipment projects, the buyer's manufacturing engineers usually developed some sort of over-all design concept for the equipment, that is, its basic configuration — dial, transfer, or other type — and a preliminary designation of the number of work stations, plus the sequence and the nature of the operation or operations to be performed at each. Consideration was usually given to making some workpiece design changes which might facilitate processing. The gaps in the specifications were just as broad, however, as in the case of machining equipment with respect to needed or desired inspection stations, allowable scrap rate, the types of electrical and mechanical components desired, the variation in the characteristics of the flow of incoming workpieces, and the nature of "satisfactory performance."

There is no doubt that the performance criteria comprise the crux of the specifications for special automatic equipment of all types, and these were always specified. The primary objective of acquiring the equipment, of course, is to obtain a certain production of good pieces per hour. But over a run of how many hours? With an input of what kind of workpieces? At the cost of how much scrap and rework?

Some buyers, especially those in the automotive industry, specified in detail the nature of selected components, notably electrical elements and circuits, which were to become a part of the equipment. Usually this was done by reference to standards of the buyer, or to the JIC standards we described in Chapter III. In the absence of other standards, some construction elements of special equipment analyzed often (but not always) complied with standards promulgated by the National Machine Tool Build-ers, an industry trade association. Specification of standards can involve establishing the quality of components, but the choice of components has other implications, notably the degree of inter-changeability of parts among similar equipment. For this reason, further discussion of standard parts is postponed until we take up the topic of coordinating product design and equipment in a later chapter.

There is a question of how far the buyer's representative should go in developing the specifications for a piece of equipment. On the one hand are the quite valid and impressive arguments that elaborations beyond the basic performance specifications may undesirably restrict the approach of vendors to the problem, per-haps precluding them from suggesting a different and better ap-proach. Likewise, there is the argument that the further a buyer goes beyond the performance specifications, the greater the de-gree of responsibility he assumes, practically and morally (no matter how the contract reads), for the equipment ultimately delivered by the successful bidder. Then, too, vendors may hesitate to bid, fearing that in the end these detailed specifica-tions may be applied too rigidly and to their detriment. On the other hand are cogent arguments favoring more extensive devel-opment of specifications by the buyer, arguments which are some-what more persuasive despite the admitted disadvantages of such a course of action. These advantages are the anticipation and solution of many problems which otherwise may not be clear un-til the equipment has been assembled and tested; the knowledge necessary for adequate description of requirements to all bidders and, later, to the vendor to whom the award may be made; and the detailed awareness of the potential trouble spots in building equipment for the project at hand, since developing such de-tailed specifications forces the thinking through of a project. In other words, the buyer will be better prepared to evaluate speci-fic vendor proposals and to weigh the risks entailed in the use of particular methods and novel devices. Such additional develop-ment of specifications is likely to be more beneficial, in some cases even mandatory, when assembly equipment is involved. Nevertheless, it seems that the development of supplementary specifications is generally desirable, for they can probably be de-

veloped somewhat faster for most machining projects than they
can for most assembly projects and therefore are likely to yield
at least as much return per hour of a manufacturing engineer's
time.[2]

In the author's sample the Rush Company was the one which
developed its specifications for machining operations to the maximum degree. The first step in its procedures was to decide
which machining process to employ (i.e., broaching or milling)
to finish each surface. This step was gradually expanded to include considering other processes, such as cold forming or die
casting, combined with alternative product designs. Having selected a process, the manufacturing engineer in charge of the
project then proceeded to determine the design of the cutting
tools to be used, the speed and feed at which they were to be operated, and the sequence in which the desired operations, including inspection, were to take place. The specific operations to be
included at each work station were also sometimes decided before
potential builders were called in.

The typical piece of equipment was designed to process only
one workpiece, so consideration of setup changes was not usually involved. The Rush project leader not only fixed the cutting
tool design and its feed and speed, but also usually estimated the
time needed for tool changes and maintenance allowances, added
the appropriate operator allowances, and informed the bidders
what percentage efficiency rates to employ in designing their
equipment to achieve the required average output.

The Rush Company attempted to capture the originality of
thought which vendors might apply to each project by specifying
that, while an interested vendor was required to submit a bid

---

[2] The development of a good specification is stressed by Bernard Lester
in *Marketing Industrial Equipment*, 1st Edition (New York, McGraw-Hill,
1935), pp. 256–259. Especially relevant is the following (p. 258): ". . . it
[the specification] must exactly define the extent of the work.

"It must state in detail the results to be obtained within the defined
limit. It must state all essential requirements as to the final form of the
product and the service which the product is expected to perform. It must
define the type and quality of materials to be used. It must provide complete qualitative information.

"The specifications should restrict the supplier as little as possible in his
method of procedure, as long as the results are in accordance with the
requirements for the finished product."

which would process the piece as set forth in the invitation to bid, the firm was also encouraged to submit a layout and a bid for any alternative processing believed to be superior.

Rigorous analysis alone is not always sufficient to develop full specifications. When substantial process changes or new and untried mechanisms, or both, are involved, some experimentation before asking vendors to bid will not only help refine the specifications but will probably avoid some debugging problems which would otherwise appear. Under many circumstances the prospective buyer may not succeed in obtaining any bids until a preliminary investigation has solved, or at least clarified, obvious major problems.

In talking with vendors of both machining and assembly equipment, it was clear that they were usually careful not to take on, on a firm bid basis, any projects which were certain or even likely to include these kinds of process changes and new mechanisms. Even though the prospective buyer was not always so informed, this policy underlay many refusals to bid. It follows, therefore, that there would seem to be a danger that if a prospective buyer did by chance succeed in getting some builder to bid under these circumstances, either the problems would have been overlooked (and therefore likely to be a reflection on the general ability of the builder); or they would have been understood, but the builder for some reason (such as lack of other business, or desire to "break into" a new company or a new market) had decided to "take a chance." In either of these cases, the possibility of late deliveries, and perhaps unsatisfactory equipment in the end, would seem to be quite large. A pre-award investigation that tests process changes or new mechanisms, on the other hand, might result in specifications against which more (and probably more reliable) builders would be willing to bid. Some builders interviewed stated their willingness to undertake such exploratory investigations on the basis of payment per engineering hour expended, rather than on the basis of results obtained. A few indicated that for established customers they would occasionally be willing to undertake such investigations on the basis of essentially out-of-pocket costs when the circumstances indicated the vendor would have a good chance of getting an equipment contract if the investigation resolved the problems. These investigations are often, however, likely to be of such great interest to the buyer that he probably would prefer to carry them out inside his own organization if he has the available personnel.   Another source of aid on investigations like this, of course, are professional engineering consultants; one company interviewed had used such consultants in connection with several preliminary investigations.[3]

An additional advantage to be gained by having the buyer develop specifications in detail arises from his obviously superior knowledge of the use to which the equipment is to be put, including an appreciation of what might be called the "unwritten specifications" for the product.   Sometimes, these may be essentially indescribable by using the written word or a drawing; more often, however, they can be quickly and effectively communicated orally and by demonstration once the need to do so has been appreciated by the buyer.   Working out detailed specifications and sketches — even if they are later superseded by counterproposals put forward by the vendor — is likely to insure that many, if not all, of these unwritten specifications will be recognized and taken into account.[4]

A vendor has a strong incentive to try to design equipment the

---

[3] This kind of preliminary investigation may be important, of course, to any project, irrespective of whether it is a case of making or of buying. In the field cases the Hill Company, which made almost all its equipment, undertook a project estimated to cost well over $100,000 without making preliminary studies.   In the end, the cost was a little more than double the original estimates.   There was good evidence that at least a significant portion of the actual cost and an even greater portion of the elapsed time consumed would have been saved by a pilot study.

[4] A specific example of how a buyer's background of knowledge of the product can beneficially affect equipment specifications may be found in Ray A. McCarroll (then master mechanic of the Plymouth Division and now division manager of the Engine Division of Chrysler Corporation), "Many Technological Improvements Made in Plymouth Engine Plant," *Tooling and Production,* October 1955 (p. 17 of special reprint for Plymouth Division, Chrysler Corporation).   McCarroll notes the difficulties of achieving close tolerances in the alignment of several holes in one workpiece when the holes are machined at more than one station, because clamping is never exactly the same from station to station.   Therefore, in acquiring equipment which would machine valve guide holes in close alignment to the valve seat (an operation which he describes as one of the most critical of all in engine manufacture), one clamping operation was specified. McCarroll states, "This operation, usually performed in two stations, is now being done in one, and a concentricity of 0.0005 inches is held between the seat and valve guide hole."

cheapest way possible, from the standpoints of both engineering time and fabrication cost. In most cases a vendor will assume the award will be strongly influenced by the amount of the bid, and so he will try to submit the lowest bid he can to maximize his chances of getting the contract. He will try to do this, however, within the restrictions of the buyer's specifications; hence the importance of a careful and complete statement of the buyer's requirements. Once the user's needs are fully understood, and their importance comprehended, the design proposal a vendor submits cannot help being far more useful to the buyer.

Time pressure is often the reason for inadequate pre-award planning. Not to do this planning thoroughly, however, is to expose the company to the possibility of substantial losses, such as we have just described. The risk of loss is so great that it probably will be better to reduce the work load by dropping or postponing some projects. Or, the scope of a project may be reduced, such as specifying hand loading in lieu of mechanical feeding. The job of defining the specification for each piece of equipment is so basic and a job well done so essential that there is no alternative to scheduling whatever time may be required to permit this to be accomplished.

Preliminary Discussions with Vendors

One vendor proposed that a buyer get vendors' ideas on a project not simply by issuing invitations to bid but by first systematically getting vendors' ideas about the general approach before asking them to submit formal quotations. Specifically, this suggestion would call for the project leader to ask selected vendor representatives to call, at which time he would set forth the nature of the project involved. Various approaches to the general method to be employed could be discussed, and a price range for the equipment involved could be set, for use in preliminary economic analysis. Alternatively, the project engineer might visit the vendor's plant, especially if the vendor's sales representative played little or no part in the development of over-all approaches but merely forwarded data to the vendor's engineering organization for development of a proposal.

After a project leader had held such discussions with several potential builders of the equipment involved, the proponent of this method argues, he would be able to issue a formal invitation to bid which would present the requirements of the project much more clearly and in more detail. Furthermore, vendors' representatives preparing a formal proposal would have the benefit of the background discussions and, in some cases, observation of existing processing.[5]

This approach calls for vendors to provide free consulting advice for a project for which they may not receive a contract, either because it is dropped or because the award is made to another builder. For a particular project, any one vendor's chances of getting something in return for his free consultation are pretty low. The only justification for a vendor's participation in such a program is the expectation of getting a proportion of a continuing series of awards, at prices which on the average recoup the "free consulting" he may have contributed to several projects for which he did not receive any award.

The vendor's dilemma under this proposal is really no different, however, from that which prevails under much existing practice, according to which the prospective buyer sends ten or twelve special equipment vendors a set of prints for a part, possibly along with a sample workpiece, and an invitation to bid setting forth a requirement of, say, "200 pieces per hour at 80% efficiency." The vendors are expected to work up a proposal and submit a firm bid, based upon these simple data, which may sometimes be supplemented by a few pieces of additional information culled by their local sales engineer or manufacturer's agent. The data are quite likely to be inadequate for a thorough job, in addition to which the chances of a particular vendor's getting the job are so low that he cannot afford to come up with anything more than a schematic diagram in lieu of a full layout drawing. It follows that under normal market conditions, and assuming that a vendor

---

[5] A similar course of action is advocated by Kenneth R. Treer in the third installment of his series of articles on "Automated Assembly," *Automation,* December 1956, p. 57. His proposal, however, calls for the user to choose a vendor on the basis of a "preliminary survey" by the user, during which the vendors consulted are asked to make "preliminary quotes or estimates," on the basis of which the buyer chooses one vendor. This chosen vendor then prepares a layout and submits a final proposal, on the basis of which the user decides whether to go ahead with the project. Another similar proposal is contained in William C. Goeckle, "Engineering Small-Plant Automation," *Tool Engineering,* November 1956, pp. 99–102.

attempts to quote a price providing neither plush nor skimpy margins, there is a fair chance that after the award, as he begins to work out an adequate layout drawing and details each work station, the successful bidder will find that he has overlooked one or more major problems.

The following quantitative data on the effort put forth in developing proposals and on the proportion which resulted in awards were gained from discussions with special machine tool builders who customarily operate on this basis. For the large majority of vendors interviewed the usual proposal took from four to six hours of work by the engineer developing it. Furthermore, the number of proposals made compared with the number which developed into contracts ranged from a ratio of five to one to a ratio of fifteen to one and averaged about ten to one. Two vendors, each of whom was particularly careful in limiting the projects on which he submitted bids, reported ratios of proposals made to contracts obtained of five to one and eight to one. Both companies manufactured very complex equipment which demanded more man-hours per proposal, even on a minimum basis.

With such low return ratios, it is small wonder that many proposals are superficial. A number of builders admitted that on successful bids, they frequently found it necessary after thoroughly investigating the project to use a substantially different approach from that which they had used as the basis of the original proposal. As a result, most vendors interviewed avoided specific details in presenting proposals; instead, proposals were couched in the most general terms possible even though specific assumptions had been made in building up the quotation figures. In a few instances, the lack of detail accompanying proposals was excused on the grounds that it would be possible for an unscrupulous buyer to use a detailed proposal to make the equipment in his own shop, or to contract with someone other than the bidder for finishing the design work and constructing it. While this argument has an element of truth in it, especially for cases requiring a large portion of custom design, in some cases it was apparently used as a red herring to justify a skimpy job on the layout.

It is difficult to escape the conclusion that to get very many worthwhile and well-developed ideas for a piece of special automatic equipment, a prospective buyer will have to pay for them, either by paying a builder or a consultant to undertake a development contract, or by having his own organization (if qualified) do the job. The smaller a prospective buyer's program for acquiring special automatic equipment, the more clearly inevitable is this conclusion. The relatively few firms which annually spend millions of dollars for this type of equipment may be able to create so much competition for their equipment business that some vendors, at least occasionally, will be willing to risk larger engineering expenditures in preparing quotations. But for the most part vendors simply cannot afford to do very much simply because of the low odds that they will receive an award.

Implications of Pre-Award Planning

A company's decision to follow a policy of extensive pre-award planning before asking vendors to bid — a sensible policy where a continuing series of special automatic equipment proposals is envisioned — assumes three conditions. First, the company must be willing to bear the cost involved. The expectation, of course, is that these costs will be more than recouped by one or a combination of the following benefits:

1. Procuring machinery making greater savings (and fewer losses); or
2. Reducing investment expenditures (the invoice price or the costs of debugging, or both); or
3. Avoiding the types of indirect cost usually associated with late delivery or delivery of substandard equipment (such as excessive debugging, high-priced temporary parts supply, lost sales, and customer dissatisfaction).

Second, some arrangement must be made to weed out the less desirable projects as soon as possible during the planning stage, rather than depend solely upon reviews at the appropriation request stage to cull out unsuitable projects. When preliminary bids are obtained and again when final bids are obtained, economic reviews should take place. A series of economic analyses, even though they involve some slight expense, would probably save the funds and, equally important in many cases, the time of project engineers, spent in working up proposals which are subsequently rejected.

Third, enough capable personnel must be available for doing such pre-award planning well and they must have time in which to do it. For consultation to be worth while, the user's personnel must be technically capable of understanding what vendors propose and must be able to discriminate among the various proposals. Qualified personnel are likely to be those with either work experience or training, or both, which enables them to analyze the technical aspects of the job and to originate some of the ways of doing it with special automatic equipment: in other words, personnel capable of coming up with ideas for a general approach, developing such ideas into a layout drawing or sketch, and sketching selected details — such as holding fixtures, tool slides, and gaging equipment — which may be critical to the success of the particular piece of equipment.

Selecting a Contractor for a Project

There are manifestly some general types of qualifications which any potential contractor for this type of equipment should meet. One set of qualifications was obtained during the field work from the head of a prominent builder of this type of equipment:

1. Capacity to produce.
2. Size and capability of the engineering department.
3. Size and capability of the service department.
4. Reputation for meeting delivery dates.
5. Policy and availability of service parts.
6. Ability to expand in an emergency period.

The sum of the criteria suggested by all the users interviewed lay in appraising three things: the physical facilities of the vendor's shop, the quality of the shop organization, and the ability of the engineering group. Of these three, the greatest in variability and the most difficult to evaluate is the ability of the engineering group to cope with the project in hand.

Beyond these general types of qualifications there may be others, more specifically tied to the nature of the particular special automatic equipment project and even to the individual plant's special needs. The need to be qualified in drilling or milling or grinding or welding or diecasting — whatever processes may be involved — is clear. But other types of essential qualifications may be less obvious. For instance, one leader of a special automatic equipment group stated: "We have found that there are two general characteristics associated with our work in assembly equipment for product 'X': first, the ability to handle small sized parts; and second, ability to work to close tolerances." Another commented along similar lines on the basis of his experience with assembly equipment and a variety of other types of special automatic equipment: "I have become convinced that a key question is whether a vendor has had actual prior experience with the mechanical feeding of small parts. Mechanical feeding of small parts is the backbone of the design job for almost every project we have." Gaining a knowledge of these special qualifications, whether they are common to many or to all projects, or whether they are unique to one particular project, is certainly the first step for a project leader in search of qualified vendors.

One finding during the field work was the apparently minor role of the financial capability of the proposed contractor. No case was discovered in which a potential contractor had been considered but was subsequently ruled out because of weak finances. It seems probable, however, that many financially unstable firms may simply never have been invited to bid, as many firms reported that they followed a policy of making a financial check as a matter of routine. Such a check usually consisted of the purchasing department's sending for a Dun and Bradstreet report on the potential source. On the other hand, it is known that many of the vendors actually given contracts were small and new firms which did not have strong finances. In some cases, they have subsequently gone out of business as contractors for this type of equipment. Financial ability sufficient at least to assure completion of a proposed contract should certainly be a condition of any award.

Once the project leader has worked out the particular qualifications which a vendor would need in order to undertake a given project, there remained the task of determining whether a particular vendor met the qualifications being sought. When a vendor had been awarded and had completed previous projects, the user had a fund of experience to draw upon. When the vendor was a new one to the equipment user, however, some sort of appraisal was necessary. For a using company just starting a special automatic equipment program this task was especially important since all potential contractors were likely to be unknown quantities.

Any one or a combination of all three methods used to appraise a potential contractor might be employed. The first method was to have one or more of the user's personnel visit the plant of the potential vendor. When the visit was made by only one person, the user's representative was usually the project engineer or his immediate supervisor. When more than one person was involved in the visit (which was usually the case when a large, difficult, or critical project was concerned), other persons who might be involved included a representative of the user's quality control organization, the foreman of the department which would use the machine, and perhaps the factory manager or chief manufacturing executive. The visit usually consisted of discussing the proposed project with the potential vendor's executives and design engineer(s), inspection of the shop facilities, and examination of the equipment currently being manufactured in the shop. The factors considered and the weight accorded each in the over-all evaluation were invariably left to the discretion of the persons making the visit, rather than being prescribed and standardized. This general type of pre-award survey has been prominent in the general procurement procedures of the United States Armed Forces.[6]

In a few companies a second method of pre-award evaluation of a prospective contractor was the inspection of equipment built for other users. Obtaining a list of recent customers from the vendor, the using company would make arrangements to view the equipment and to talk with the owner's operating and manufacturing engineering personnel. The equipment would be examined with a view to determining how closely it approached the project the using company was considering. A judgment on this point would depend on such factors as the size and shape of the workpiece(s) involved, the operation(s) performed on them,

---

[6] For examples of the more formal surveys of this type, see the survey report forms used by two aircraft manufacturers in selecting subcontractors, set forth in John S. Day, *Subcontracting Policy in the Airframe Industry* (Boston, Harvard Business School, Division of Research, 1956), pp. 313–317 (Appendix A and Appendix B).

the material involved, the principal tolerances specified, the spatial relation between critical tolerances, and the method(s) of handling and positioning workpieces. If the prospective vendor had already constructed somewhat similar equipment, or similar major assemblies, then the user's representatives reasoned that fewer difficulties would be encountered in that vendor's executing the project under consideration.

The experience of the Strand Company in acquiring some special automatic equipment is a good illustration of maximizing the usefulness of inspecting similar equipment. In this instance, an important question was whether the equipment could hold close tolerances on two critical dimensions. Through the vendor, Strand personnel arranged to visit the Rollo Company and inspect a similar piece of equipment. The Rollo equipment was performing like operations on a workpiece of different shape and dimensions from Strand's workpiece but not greatly different in total bulk. A Strand quality control engineer was included in the group making the visit. The latter's principal task was to select two dimensions on the Rollo product which bore some resemblance in location and magnitude to the two critical dimensions of Strand's product. He then proceeded to gather a sample of eighty workpieces and from their measurement to construct statistical control charts. The evidence thus acquired indicated that like equipment would in all probability be easily capable of holding the tolerances which were critical in the manufacture of the Strand product.

A third method of pre-award evaluation of a prospective contractor is to make a critical analysis of his proposal, from a technical point of view. How does he propose to divide the operations? What inspection and safety features does his approach contemplate? What kinds of hardware (limit switches, motors, and other purchased parts) does he intend to utilize: rugged models of high-quality manufacturers, or light, inexpensive items likely to give only minimum performance? Evaluating the answers to questions of this sort requires a background of skill and knowledge on the part of the buyer's project leader. Experience in acquiring special automatic equipment will develop some such skill and knowledge. Even in the early stages of a first program of this sort, however, there will probably be much to be gained from making a comparison between the approaches of two or more potential vendors who submit proposals for a single project, sketchy as they may be.

From all that has been said so far, it might be inferred that only large, well-known vendors should be employed. This conclusion is not warranted. If all other qualifications are satisfactory, a smaller and less well-known company may be the most satisfactory choice. The following example illustrates this point. Arthur Company desired to develop several metalworking presses for a special application. It contacted the well-known building companies in that field but found them all unwilling to undertake the project, their general objection being that the application sought was too specialized — in other words, the market among other users was probably slight or nonexistent. Finally, Arthur Company's representatives approached the Simpson Company, a smaller press manufacturer, and found that company's management was interested in the project. To Simpson, the project was a substantial piece of business in its own right, even if there seemed to be few chances of selling the same kind of press to others. Simpson undertook the project and brought it to a highly satisfactory conclusion. Arthur Company has subsequently awarded other projects to Simpson, this time on a first-choice basis.

Surprisingly often, no difficulty was encountered in choosing a vendor because only one was found who could and would undertake the project at hand. Possibly in some instances this condition was the result of a superficial search by the buyer's project leader. In many instances, however, there was evidence that this was not the case, particularly when specialized processing or assembly equipment was involved. For some types of equipment, it was simply very difficult to locate qualified vendors — and in a few cases, the acquiring company believed, with or without great justification, that no qualified vendors existed for certain of its requirements.

When two or more qualified vendors were discovered, the investigation to determine their qualifications frequently disclosed facts upon which the final choice would be based. The visits to the vendor's plant, the inspection of equipment in the plants of the vendor's clients, and the review of his proposal all supplied data which would be used to make comparisons between qualified vendors.

In addition to ranking the vendors according to their general qualifications and probable capabilities, the specific proposals of each could be ranked in order of merit. A wide range of criteria could be considered in evaluating these proposals. One builder interviewed suggested the following list:

1. Direct labor cost (of item[s] produced on the machine).
2. Safety.
3. Ease of maintenance; accessibility of perishable and semi-perishable items.
4. Convenience of operator to controls.
5. Degree of flexibility and convertibility to other uses.
6. Ease of setup, including the time to change over from one job to another.
7. Convenience of tool changing, including the time to change tools.
8. Floor space.
9. Degree of standardization, including the use of standard parts, components, and subassemblies from other machines.
10. Degree of rigidity and proportions of elements.
11. Chip disposal system.
12. Way construction, including load per square inch, ratio of length to width, and overhang.
13. Spindle construction, including the availability of special spindle bearings, drive gears, etc.
14. Feed mechanism and application.
15. Selection and application of electrical components, hydraulic components, lubricating devices, and systems and bearings.
16. Provisions for straining coolant, filtering out dust, and other objectionable elements.
17. The ratio of tried to untried ideas.
18. Price.

In specific instances, some of the factors listed will be given considerable weight; others will be given little weight; and some might not be considered at all — depending upon the buyer and the particular type of project involved. For assembly equipment, for instance, point 5, the degree of flexibility and convertibility to other uses, was often not considered because it was assumed that the equipment would not be converted to other uses but would be junked if its primary application became obsolete. In the case of machining operations, however, this factor was often given more weight in a considerable number of cases.

Finally, there was the criterion of price. The role of this factor was more subordinated to other considerations than in other types of procurement. Within a range of 10% to 15% above the low bidder, the factor of price generally seemed to be given little or no weight — and in several instances in which bid data were obtained, most vendors' proposals were within such a range.

In practice, the step of determining whether a vendor was qualified and the step of selecting the one to whom the contract should be awarded were usually combined into one. Contractors to whom awards had not previously been made would not be considered unless their proposal — its general approach, promised delivery date, and price — indicated that it should be considered. Subsequent investigations were then undertaken to determine whether a new firm was qualified in an absolute sense and, if it was, how its qualifications compared with others being considered for the particular project in hand. The question of general qualifications, however, was nevertheless important because it determined whether the new vendor, if not awarded the particular contract in hand, should be asked to bid on subsequent projects.

Furthermore, the standards which might be desirable for a truly qualified vendor could not always be realized in practice. For one reason or another, the kind of vendor desired may simply not be available for a specific project. Often the most desirable vendors were so committed to other work that their estimated delivery dates fell nowhere near the prospective users' requirements. In some cases, the user's needs could not be deferred, and they settled for "second-best" sources, vendors whose qualifications were quite a bit less than the standard we have been describing. The cases were too few to weigh heavily, but the results of these projects were at least consistent with the conclusion that such a course of action is likely to be justified only in the direst straits. A change in method, employing different processing or less mechanization, or both, would seem to be a better procedure in instances in which the project cannot be deferred.

Another factor bearing on selection of a contractor for a project when much equipment like this was being bought was the buyer's desires with respect to the number of sources of supply. Are too many or too few vendors for this type of equipment being used? This is a factor which users seemed to be slighting unduly. Only one firm was found which had three or four potential sources available to it but which had made a conscious policy decision to buy all of its requirements for a particular type of special automatic equipment from one source. Such a policy we might term "selective procurement," to parallel the concept of "selective distribution" in marketing. There is much merit in establishing some restrictions on the number of suppliers for each principal class of equipment. A policy of dealing with only one or two sources for each class of equipment means that repeat orders will enable a vendor's designers and other personnel to become more fully aware of the user's requirements and to absorb more detailed knowledge of the user's product, the nature of his processing, and his operating conditions. There are other obvious, but less important, potential gains from the standpoint of easier maintenance because the equipment is from only one or two vendors rather than a hodge-podge from many sources. There is also likely to be a somewhat greater opportunity for re-use of part or all obsolete equipment if several pieces are obtained from one supplier. Finally, the more that the procurement of any given type of special automatic equipment is concentrated with one supplier, the more important that user becomes in the eyes of the vendor. This fact in turn means that the vendor will feel justified — and rightly so — in expending more effort to satisfy that particular user and insure his continued patronage. This argument will bear on meeting difficult delivery dates, on the extent and expense of debugging done by the vendor, and on the vendor's willingness to undertake jobs that are a little risky from a technical standpoint. If the vendor makes a little less on one project, but expects to get more business from a particular user, he can expect to average out the difference over several projects.

These advantages are likely to be most pronounced where assembly equipment (and probably specialized process equipment) is concerned. There are undoubtedly risks in following such a policy. Emergencies may arise in which the usual sources of supply cannot meet the buyer's requirements, especially with respect to the delivery date needed. Furthermore, continued reliance on only one or two sources runs the risk of overlooking progressive ideas which develop in other companies. Then, too, lack of competition for the available business may result in higher costs for the special automatic equipment program. It seems preferable, however, to accept these risks, taking such steps as may be feasible to mitigate them. In any emergencies when the regular sources are not available, other alternatives may be utilized. For one thing, in many instances a buyer's requirements can be deferred. For another, alternative production methods are often available which will involve no special automatic equipment (sometimes at surprisingly little difference in production costs). Finally, other builders are likely to be amenable to taking on occasional projects in such emergencies, provided they are well paid for the effort. This is especially likely to be true since such a vendor will always give some consideration to the possibility that a good job on the project may enable him to supplant the former regular source permanently.

To escape from being saddled unknowingly with high-cost equipment or with second-rate design or construction, or both, a continuous evaluation by project leaders of both current suppliers and alternative sources should be made. To some extent this can be accomplished by a general program of visiting the plants of other users, attending meetings of professional societies, and following developments in trade and other journals. It is too much to expect that large numbers of other builders will be very much interested in bidding on a user's project proposals when such a policy becomes apparent, as it inevitably will. It is probably not too much to expect, however, that an occasional, special invitation to one or two alternative sources will be accepted on the basis of possibly supplanting the regular source. If the policy of continuous review of sources is made plain, both to the occasional special bidders and to the usual sources, the buyer should gain doubly. He should be able to keep the usual source on its toes, as to both design and price, and he will gain a kind of standard against which to measure the performance of his regular sources, a standard which may indicate that a change in sources should be made on a long-run (rather than a project-by-project) basis. Certainly a policy of using two sources, rather than only one, has great merit and should be followed when the volume of the particular equipment is sufficiently large that little or nothing will be lost by dividing it into two portions.

Communicating Additional Data to Vendors After Awards

As a rule, even when the buyer has prepared relatively detailed written specifications, there remain important additional facts to be communicated to the vendor. The buyer usually has a large body of information of potential value to the vendor, ranging from the nature of operating conditions to process information about special applications peculiar to the buyer's plant.[7] It is in the buyer's interests to get the best performance he can from the vendor, and there is little doubt that a vendor can do a better job if he is fully informed as to the performance expected, the product requirements, and the operating conditions under which the equipment must function. Plant visits by one side or the other should help to reduce errors of either commission or omission in the basic approach to the project.

In the field survey, it was found that relatively slight attention was paid to communicating specific data concerning the workpiece on one hand and the finished piece on the other. As we noted in the chapter on debugging, for the purposes of automatic handling and processing the workpiece being processed can be likened to a functional part of the special automatic equipment processing it. But many workpieces are far from being precision made. And even to the degree that some workpieces may be precision made, as many are by the time they reach assembly operations, they still may not be precision made with respect to

---

[7] As one vendor has observed, "It should be recognized that most automation projects begin with considerable study of the problems by the buyer, sometimes covering years . . . ," and therefore "Every question, every problem, every conceived answer should be presented to the vendor when he is called in." See Kenneth R. Treer, "Automated Assembly — 3," p. 58.

certain dimensions or qualities on which the proper functioning of the special automatic equipment depends. An example will demonstrate this point.

The Robinson Corporation acquired from a vendor a piece of assembly equipment which was designed to put together four parts. One of the parts was a short metal shaft. In the equipment delivered by the vendor, this shaft was fed onto the operating turntable over an inclined feeding track which held three shafts in line lengthwise, the circular front end of one resting against the circular back end of the preceding piece. To make sure that this track was full at all times, the beam of a photoelectric cell (or "electric eye") was directed at the base of the last of the three shafts in the feeding track. If the photoelectric cell beam did not register the presence of a shaft, the operation of the whole machine was automatically stopped. The assumption, of course, was that the supply of shafts had been cut off for some reason. In determining the location and the width of the photoelectric cell beam, the vendor had taken into account the tolerances specified on the part drawing. Furthermore, to protect the equipment against "short ends" and similar foreign objects which might contaminate the normal supply, the beam was pinpointed so that it would take three shafts of the minimum specified length, abutting one another in the track, to register in the photoelectric cell beam.

When the machine was installed in Robinson's plant, however, this mechanism frequently shut off the machine even though inspection revealed that three apparently normal shafts were in the track. Investigation finally revealed that the shafts were not within the print tolerances, but deviated from the nominal specifications by relatively large amounts. Because the distance measured was the length of three shafts, these deviations were sometimes cumulative on the short side in sufficient amount to cause the photoelectric cell beam to miss the end of the last piece in the track, and therefore to shut off the equipment and bring the operator to this station to find out the cause of the trouble. In the assembled product, these deviations in tolerances of the length of the shaft were of no importance. As a result, they had not been subjected to close quality control efforts, and, of course, they had never been the cause of problems in the prior hand-assembly method.

The Robinson example cited was by no means unique — vendors in several cases relied on dimensions specified by blueprints in designing fixtures or handling devices, only to find that in reality the workpieces were different in important ways from the specification.

Sometimes we found the reverse situation obtained; that is to say, there were important product specifications which were not recorded, but which the user's personnel appreciated fully. Evidence of this kind of inadequate communication of requirements was the frequently encountered statement, "The vendor didn't realize the high quality our manufacturing demands." The Robinson equipment referred to above also provided another example which demonstrates this second type of problem arising from furnishing insufficient data to vendors. During one stage of the assembly operation on this equipment, considerable pressure was generated by the machine in holding one major part while screws were driven into the assembly. As a result, one edge of the major part was sometimes bent, imperceptibly to the naked eye, but bent nevertheless. Unfortunately, for Robinson's particular product a slight bend was very likely to make a considerable, sometimes critical, difference in the functional performance of the finished assembly. The prints of this part and of the assembly, however, made no mention whatsoever of this fact, and neither did Robinson's personnel until the equipment began operation and rejects for defects of this type were piled up at final inspection for the fully assembled product.

To communicate the required characteristics in full, the special automatic equipment vendor must be furnished with several, sometimes several hundred, workpieces. The range of actual dimensions in these workpieces can then be measured and checked against the print when desired. One firm noted that occasionally a vendor would ask not only for several workpieces but also samples of mating parts and prints thereof. Inspection of these would then indicate critical working relations. The user should also supply data on the inspection procedures and instruments which will be employed to check the quality of workpieces coming from the special automatic equipment. Note that even this type of information might not prevent an incident such as the second problem on the Robinson project referred to above. A description should be supplied of the inspection procedures for the part or parts involved up to the time of entering the special automatic equipment, including a list of the dimensions and characteristics inspected. If the using company has no inspection of a dimension with which the vendor's design is concerned, prudence would certainly suggest not relying on the print, but requesting a sample lot for measurement (or perhaps a sampling inspection of this dimension by the using company). Supplementing such information with quality control charts on incoming pieces which the machine will process would likewise seem to be a useful practice if a large sample of actual parts cannot conveniently be furnished.

Competing Philosophies: "Hands-Off" vs. "Close Cooperation"

Here may be as good a point as any to focus attention on a policy question about which widely divergent opinions were uncovered. This is the matter of how closely the user works with the vendor once a particular vendor has been selected, and how much freedom (or, on the other hand, control) is allowed (or imposed upon) the vendor.

One school advocates a "hands-off" policy. Its proponents believe that it is best to allow the vendor to make his own decisions with respect to the method of processing (for example, milling vs. broaching), and design of tools, fixtures, and auxiliary equipment. Should the vendor's representatives ask for specific information, however, the adherents to this policy usually seemed quite willing to comply. It is argued that this kind of relationship prevents the vendor's originality from being subdued or perhaps even stifled by the buyer's habitual ways of thinking and of doing things. A prerequisite for this policy is that the specifications, and especially the performance requirements, have been carefully drawn before a contract has been awarded and accepted by the vendor.

An important qualification to the concept of a hands-off policy was reserving the right to examine and approve the layout or over-all approach, usually set forth in a blueprint, to the equipment's design. Such a layout discloses the general nature and sequence of operations (for example, mill surface "x" is the third operation) without getting into the details of speeds, feeds, handling, holding, and like aspects of each operation. It also shows the over-all physical shape and size of the equipment. Thus the buyer has the opportunity to disapprove of the vendor's basic approach. No case was found (although one is not inconceivable) in which the procedure of submitting layout drawings to the buyer was omitted. In other words, getting the buyer's approval of layouts was standard operating procedure. On the other hand, neither was any case found in which a buyer's disapproval of the layout resulted in termination of the contract, although again, such a case is not inconceivable. In some instances no changes were suggested, while in others minor modifications were proposed and implemented by the builder, usually without any extreme difficulty.

One implication of the hands-off approach is that if the equipment delivered by the vendor fails to meet specifications, and especially the performance requirements, then the responsibility for failure is wholly and clearly his and not the user's. A corollary follows that if the equipment delivered by the vendor has any defects, the vendor has not qualified to receive any payment and he need not be paid until and unless he has cured these defects to the satisfaction of the buyer. Another advantage alleged is that such a policy discourages vendors from taking jobs on which they foresee trouble. Knowing that he and not the buyer will have to foot the costs of any mistakes in this evaluation, the vendor is encouraged to examine the project carefully to be certain that it is within the capability of his organization before he bids. Finally, the hands-off policy tends to minimize the man-days spent by the buyer's personnel in following up a special equipment project from the time the contract is let until the finished equipment is ready for try-out.

A second school — and it had fewer adherents among companies visited during the field work for this project — holds to the philosophy that there should be close cooperation between the buyer and the vendor, even to the extent of lending the services of engineers or skilled workmen to assist the vendor's personnel. In sharp contrast to the hands-off philosophy, for instance, immediately after an award had been made, one buyer's project engineer sent the vendor a drawing for a suggested approach to designing a necessary automatic feeding mechanism. We have earlier described how another company closed the door on some of the vendor's freedom, and therefore likewise on much of his responsibility, by spelling out in detail the cutting tools to be used, including speeds, feeds, and depth of cut. In matters like these, of course, there is a fine line separating suggestions which are appropriate from those which are inappropriate and likely to create more problems than they would solve. What is likely to be appropriate varies both with the project and with the particular relation that exists between the buyer and the vendor. What might not be appropriate during the first project with a certain vendor could become appropriate by the third or fourth project with the same vendor. Then, too, both the technical skill and the personality of the project leader are likely to have an important effect on what should be suggested and on the form of the suggestions.

The buyer can be helpful to a vendor in other ways, too. For example, in a number of instances the buyer reported giving considerable assistance to the vendor in procuring purchased components which the vendor found it difficult to obtain. Sometimes this involved using moral suasion on suppliers, while in other cases it involved searching out replacement sources of supply. One company reported sending cutting tool specialists and electricians into the vendor's shop to help during the period that the equipment was under construction.

What are the advantages of such a policy of close cooperation? The proponents of this philosophy start from the proposition that what the buyer wants is delivery of equipment that functions properly, and delivery of that equipment on time. They argue that their approach tends to lower the chances of ultimate failure on the part of the vendor, and that such a consequence is of more importance than is nonpayment in the event that the vendor fails to perform adequately. They argue further that close coordination between the buyer's and the vendor's personnel as the project progresses is an effective way of supplying the background of the buyer's business in general and the requirements of his product and that they therefore get a better piece of equipment and avoid many problems in the debugging phase. They argue that overemphasis on low price and strict performance specifications may sometimes be self-defeating because of the pressures upon a vendor.   For instance, in a given situation, two operations may be combined at a single station by the vendor because that construction is cheaper than if two stations were used, even though under sustained operation the single station design would be more rigid and therefore be more likely to result in less downtime for adjustments.   Speeding up tool action, at the cost of more frequent tool changes, may also be an expedient to which a hard-pressed vendor may resort.

Finally, they point out that under the hands-off approach, a vendor's problems are likely to accumulate and burst forth in the debugging phase.   If the buyer's need for the equipment is great, he will probably feel impelled to assign personnel at this stage to help the vendor's personnel, even if his policy up to this time has been hands-off.   In other words, most of the problems, and especially the serious ones, are very likely to involve the buyer in any event, although the involvement would begin later.   Furthermore, at this stage — with the entire machine in being and possibly a production deadline quickly approaching for the buyer — resolution of any serious problems is likely to be both costly and less than the optimum from the standpoint of machine performance.

Whatever the nature of the buyer's benefits, however, there is little question that a policy of close cooperation places a premium on selecting capable vendors, and — just as important — on having project leaders who are capable of doing a good selection job.   An efficient selection procedure is the only practicable way to protect the buyer from unqualified contractors.   There is also the risk, which may be only partially avoided in the selection process, that occasionally a vendor will take a chance and bid on a piece of equipment with which he foresees difficulties, counting on the buyer to help solve them in some way and probably even shoulder some financial responsibility in the event of failure.   When the vendor embarks on a project in good faith and unexpected difficulties arise, he is even more likely to look to the buyer for supplementary assistance.   Under such circumstances, the more design suggestions the buyer has made, the greater his moral, if not his legal, responsibility is likely to be. Another risk when the buyer follows a policy of close cooperation is that the buyer's personnel may tend to feel it is unnecessary to carefully spell out the initial specifications in so much detail, since much of this may be worked out between representatives of buyer and seller after an award has been made. Such an attitude seems to be a mistake, and in any program care should be taken to establish precedents from the very start of carefully drawing up specifications before any vendor is asked for firm quotations.

Despite the risks associated with a policy of close cooperation, it seems preferable because of the potential it holds for achieving greater control over the kind of equipment delivered and the date of delivery. It offers the opportunity for discovering faulty design at an earlier stage, when more freedom of choice in redesign or other alternative action is available. It is the only way, short of setting up one's own machine construction department, to promote the easy interchange of background information which, on occasion, may be of great importance in obtaining a satisfactory piece of equipment. The need for certain specific information cannot always be foreseen at the start of a contract. Frequent interactions between the buyer's and the vendor's representatives throughout the duration of the contract, however, should help both to discover and to remedy many of these deficiencies before costly errors are committed. It is likely, also, to result in the project leader's getting more extensive experience in more intimate detail, a kind of training which is likely to prove valuable on future projects. Furthermore, such a condition improves the buyer's chances of finally getting not merely an acceptable but rather a highly efficient piece of equipment in return for his contractual payment. Finally, over a term of several projects, a policy of close cooperation is likely to save time-consuming acrimonious bickering over the question of whether the supplier has lived up to the letter of the contract. When serious deficiencies appear, the spirit of the undertaking is more likely to be forgotten by the buyer under a hands-off approach.

Progress Supervision During the Contract Term

Whether a policy of close cooperation or a policy of hands-off was being followed, all the companies in the field sample did some checking on the progress of a vendor during the term of the contract. Few of the firms visited, however, did more than a perfunctory job of expediting.

A vendor's progress on a project may lag because of changes in the ability of its organization to perform (for example, strikes), because of changes in the vendor's desire to perform (for example, receipt of larger and more lucrative contracts), or simply because of apparently slipshod planning or execution, or both, by the vendor's organization. A number of firms also complained of delays caused by failure, or at least alleged failure, of a manufacturer of a purchased machine part to deliver in time to meet the vendor's original machine assembly schedule. Probably the manufacturer of the component was at fault in most of these cases, but sometimes these instances also seemed to have their roots in slipshod administration on the part of the vendor. For instance, in one case in which the vendor reported being delayed by purchased components, the buyer volunteered to lend expediting assistance, which the builder readily accepted. The buyer's representative made contact with the component suppliers and to his surprise found that they had not previously been subjected to any expediting action whatsoever on the orders. Inquiry revealed that the equipment builder's organization habitually undertook no follow-up with respect to purchased parts.

Skillful expediting is likely to involve the buyer intimately with the vendor's organization, policies, and procedures. Another buyer, for instance, expediting for a builder being held up by a purchased subassembly, discovered a fact not known to the equipment builder. This was that the major element in the subassembly was a stock item (not then out of stock) for the component manufacturer. The components which needed to be added to the stock major element, however, had to be custom-made, and the component manufacturer had a very large backlog of orders for such custom-made elements and a very small capacity to make them. In other words, the buyer's expediting discovered that it was the custom-made components which were causing the delay. The equipment buyer, however, knew of half-a-dozen other concerns which could fabricate the custom-made elements (but which did not make the major element or its equivalent), and improved delivery was achieved by using one of these sources and buying only the stock item from the original component supplier.

One buyer, faced with the necessity of completing a program involving several pieces of special automatic equipment, in effect expedited the purchased components of some of its vendors before these builders even placed orders for the components. What the user's personnel did was to find out from the builders which projects could be accelerated if delivery of purchased components could be accelerated. The equipment user's personnel then contacted the manufacturers of these components and also explored alternative sources of supply. These actions significantly improved the delivery of several components and therefore improved delivery of the various pieces of special automatic equipment involved. It was reported in one instance that the builder's promised delivery date for a piece of equipment was improved by three months as a result of using this technique.

The source of all problems arising during the expediting phase of procurement is not necessarily the vendor. Occasionally, the equipment buyer's requirements will change. For example, it may become necessary to modify the design of the part or parts constituting the workpiece(s) of the equipment under procurement. If these are of any significance, of course, they may result in a revision of the design of the equipment, the price, and possibly of the delivery date.

Any plan of expediting needs to be based upon a plan for manufacturing the equipment. In general, the principal elements in the manufacturing cycle of special automatic equipment include layout drawings, detailed drawings, ordering purchased parts, ordering fabricated parts, assembly, test run(s) of equipment, and shipment to the user's plant. It appears reasonable to expect any vendor of special automatic equipment to be able to furnish tentative beginning and completion dates for each of these principal steps. The larger special automatic equipment vendors visited did prepare such schedules for their own use in allocating their capacity and in their own follow-up activities. At times, the schedule for key individual parts may prove helpful; for instance, the ordering date and the promised delivery date for the base casting (or weldment), for motors, for feeding devices, or for drill heads. Just what is a key part, of course, is often likely to vary with the project, and its selection is a matter of judgment.

Once the vendor has submitted such time schedules, developments can be monitored and actual performance compared with the forecast. The quality of the vendor's performance during this period is much more difficult to gauge. Examining the layout drawings and discussing progress with the vendor's design engineers and shop supervisors can be helpful to a skilled expediter in judging the qualitative element, though his evaluation of this matter will necessarily lack precision.

In some instances, the concept of "percentage completed" was employed, for instance, 25% completed, 50% completed, 75% completed, and 100% completed. Usually this concept was applied to the vendor's whole job of designing and building. This approach is suspect in that the percentage completed is difficult to fix. Reports on completion of individual key tasks and milestones are preferable. Whether completion of layout drawings and receipt of the base casting constitutes 25% of the total job or not is immaterial if one ascertains these facts and can relate them to the general magnitude of the jobs which remain to be done before the equipment is shipped.

An expediting program such as the one just described requires the understanding and cooperation of the vendor from the time the contract award is made. A vendor is likely to be more interested in setting up schedules and in committing his organization to meeting them before he has the contract in hand than he will be after the project has joined others in his backlog.

Only a handful of the firms visited were using as tight control as has just been described, but this seemed to be more the result of inexperience and oversight than of deliberate policy. Only one firm dealing with vendors advocated a "loose" approach. "We don't want our contractors to feel too regimented," said the leader of this firm's special automatic equipment section. It must be admitted that a tight approach may backfire. The contractor may be forced into estimating schedules on the basis of few or unreliable data. The vendor may also commit himself to optimistic schedule estimates in his eagerness to receive the award. If the buyer's expediter then injudiciously attempts to force the vendor to comply with these shaky estimates as the project progresses, the vendor will at best be frustrated. At worst, he may be driven to adopt short cuts which carry grave risks of complete failure of the assembled equipment. A more likely risk, however, is the delivery of functioning but distinctly inferior equipment.

The risks associated with tight expediting control are not inherent in the approach itself but rather in the people who do the expediting. For this reason, the writer advocates a policy of having the engineer or team leader who is responsible for a project do the expediting personally. He is the only one who can apply the kind of judgment which is essential to appropriate use of these kinds of estimates. Such a person is also the only kind capable of making the qualitative appraisals essential to productive supervision of contractors. Making expediting the project leader's responsibility was, in fact, the practice in almost all the companies visited that used vendors. Only a few firms carried out such detailed expediting procedures as we have been discussing, so it is essential to stress the point that efficient expediting is a matter of following useful procedures *and* drawing on personnel qualified to make effective use of such procedures (including avoiding the inherent dangers).

Just how effective good supervisory practice might be in preventing excessive delays in the delivery of equipment ordered from vendors is problematical. There certainly seemed to be room for improvement. Of the sample of 26 projects tallied in Chapter III, most of which were cases of buy projects, the average performance during the design and build stage consumed nearly twice as much time as originally estimated; the typical project took nine months to go through the design-and-build cycle even though it had been estimated to take only five months. The ratio of actual time to expected time varied widely. One or two projects were completed as estimated, but some took three or more times as much elapsed time as had been contemplated, and pronounced delinquency was the rule. Much of the delay was undoubtedly related to the nature of special automatic equipment and to the difficulty of foreseeing all the problems actually encountered. Other factors responsible undoubtedly included changes neither foreseen nor, in an immediate sense at least, controllable by the vendor, which affected his ability to perform as scheduled. Part of the fault must be laid at the door of the buyers for such obstacles as failing to draw up and communicate adequate statements of requirements or changing the design of the workpiece after the contract had been awarded. Some of the delay, however, probably was caused by failure of the vendor to set up and follow closely a detailed plan for accomplishing the steps necessary to execute the contract. Good expediting practice would require a plan in fair detail for beginning and completing major steps and in purchasing major purchased elements. Regular follow-up would keep the vendor constantly aware of his original (or perhaps later revised) schedule. Finally, good expediting procedures undoubtedly would have uncovered some problems earlier than they were in fact uncovered, and less time would have been lost before remedial action was begun. The earlier that problems are discovered, the more alternatives are likely to be practicable and the easier it is to make adjustments elsewhere which may permit some extra manpower to be assigned to the trouble spot.

Expediting is not usually a very exciting activity. It is also traditionally a low status clerical job in the hierarchy of a manufacturing organization. Furthermore, while some of the job can be accomplished by correspondence or telephone calls, many visits to the vendor's plant should take place — otherwise expediting is likely to become sterile and ineffective. Thus, it necessitates travel and a certain amount of time spent away from home, probably sometimes on inconvenient occasions since expediting should be done when necessary and not when it is most convenient for the expediter. Nevertheless, good expediting should pay for itself several times over by the time a project is completed.

Acceptance Standards and Procedures

The commonly used method of determining whether the assembled special automatic equipment is acceptable to the buyer is to have a test run. This test run is usually made in the builder's shop, prior to shipment, but one buyer in the field sample for this study occasionally provided in the contract that there should be a test run in its plant, rather than in the vendor's.

Each of two buyers interviewed, however, admitted to having bought a piece of special automatic equipment without any requirement for acceptance tests. Both pieces of equipment were expensive (over $30,000), but both were first acquisitions of this type of equipment for the organizations involved. In one of these cases, the builder was accustomed to the test procedure and therefore requested the buyer to ship 150 workpiece parts for a test run even though it was not required. At the specified rate of output for the equipment involved, 150 pieces would be sufficient for only five minutes of operations. The buyer complied with the builder's request, and presumably these pieces were run off in the builder's plant, but no buyer's representative was present. The pieces were not returned and the test run results were never communicated to the buyer. In the case of the second buyer, the equipment probably was demonstrated in operation to some of the buyer's representatives, but apparently no significant number of completed parts were run. In the first case the equipment after installation in the buyer's plant performed quite satisfactorily. In the other instance, however, the project was considered to be clearly unsatisfactory by those who had been responsible for it.

In all the other instances investigated the equipment was subjected to some sort of qualifying test run, but the actual value of such runs as a criterion of acceptance varied greatly. The required rate of output was invariably stated in the equipment specifications forming part of the contract, but duration of the test period over which such an average production rate would be achieved was practically never mentioned. Instead, the length of run seemed to be determined by chance or by an arbitrary decision made when the equipment was assembled. No instance occurred in which the allowable proportion of spoiled parts was specified; only the number of good parts per hour was mentioned. Whatever provisions the contracts did contain were more often than not honored in the breach.

Very few of the tests actually conducted provided for a long enough run to be convincing; for instance, a continuous run of as much as eight hours was rare. Two factors seemed to account for this condition. The first was pressure from within the buyer's own organization to get the machine into its plant and into production. The second was the failure (or sometimes the inability) of the buyer to provide enough workpieces to permit the duration of run to which the vendor had already agreed. It is, of course, up to the buyer and not up to the vendor to see that an appropriate test run is made. One buyer said, a little critically, "Most builders seem to feel that the buyer should take delivery when the equipment has cycled once." Most reputable builders will try to do more than this, but there are limits to what they will do without urging and cooperation. If the buyer neglects to supply test parts, for instance, one cannot expect the vendor to do more than ask for them once or twice. Nor can one expect the vendor to suggest a longer test run if the buyer exhibits no concern about the matter.

It is not difficult to conceive how strong pressures for action would build up as production deadlines for new models and new products approached, and how the temptation might be great to accept delivery of equipment from contractors which might be capable of some production, even though its performance might be substandard in both quantity and quality of output. Indeed, it might often be difficult to perceive an alternative, other than the most unsatisfactory one of failing to meet the production schedule. Sometimes new models or new products were not involved, but powerful pressures for early acceptance of equipment nevertheless developed. In one instance of this sort the buyer's representative originally planned to run a test of 3,000 units, equivalent to two days' production run on certain automatic equipment before accepting it from the builder. The project ran considerably behind schedule, however, and the supervisor of the special automatic equipment unit was under some pressure from the management group to complete the project even though a new model changeover was not involved. In the end, only 300 workpieces were submitted to the builder, and the test consisted of putting the lot of 300 through the machine and then cycling it through the equipment for a second time. The performance seemed adequate, so the equipment was accepted and was moved to the buyer's plant. There a full eight hours' run was made and the project personnel were surprised and disappointed to find it did not work nearly as well as it had seemed to with the lot of 300. The unit supervisor explained, " 'Bugs' just popped out all over the place."

It is doubtful that all cases of having to accept substandard equipment can be avoided, but their number and effect may be minimized by careful planning, including making allowances for contingencies in the time schedules, by judicious selection of a builder, by effective communication of requirements to the builder, and by frequent, systematic and intelligent follow-up on progress after a contract has been let.

The time to insure that sufficient test pieces will be available when they are needed is not when the equipment has been assembled and is on the builder's erecting floor, but rather when the project is initially planned, before the construction contract has been let. Often the buyer had quite understandable problems in obtaining workpieces from parts suppliers (for example, castings, forgings, or stampings) when the item was of new design. Even so, it was manifestly his responsibility to provide whatever workpieces were to be available, and the vendors could not be blamed even though a short test run might minimize the debugging they would have to do. One company (Chrysler Corporation) involved in a very large program, equipping a new V-8 engine plant, found that the size of its program justified the assignment of following up on the availability of castings and forgings to a special task group, to insure that pieces would be available for equipment tryouts.[8] Under ordinary circumstances, however, the project leader should be explicitly charged with this responsibility if for no other reason than that having the part available for the test run probably means more to him than to anyone else, and therefore his efforts are likely to be more persistent and more effective.

<hr>

[8] Carl J. Demrick, "The Plymouth Story," *Tooling and Production,* October 1955, p. 10.

In the field work, it became clear that the results of test runs were a potential though unutilized source of valuable information. Data from the test run can be utilized not merely to determine whether the resulting product of the equipment meets quality standards, fundamental as this is, but they can also be used to reveal the tolerances within which a machine is able to perform various operations, to pinpoint the chief areas of breakdown or malfunction, so that they may be made the objects of searches for improvements in design, and to yield a more reliable estimate of the ability of the equipment to produce at required production rates. Analysis should include measurement and tallying of the quality of workpieces used as the input for the test run, comparison of items produced by the equipment with the product specifications, classification and tallying of defective products in a manner that will permit identifying the operation responsible, and identification and tallying of the various causes of downtime during the run, along with the duration of each. A few firms made a practice of sending a quality control engineer to monitor the test runs, and there seems to be much to commend this practice. Failure to note the causes of downtime, however, appeared to be common in instances of test runs, attention of the observers seeming to be concentrated more on the quality of the output. One special equipment section supervisor, after more than two years' experience with a variety of projects, succinctly put what he had learned as follows:

> In dealing with vendors of special automatic equipment, we have learned to be more picayune in analyzing the equipment before accepting it. We check each and every jam to find out why it occurred and to determine how easily it might be rectified. We also ask ourselves, "How often will this event occur under operating conditions?"

Even though practically every project examined in the field work provided for some performance specifications, at least for a given production rate per hour, very few spelled out in detail the method by which quality would be determined; usually the quality definition was simply the expectation that the finished parts would match the blueprint. But the print sometimes omits elements of the quality control specifications, such as which dimensions were critical and would be inspected, as well as the sampling and measuring procedures. Sometimes, too, the print was incomplete and current inspection practice applied criteria not stated or implied by the print. The specific basis for appraising quality should be carefully pointed out in the contract, order, letter, or other document authorizing the builder to begin work on a piece of equipment. But such a procedure was followed in only a small minority of cases. In one case the failure to spell out the bases and procedure for determining acceptance was deliberate, for it was the buyer's intent to use the withholding of payment[9] as a bargaining weapon to assure maximum cooperation of the builder in seeing that the equipment performed satisfactorily in the plant. In most instances, however, it was not deliberate at all, but was by default.

There was also considerable variation in the practice of buyers in the matter of holding the builder strictly to the specifications. Some buyers construed these as minimums which had to be met in all respects, while others held the builder responsible only for a reasonable effort. At the one extreme was the firm which deferred accepting the machine, when possible, until all defects, major and minor, had been remedied. If it was necessary for this buyer to take delivery before all the defects were cleared up, its practice was to set forth in writing just what was wrong and then get the builder's agreement, also in writing, to remedy these defects after the equipment had been installed in the buyer's plant. If the defects were major, this buyer would continue to withhold payment even though the equipment was in use in its plant. In keeping with this policy, this buyer once withheld payment for four months after a machine had been installed in its plant. At the opposite extreme was the firm which went so far as to reimburse a builder, who had exerted his best efforts on a project, for certain extra costs which had developed, costs of a type which neither buyer nor builder had foreseen at the beginning of the project and over which the vendor could have had no control. This firm's policy did not go so far as to make the contract a cost-plus-fixed-fee arrangement, but it did have the effect of leaving the builder with only a nominal out-of-pocket

---

[9] Often this amount might be as much as the whole contract sum. Frequently, however, progress payments might be required by the builder; for instance, one-third down, one-third at the half-way point, and one-third payable on final acceptance.

loss. One of the aims of this firm's policy (the firm was a large one, incidentally) was to be fair in dealing with its builders so that they would be quite willing to take on further contracts, even though a builder might have been "burned" once. A second firm in the field study followed exactly the same practice, not as a general policy, but only on a single contract on which a well-regarded builder would otherwise have suffered a sizable loss.

At a test run it seems reasonable to expect a builder to meet the agreed-upon specifications with respect to both quality and quantity of output, provided that at the time the contract is signed he has a clear understanding of the standards he is expected to meet. The proviso places an important responsibility on the buyer which was often not fully met. Even when there has been a clear understanding initially, however, many matters are bound to come up which cannot be foreseen, and a reasonable attitude will probably serve the buyer best in the long run. Nor can one expect to shift all the risk to the vendor by establishing too stringent and too detailed test run specifications, or by requiring exhaustive evidence that they have been met.

Responsibility for Debugging After Delivery

One of the indistinctly defined areas of buyer-vendor relationships is the degree of responsibility on the part of the builder for bringing the equipment up to production standards once delivery has been accepted by the buyer. In the cases investigated production standards seemed invariably to be more stringent than those required for mere acceptance of the equipment from the builder. Thus there almost always remained some additional debugging after the equipment had been installed in the buyer's plant. Sometimes the amount remaining was small, but sometimes it was considerable. To what degree should the buyer expect the vendor to help in remedying defects uncovered after delivery and in bringing the equipment up to production efficiency?

The general answer to this question seemed to be, not very much. Vendors try to minimize the amount of work for which they are responsible after physical delivery of the equipment has taken place. They typically provide some help to buyers in installing equipment and then in getting into production, but such help is sharply limited, usually amounting to no more than a few days' time for one or two men. Anything more typically required special arrangements or was up to the buyer to provide. The problem of coping with defects discovered after delivery is naturally very closely related to the matter of acceptance standards, for how much debugging remains to be done after delivery depends very heavily upon the kind of debugging done before delivery. If a buyer sets reasonably high acceptance standards, he can avoid many of the tasks which would otherwise fall to his lot, and vice versa, if his acceptance standards are low, or so loose that they become subject to such an interpretation, his share will be larger. Drawing the line on responsibility for such work involves, of course, something other than mere physical acceptance of delivery, important as that factor is in the absence of other factors. Physical delivery may be accepted, for instance, but subject to a written list of tasks still to be accomplished by the vendor after the equipment has been installed in the buyer's plant. What we are concerned with, then, is the appropriate apportioning of responsibility and the devices which may be used to accomplish it.

Policy-making in this area must begin with acceptance of the fact that the buyer must shoulder a considerable part of the costs of debugging needed to bring equipment to the point that it is acceptable for day-to-day production. Particular operating conditions, the fact that the equipment and the product are so intimately related, and, often, unique elements of process application all join to make this condition inevitable. It is both cheaper and faster for the buyer, rather than the seller, to do some of the things which have to be done.

Insuring that the buyer shoulder no more than his just share of the debugging costs depends greatly on his understanding with the builder on two matters: first, the nature of the defects remaining to be corrected after the test run; and second, the contract provisions governing final payment to the builder. To be able to negotiate an agreement on the first requires that the major faults be clearly identified as such during the test run, and this fact emphasizes once again the desirability of having a carefully planned test for this type of equipment. Each case also calls for a determination of the defects for which the buyer will accept responsibility and those which the vendor will be asked to remedy. There are likely to be many and varied factors which should be considered besides whatever may be the vendor's strict legal responsibility. Such factors as the nature of the problem, the skills of the vendor's and of the buyer's personnel who might work on the problem, the seriousness of the matter, and the immediacy of the production deadline must be considered.

In addition to providing help in debugging, vendors almost always gave buyers some assistance in training operators and setup men. This training was accomplished either at the builder's plant, usually at the time of tryout, or at the user's plant just after the equipment had been installed there. Since the operator rarely was expected to do more than attend the machine and sometimes make tool changes or adjustments, the training job was not usually a prolonged one, but it was necessary. In a few cases the user considered it desirable to send to the trial runs the foreman in whose department the equipment would operate. The motive behind this practice was probably as much to spur the foreman's interest as to impart general information to him. The merits of this procedure probably depend upon the training and background of the individual, the degree of responsibility he or his subordinates will have for making adjustments and performing maintenance work, whether there is much special automatic equipment already in use in the plant, and the degree to which the equipment will make major changes in the way he must operate his department.

Other Policies and Practices in Dealing with Vendors

In most instances investigated, the purchasing group did nothing more than handle the paper work of filling out orders and processing data for payment. There were, however, significant exceptions. Three companies, all large ones, had specialists in their regular purchasing organizations to assist in buying this type of equipment; in some cases, these specialists also bought other types of engineering supplies and equipment. These specialists not only handled the paper work but also suggested sources of supply for individual projects, sources which would be considered along with the vendors of whom the project engineer was aware. The specialists often did a good share of the routine expediting, but in one case he only scheduled expediting calls and the project leader made contact with the builders.[10]

Arrangements like these help assure that good purchasing practices are incorporated into the process of acquiring special automatic equipment. As one purchasing representative pointed out, the project engineers were so aware of the deadlines set by an impending production schedule that they lost sight of good buying policies. Nevertheless, the nature of the equipment involved in these cases generally dictates that the project engineer must bear full responsibility for what is done and what is not done. Any attempt to divide responsibility here would undoubtedly be a mistake. Even in the company with perhaps the most aggressive procurement group encountered in the field study, the procurement head was careful to stress that the role of the purchasing agent in buying special automatic equipment was solely that of an adviser.

A fixed-price policy with full responsibility was followed by all the buyers we visited. When the equipment was bought, the vendors were held responsible for both design and construction of the equipment — there were no instances of design-only contracts. The argument advanced for avoiding contracts for the design phase only was fear of "buck passing" between the designer and the builder if responsibility were to be divided this way. Despite the advantages to the buyer of placing equipment contracts on a fixed-price, full-responsibility basis, this policy was not foolproof. Changes made during the design and construction period often raised the ultimate cost of equipment. A buyer may also suffer loss even with a fixed-price, full-responsibility contract. When the builder defaults, the project is terminated or placed elsewhere. When a second contract is placed elsewhere, as a minimum there will be the added cost of the project engineer's time from the start of locating possible vendors to the point at which the first contract is terminated. If the project is dropped, the buyer's investment in the development of the proj-

---

[10] Some additional examples of how a specialized purchasing agent aided in negotiating to safeguard claims in a contract for acquiring equipment can be found in John M. Kelly, "Techniques for Safeguarding the Buyer," *Essentials of Machinery Procurement and Development,* (New York, American Management Association, 1956), pp. 18–23.

ect will also be a loss. And if production deadlines are involved, there may be further costs, whether the project is eventually completed or not, of developing a temporary source to perform the operations required until the equipment becomes available. Finally, there will be the loss during the period of additional delay, equivalent to the cost reductions which would have been achieved if the first contract had been completed in a normal period of time.

Ideally, there should result from every project an evaluation in writing by the project engineer which could be put in a suitable file for use in the event there were any further dealings with that vendor. A discussion of such a summary by all project engineers probably would also result in benefits for other project engineers, including but not limited to dissemination of knowledge about contractors' strong and weak points. Another main product of such analyses would be their training value. Specifically, one would expect project leaders exposed to such reviews to learn a great deal both quickly and well about dealing with vendors, as well as gathering specific information about the foibles of specific vendors. The time expended by the project engineers and their supervisors would be repaid many times. Of course, there is no doubt that the project engineers in the plants visited did get opinions about a builder's performance as a contract drew to completion, and it is quite probable that there was a considerable although haphazard exchange of views and experiences among project leaders. It seems that much more is to be gained by a systematic analysis in each case. Furthermore, such an analysis would probably be of greatest use if it were in writing, both to gain the additional thought and precision of analysis which should inevitably follow and to provide a record which will be available to other project engineers. Otherwise, it is extremely likely that turnover of personnel in project leader assignments will result in losing much of the value of their experiences if there is no written record.

Summary

The use of vendors, rather than one's own organization, to acquire special automatic equipment makes it necessary for the buyer to perform two important additional steps: one is to find

qualified vendors and the other is to communicate his requirements effectively to them.   For the companies interviewed during our survey and over the time period we covered, finding
qualified vendors for this kind of equipment was not an easy
task, and the more complex the project or the less experience the
buyer's organization had with special automatic equipment, the
more difficult this task became, especially the appraisal of the
qualifications of possible vendors.   The choice of vendors was,
or more precisely, should be, an important one because of the
intimate association which is necessary to achieve optimum results.   The relationship possesses many of the attributes and
many of the potential problems of a business partnership, rather
than the hands'-off and arm's-length bargaining features which
have often typified vendor-vendee relationships in which standard commodities have been concerned.   If this is so, then the
advice to choose one's partner well automatically becomes fundamental.

Once a vendor had been chosen, the next major task was for
the buyer to communicate his requirements.   Some projects were
fairly simple for qualified vendors and required only routine handling as far as effectively communicating the essential information
to a vendor.   On more involved projects, and indeed on some
which initially appeared to be simple to the parties concerned,
there were important background facts which the vendor needed
in order to do his job well.   Perhaps the most notable of these facts
were the conditions under which the equipment was to operate
in the plant, the characteristics of incoming material or parts, and
the qualities required (or, conversely, those unacceptable) in the
product resulting from the machine's operation.   Several methods or combinations of methods might serve to communicate
these kinds of data effectively, but it was essential for the buyer
first to appreciate that the data were relevant, and then to arrange
some way in which they could be effectively communicated to
the vendor's representatives.

The experience of the firms consulted heavily underlined the
importance of carefully defining specifications for proposed
equipment.   Perhaps it is self-evident that this step, taking place
before much or even any contact with vendors, was fundamental
to the success of any project, whether it was a buy project or a

make project. Nevertheless, in some cases an inadequate job of developing specifications was the cause of considerable, and even fatal, difficulties which came to light only after the vendor had constructed and built the equipment. And sometimes, although he had knowledge of a requirement, the project leader failed to include it in the specifications given to the vendor, with similar consequences. Accurate and detailed specifications, primarily in written form, but supplemented by oral communications as needed for clarity, are of greatest importance in a buy project.

Another important facet of dealings with vendors should be progress supervision. Once the contract had been let, most of the firms interviewed followed developments perfunctorily at least up to the time the equipment was ready for a test run. Fully planned and fairly detailed monitoring of progress is likely to result in earlier vendor performance than would otherwise be the case, and also is likely to discover serious delays and other problems earlier than otherwise, maximizing both the degree of flexibility available to the buyer and the ability to use any resources the buyer may have to help the vendor's personnel. Effective supervision presupposes a target schedule for starting and for completing the key steps in fulfilling the contract, a commitment which is probably best and most easily obtained from the vendor prior to the formal award of a contract.

Finally, another key area in dealing effectively with vendors is that of carefully planned acceptance procedures, notably the conduct of the test run of the assembled equipment and the analysis of its results. On one hand, the specifications for the level of quality required and the duration of the test run are part of the specifications for the equipment and should be available to the vendor before he commits himself to undertake a project. On the other hand, the data collected as a result of the test not only bear on the decision whether to accept the equipment as satisfactorily fulfilling the contract, but they likewise may provide clues to the way to go about further debugging so as to minimize the additional time required before full production operation may become a reality.

CHAPTER VI

Builders Look at Buyers

As a method of throwing further light on the problems involved in achieving more efficient builder-buyer relations, the writer visited nine special automatic machine builders at their plants. This phase of the study was based on the assumption that a look at vendor-vendee relationships from the vendor's point of view would confirm and possibly supplement the conclusions derived from data supplied by the users of such equipment. Six of these builders designed and constructed relatively straightforward pieces of equipment, each of which typically comprised a few machining operations and, occasionally, a simple assembly operation or two following the machining. The selling prices of equipment produced by these six builders ranged usually from $15,000 to $65,000. A large part (say, about one-half) of the production of two other builders visited was quite complex assembly and nonmachining processing units, selling usually in the range from $30,000 to $65,000. The final company included in the nine was a designer only — it did no construction — and its customers were firms like the six described above.

For the most part, customers of these vendors were very large firms. From a half to two-thirds or more of their business came from the automotive industry and a large part of the remainder came from the electrical manufacturing industry (especially the appliance, industrial electrical gear, and electronic subdivisions). On the other hand, a variety of other industries were represented among their customers even though their purchases did not comprise a large proportion of the total. Probably at least 90% of shipments were made to plants employing 1,000 or more people.

*Major Problem Areas: Getting Full Data
   on Equipment Specifications*

The area stressed far more than any other by the builders was
that of getting full data on equipment specifications.   One reason
for deficiencies in the data furnished lay in the buyer's failure to
know what he wanted.   There was evidence that some requests
for bids were fundamentally attempts to develop specifications by
first getting the vendors' ideas about ways to approach a problem.
Buyers commonly modified and amplified their specifications
after the first round of invitations and then resubmitted the item
for a second and occasionally for a third proposal and bid from
several vendors.   There can be little quarrel with the idea of
seeking vendors' ideas about how a project might be accomplished.
It does seem, however, both desirable and reasonable that the
buyer's representatives first do a considerable amount of preliminary analysis rather than just select ideas from those vendors
present.   It also seems desirable that a preliminary round of invitations to bid be identified as just that, although it must be
admitted that there is a clear danger of the builder's doing a
superficial analysis himself in this case, and perhaps subcon-
sciously quoting a very low bid to keep himself in the running,
since he knows that he will have a chance to revise his bid upward, if necessary, on a second round.

In other instances, the problem of getting full data on specifications was not the result of a lack of specifications, but simply a
failure to communicate needed data, either because of careless-
ness or because of ignorance that it was needed.   Several builders had forms they had devised to insure that the data they required was submitted, but they reported difficulty in getting
buyers to fill out these forms.   Another stumbling block was
data on the product to be processed.   Builders invariably reported that the specifications set forth on the buyer's prints were
inaccurate.   When it came time to test the equipment, the parts
furnished for the test did not conform to the print.   By that time,
unfortunately, the equipment had been built to process the items
described in the print.   All builders preferred to start developing
a piece of equipment with not only a set of prints for the product
on hand, but also several samples of the product, each in the

condition in which it would enter the machine. Not only was it desirable to check variations from the print in the configuration of the workpiece, which might vary from piece to piece, especially when it was a casting or a forging, but it was also desirable to check the variation in the quality of the material of which it had been made. The hardness of the material, for instance, was important in fixing the cutting feeds and speeds, as well as in providing cutting tools sufficiently sturdy that broken tools from hard castings would not result in excessive downtime. Getting parts for a piece of new design, of course, was usually impossible, and in these cases the builder was forced to work solely from prints. Some builders reported that they were asking for assembly drawings, as well as parts processing prints, to get a better idea of the specific job the customer needed to have done on a particular part.

One of the most difficult and often the most important type of specification data builders found missing can best be described as the "standard assumptions" involved in processing a workpiece. One builder interviewed used as an illustration the case of a part already in production, for which the customer had found that a slightly off-standard grinding of a drill point was necessary to accomplish a certain operation. Often this type of change was forgotten when the buyer commuuciated his requirements to the builder. Two reasons were advanced to explain why a buyer neglected to communicate these data: one, because he did not realize it was necessary or, two, because he realized he had a troublesome processing problem and hoped to get the builder to solve it as well as provide him with a piece of special automatic equipment.

Changes After the Contract Award

Perhaps the second most frequent complaint of the builders interviewed was that the buyer changed his specifications after a firm order had been placed and while the contract was in progress. Most often mentioned was the problem of changes in the design of the parts to be processed, either in their shape or other quality or in the processing required. Changes of the first kind might make changes necessary in the holding or transporting devices, or both, and sometimes changed the nature of the processing problems (as when the basic material was changed), while changes of the second type by definition caused obvious equipment design problems. Many if not the vast majority of these complaints seemed to be based on the builder's experience in the automobile industry, which frequently made last minute changes in the design of a part for a new model during the acquisition cycle for special automatic equipment. But instances of this type were also noted in which the part was used in the appliance, electronic, and electrical manufacturing industries.

On the whole, most of these changes in equipment specifications were irritating and caused delays and some increase in costs but did not seriously jeopardize the basic equipment design very often. There were some exceptions to this generalization, however, especially when a change in the performance or capacity of the equipment was involved. For instance, one buyer contracted for two identical machines to be delivered sequentially; after the first machine was completed, the buyer decided that the capacity of the machine to handle workpieces up to a major diameter of four inches should be increased so that the equipment could handle workpieces ranging up to four and a half inches in diameter. Apparently the change was made solely in an attempt to hedge against possible future design changes which would require this additional capacity. In any event, this change added substantial engineering and construction costs for the builder.

In practically all instances of changes the builder was both contractually and morally justified in charging the buyer an additional amount to cover the full additional costs incurred. In practice, however, the builders all stated a reluctance to charge the full cost because as far as the buyer was concerned it usually seemed out of all proportion to the changes made. The builder was concerned about the possibilities of a dispute over the charge and its effect on the builder's eligibility for future business. Repeat business was most important, of course, in the case of the larger automobile manufacturers.

Liaison Problems After Award of the Contract

Another problem frequently mentioned by the builders was created by the length of time taken by buyers in acting on bids and in approving drawings. Typically, the buyer approved drawings after the basic layout was completed and then at a later stage approved the detailed prints of fixtures and other tooling. Acting on bids sometimes took as much as two or three months, a period of time builders regarded as far too long not only because it created problems in furnishing delivery quotations to other customers but also because it delayed work on the project, impairing the builder's ability to meet the delivery date required. Builders considered a reasonable period of time to be two to three weeks. A random sample of ten orders was obtained from the Richards Company, one of the builders visited. In only half of the cases did the buyer meet the builder's desired standard of three weeks or less; the other half took from five to more than eight weeks in accepting the Richards Company's bid. Delivery requests on these cases varied from 15 to 30 weeks, so that the 5 to 8 weeks' delays were a significant portion of the procurement cycles. Perhaps the most obvious abuse was in one case in which the buyer requested delivery in 15 weeks but delayed acting on Richards' bid for 8 weeks. Builders' quotations on delivery are usually made in terms of a specified number of weeks from date of receipt of order, technically giving the builder a fixed time for doing the job. Often, however, the buyer faced a specific deadline date for starting production of the part and therefore insisted on a specific date which would not be changed by the delay. If the vendor insisted on holding strictly to the letter of his quotation he ran a grave risk of not getting the order, so he frequently "took a chance," accepted the order, and said nothing. Delays in returning approval of prints, when the contract was actually in process, were likely to be an even more serious matter, as the builder suspended further work on the order during this period. Delays on approval of fixtures were reported to be caused often by the fact that the buyer's project engineer withheld approval while his product designers were debating possible changes in the design of the part involved. From the builder's standpoint, prompt approval of equipment prints was desirable to minimize his investment in work in process — the shorter the approval times, the faster the turnover of his capital. Aside from this selfish interest, however, excessive delays by the buyer will probably lengthen the period before delivery of the equipment and, if the pressure for delivery becomes great, there is the chance that hurry may result in more debugging problems.

Another area of excessive friction, according to the builders interviewed, was the liaison with the buying company during the procurement cycle. For one thing, it was alleged that the personnel involved were not always technically competent to make necessary decisions or to supply necessary data. In some instances, the problem was that expediting was being performed by a clerk instead of by a qualified technician. In other instances, however, the top management insisted on being involved in basic decisions, even though they, like the clerk-expediter, lacked the necessary technical training or background.

Top management, the builders reported, created problems in two different ways. The first was when management issued an edict to "buy automation" and parts or assemblies had been chosen in a hurry by personnel "down the line" without considering whether the particular part or assembly chosen for the project was a good one to automate. The real difficulties with the project appeared only after the builder had spent considerable time and effort on it. A second type of situation, described by builders who often had large contracts (over $100,000 for one piece of equipment), was one in which top management as a committee insisted on deciding which builder would get the job. Usually few members of the top management group would have the background required to compare alternatives under consideration and often the person technically competent to do so was not a very influential member in a group meeting of this kind. One builder reported that more than once in his company's experience top management had alienated their own people at the working level by insisting on one basic approach — transfer-type equipment, for example — for a given project when the working level people were convinced that only another type of machine — indexing-type equipment, for example — would work. As this builder pointed out, it was not usually a matter of the merits of the case, for both types of equipment might be workable even if not equally suitable; rather, it was more likely to be a matter of willingness on the part of the working level people to put forth their efforts to make an idea work in which they did not believe. "In this kind of cross-fire, the odds are very great that if top management attempts to force its ideas on middle-management," said this builder's representative, "the equipment you provide will not work after it has been installed in the customer's plant."

According to one of the builders, there was bound to be an abnormally large number of problems with equipment destined for a brand new plant, one which was being equipped for production for the first time. Not only were many people in such a plant likely to be overworked but they were likely to include a high proportion of "green" personnel, and both of these factors adversely affected the quality of the liaison work during the procurement cycle.

Effect of Personnel and Organizational Factors

It is essential that a company which plans to buy much special automatic equipment meet two conditions. First, it must have on its staff personnel competent to deal with outsiders on technical grounds; and second, it must allow them to conduct such dealings. As described by one builder, such persons must be able to judge the ability of various builders to deliver on time equipment of satisfactory quality and output, to perceive significant differences in alternative designs from the standpoint of maintenance, to estimate probable obsolescence, to decide whether a design can be expected to stand up under the daily pounding of production, and to judge whether a piece of equipment can be expected to serve a second application, after retooling, when its first service assignment has gone by the board. This builder went on to say that in his opinion the preferred technical training of project leaders should be machine design. There is no question that the list of functions is elementary, and the kinds of decisions listed must inescapably be made, consciously or by default. As a minimum, competent personnel can probably be expected to avoid obvious mistakes, and to recognize most mistakes early, so that in all but a rare case a quick recovery can be accomplished that will lead to a satisfactory if not to an inspired conclusion to the project.

Comments of builders pointed out, however, that it is not simply a matter of having competent persons assigned to special automatic equipment projects. Even with competent personnel, turnover is likely to lead to difficulties on a project. Not only is a change in personnel likely to entail lost motion in acquainting the new project engineer with the project, but there may be a significant change in background and in likes and dislikes when turnover occurs, which may affect the progress of a project. As one vendor has explained, "No two engineers can be counted on to solve machine and tool design problems in identical ways, and changing engineers during the program can lead to an excessive number of costly changes in tooling." [1] There may also be a feeling of less responsibility when a project leader is completing projects originated by others. Since the kinds of background and skills sought in a project leader are often in short supply, there may also be some lessening of competency, at least competency to deal with particular projects. Occasionally the transfer of management personnel was said to have similar unfavorable effects.

Of course, some changes in personnel are necessary to provide for filling vacancies elsewhere and because a project engineer may move from one employer to another. It is also probably impossible in most cases to complete all pending projects before making necessary personnel changes. Nevertheless, no fewer than five builders pointed to personnel turnover as a cause of problems during the procurement cycle, and, what is probably more significant, they indicated that over the years some buyers seem to hold turnover to a lower rate than do others.

Finally, with regard to effective liaison during the procurement cycle, there was some evidence that the organizational scheme of the buyer may impede effective relations between builder and buyer. As several builders pointed out, only in large companies, and not by any means in all of these, has the project approach been used to carry out procurement of special automatic equipment. The procurement assignment often has been made a part-time assignment for someone who also has other and more primary duties. Sometimes this person was a line manager, concerned intimately and primarily with the day-to-day operation of the plant. In smaller plants it is easy to see how such additional duty may be slighted as far as time and effort are concerned. If only an occasional piece of equipment is acquired, it is difficult

[1] George H. Kendall, Sr., "How to Plan for Automatic Assembly," *Tool Engineer,* February 1957, p. 98.

to advocate assignment of one man full time to effect liaison with the builder. Nevertheless, in any large project, say for equipment costing $50,000 or more, this may still be the most desirable approach even if such an arrangement does not seem to be completely efficient in the use of manpower. It is probably at least possible, however, to vest primary responsibility in someone not so burdened with administrative responsibilities that daily events effectively crowd the special automatic equipment project into the background. From the observations of buyers as well as the comments of builders, it appears that the project approach — assigning a project engineer the responsibility for one or more projects involving the acquisition of special automatic equipment — is by all odds the most satisfactory organizational arrangement.

Test Run Problems

Another area of difficulties was the test run of equipment. Test runs were almost invariably made on the builder's erecting floor, provided workpieces were available to conduct them. We have already noted that obtaining sufficient workpieces was a frequent and important problem and we have emphasized the importance to the buyer of having a good test. It is sufficient to note that from the point of view of a reliable builder, it is also important to conduct a test run. When there was no possibility of getting test pieces before the machine was shipped, the builder had to do his portion of the debugging job in the customer's plant, without the range of equipment and personnel usually available. Under these conditions not only was it more difficult to work effectively but the amount of debugging done by the buyer might well be increased. It was possible that problems would arise because of differences in operating conditions in the buyer's plant and that the builder would be held responsible for remedying these, too, because of the inherent difficulty in authoritatively fixing responsibility for bugs without first, in effect, doing much of the whole job of remedying them. Thus vendors by and large preferred to obtain a buyer's acceptance after a trial run on the builder's floor. When a trial run was not possible, some builders tried to protect themselves by a contract provision which limited the amount of service they would be required to provide in the customer's plant. It is not hard to see, however, that invoking these terms would run a grave risk of alienating a customer who had a machine in his plant that would not work, whatever the reason. On the whole, then, there seemed to be little question that a test run in the builder's plant was a clearly preferable alternative from the standpoints of both buyer and builder.

Another aspect of the test run also developed some important problems for the builders. This aspect related to the observer or observers sent by the buyer to view the "run off" of the equipment. One builder noted that buyers frequently did not send some of the men who should have been sent, specifically, the setup man and the foreman involved. Training these men in the buyer's plant, after erection of the equipment there, is likely to be a cheaper alternative for the buyer and a more expensive one for the builder. There may, however, be an opportunity to obtain training in both places, speeding up the day when production can begin. More important is the fact that in a significant proportion of cases builders reported that buyers sent no one to observe test runs in the builder's shop. As reported by the builders, the proportion of ordinary equipment projects in which no one representing the buyer observed the test run varied from a high of 75% to a low of 25%, with a tendency for the high proportion of nonobservance to be correlated with the less complex, less costly equipment. In the case of complex and costly equipment, such as assembly machines, or any type of equipment costing, say, $50,000 per unit, there was no case in which trial runs were not observed by one or more buyer representatives.

Apparently conscientious buyers also presented problems at the test run. Buyers would send gauging instruments for the purposes of testing the output of the equipment, but it soon became clear that the gauges needed calibration. To make matters worse, the customer frequently lacked the foresight to send the instruments and prints necessary to do the calibrating. One builder related an amusing, if also frustrating, incident involving inspection of test run production. The buyer's chief inspector was a member of the observation group, and after examining some of the items produced by the equipment announced that they were all "off spec." The builder immediately proposed that the gauges be checked, and when this was done it was evident that it was the gauges, and not the test pieces, which were "off spec." Finally the chief inspector admitted that he knew from the start that the gauges concerned were slightly "off" specifications, but, unfortunately, the manufacturing process for other matching parts was geared to meeting the dimensions of this particular gauge rather than the print specifications. The difference was of sufficient importance that the builder ended up reworking the equipment in order to meet the standards of the off-specification gauges! Aside from its humorous aspects, the incident is, of course, a reflection on the buyer for failing to revise his blueprints to bring them into accord with shop practice, if this was the most desirable adjustment under the circumstances.

Other Problem Areas as Defined by the Builders

One builder reported that occasionally his customers reported malfunctioning of equipment after it had been used in production. On investigation, he would discover that in many of these cases the problem was failure of the buyer's workmen to perform simple housekeeping chores. More than once, he noted, the customer's workmen had failed to maintain cutting tools in proper operating condition, perhaps so simple a matter as proper and systematic sharpening of twist drills. The significance of such incidents probably lies in the kind of management control over detailed plant operations which the use of special automatic equipment demands and which a builder is entitled to assume exists.

A complex of other problems revealed by builders might be summed up under the heading of unreasonable and sometimes impossible demands. Again, it is important to keep in mind that these complaints are not necessarily objective evaluations but are based wholly on comments from builders. One of these was fixed and inflexible guarantees. Some of the builders felt that occasionally the buyer adopted an attitude with respect to contract performance which was "trying to get blood out of a stone." In other words, the customer did not recognize the uncertainty inherent in a project of this sort, and was either unable or unwilling to recognize that some compromises must be expected. No doubt the degree of unreasonableness in evaluating incidents of this type is significantly affected by the side of the fence upon which one is standing. Another matter about which three of the builders complained was the practice of some companies, especially some in the automotive field, of requiring that all equipment drawings be in accordance with the buyer's standard drafting practice, and in some cases be reproduced on the buyer's own paper. At least one builder indicated that he automatically added something to his quotation in these circumstances, but in some cases the added burden was simply borne in silence — the continuous uncertainty associated with this type of business seems to have made some builders surprisingly tolerant.

The stipulation of electrical, mechanical, and other standards was a constant irritation to many of the builders, especially among those dealing with the automotive industry. As noted earlier, the National Machine Tool Builders (NMTB) have attempted to establish industry standards, while on the users' side the Joint Industrial Conference (JIC) has published another set of standards. Some vendors have also developed internal standards overlapping the other two in coverage. In some instances, users have apparently decided to require part, but not all, of the JIC standards and have accepted NMTB standards or the builder's standards for other areas. On several occasions, cases were alleged in which the buyer's order did not say which of the JIC standards were mandatory but notified the builder of specific "violations" of those standards after the equipment had been assembled. In one instance of this type, the builder was forced to rewire a piece of equipment completely at a cost of over $1,000 because the customer did not notify the builder until wiring was practically finished that it had adopted a particular JIC standard. This whole area of industry-wide standards is a difficult one, with buyers not only attempting to insure adequate quality of work but also trying to make more efficient their maintenance function, while the builders are trying both to be economical and to standardize the work tasks of draftsmen and shop employees. Unless and until comprehensive, generally acceptable standards evolve on an industry-wide basis, the buyer's explicit statement of standards to be followed seems to be an essential component of equipment specifications.

Another area of complaint by builders was the fact that occasionally prints on new parts would require impossible operations.

Or, as one builder put it, "The product designer doesn't seem to give a hoot for the man who has to make it." By and large, the builders all seemed to hold to a policy of either trying to do the best they could and submit a bid to process the part as designed or to decline to bid at all if the problems seemed to be too great. If they saw possible modifications in design which might make the part easier to handle or to process, they might suggest them to the customer, but as a rule not before they had an order in hand for the special automatic equipment. One notable exception was discovered in which the buyer had called in one of the builders well before the final product designs of a new model had been determined. As a result of the suggestions made by the builder, the final design was considerably influenced (in the opinion of the builder, that is) by the requirements of automatic manufacture. When special automatic equipment is being purchased from vendors, the problem of coordination with product design activities is certainly likely to be more difficult than when the equipment is being designed and built by the using organization.

Characteristics of Buyers Doing a Good Job

Each builder was asked to identify one or more buyers of special automatic equipment who, in his opinion was doing an exceptionally good job of buying from equipment vendors. One buyer so designated was the Military Products Division of the Mills Corporation. The builder mentioning the Military Products Division said he did so because that plant was so easy to work with. The builder said, "We can always get the information we are seeking, or at least find a sympathetic ear." The builder noted that this easy working relationship had persisted despite more than one change in divisional managers.

Another builder nominated the Vogt Company because of its thorough, systematic approach, which included well-developed specifications, careful analysis of drawings sent to it for approval as well as their prompt return, and a policy of always visiting the builder's plant and inspecting the equipment before it was shipped. The same builder also enthusiastically nominated the McCord plant of the Hauser Products Company. It was the McCord plant which, as was briefly mentioned earlier, had called in this builder early in the product design stage, to obtain his comments on product characteristics which might make automatic manufacture easier. The McCord plant had set up a special equipment group to coordinate product design and special automatic equipment development. This group also experimented with mock-ups of machine elements to test various approaches, and it assumed responsibility for debugging activities necessary when the equipment reached the McCord plant.

The Broderick Company and the Hess Company were users nominated by two different builders, in each case for the identical reasons: great skill and experience with special automatic equipment. They knew thoroughly the problems involved in building special automatic equipment and were able to work with outstanding effectiveness with outside builders because both Broderick and Hess themselves had designed and built a fairly large amount of special automatic equipment over the years.

Comment was not specifically requested on companies performing poorly in buying this type of equipment but some names were nevertheless volunteered. The characteristics alleged to be responsible for poor performance, however, have already been thoroughly explored and will not be repeated here, except to note that one firm, the Wendell Company, was identified by two different builders as habitually doing a poor job. The Wendell Company had several divisions, and normally one would expect some variation in the level of performance among various plants. In this instance, however, the builders' condemnations were company-wide. One builder pointed out that Wendell was a big company, and that this fact probably contributed to the difficulty of getting coordination. He also noted that some Wendell representatives lacked the necessary skill in acting as project leaders; one reason for this probably was the fact that Wendell had, relatively recently, significantly expanded its rate of activity in acquiring this type of equipment, and it undoubtedly found its experienced personnel spread too thin in many plants. But the third reason for Wendell's alleged poor performance is probably more significant than the others because, at least superficially, it seems to be more easily controlled than the others. This was the fact that the turnover of personnel assigned to special automatic equipment projects was higher than for other companies.

One builder summarized the differences in performance among buyers as follows: "The difference between a good job of procurement and an ordinary or a poor one is in the people. The people doing a good job are likely to be better trained; they do a better job of analysis; and there is a good balance between old and new people." To this should be added the stipulation that they leave their men on one job long enough to turn in the good job of which they are capable.

It was also the consensus of the builders interviewed that small companies were not likely to do a good job of buying special automatic equipment. They were unlikely to have skilled representatives. The procurement task was always a part-time, additional assignment, often given to line operating personnel, such as the plant manager. Finally, it was a common criticism that the small buyer typically tried to get too much flexibility in a single piece of equipment. He wanted equipment to be designed to process many parts on the same base, with indexing mechanisms, holding fixtures, tools, and probably one or more of the tool heads needing to be changed between relatively short runs of different parts. Such versatility required a great deal of engineering to be done by the equipment builder, for the machine elements to be changed each time were likely to be custom assemblies. And in the end, the total equipment cost became difficult, if not impossible, to justify by savings over existing production methods. Implicitly, then, this criticism indicated that the small companies referred to did not need long enough runs of any one, or perhaps of any two, items to make economical the use of special automatic equipment.

The Buyer's Lack of Understanding of the Builder's Role

Many of the problems we have noted originated from oversights by the buyer's representatives. There is considerable evidence, however, that many were the direct result of a lack of understanding by the buyer's representative of a builder's capabilities and his method of operation. One piece of evidence that this was so was a builder's observation that some companies tried to dictate what they wanted rather than what the builder was capable of doing. In this case, the demands took the form of trying to hold tighter tolerances than the buyer was currently obtaining in his day-to-day production of a part. In another case, a builder noted that the Monitor Company, a large well-known company with much experience in the special automatic equipment field, nevertheless frequently sent this builder invitations to bid on highly complex equipment which he simply was not equipped to make—it demanded kinds of engineering and mechanical skill the builder's organization did not possess. Finally, one builder noted that he had had some fairly steady customers who had never sent a representative to visit his plant.

There were also some strong suggestions that buyers were not familiar with the economics of the vendors' operations in this field of special automatic equipment. One of the key areas in the operation of the builder was preparation of bids, as perhaps would be expected. In the procedures of all builders, invitations to bid were first screened by senior engineers (in small firms, often the owner himself) before a bid was prepared, to determine whether the equipment was suited to the capabilities of the builder's organization. Nevertheless, the average experience of the builders interviewed was that they obtained a contract in only a small proportion of cases in which they submitted a bid, ranging from one case in five to one case in fifteen. One builder estimated that in a year from 700 to 800 quotations were made in order to obtain between 50 and 60 orders. Only one builder interviewed reported as good an experience as one order for every five quotations. The kinds of processing in which this builder specialized, however, were not as widely employed as those of other builders, and both its market and its direct competition were more limited. These conditions, plus careful screening of bid invitations, made a lower ratio possible.

As a result of the low probability of getting an order, most of the engineering estimates were reduced to the bare essentials, and maximum use was made of broad standard estimating elements, even as broad as a "station," without developing detailed engineering sketches which would permit a more refined estimate in individual situations. If careful comparison with projects previously completed indicated significant areas of trouble or uncertainty, a liberal contingency allowance was usually added to the estimate or no bid was submitted. Of course, many of the components and subassemblies used were standard items, and could be priced very closely. For instance, many builders used standard machine bases and standard drill heads (either purchased or of their own design and manufacture), and on such items the builder invariably had carefully developed cost data. The man-hours an estimator spent in preparing a bid ranged from four to twenty-five, being generally proportionate to the cost of the equipment.

For equipment priced at $100,000 and more, the man-hours might run as high as 100 to 200, but most of the builders interviewed were not prepared to invest that much engineering time in a bid. Instead, when anything like that much time was required to work on a bid, the typical procedure was to propose to the customer that he sponsor a development-type contract, as the result of which more detailed sketches, drawings, and other specifications would be developed by the builder and paid for by the potential buyer, either on a fixed-price or occasionally on a per diem basis.

Essentially, the builder was faced by a dilemma when it came to preparing bids. "We can't afford to develop detailed layouts of proposed equipment before getting an order — but we need to develop detailed engineering layouts to make up our bid." The usual practice, therefore, was a compromise, the builder preparing a rough layout, making a bid, and depending upon his skill and experience to work out the design of the equipment when and if he got the order. The justification for this kind of risk-taking, of course, rested heavily on the ability of the screening personnel to select only projects within the capabilities of the builder's engineers and shop personnel. The amount of engineering which a builder would do sometimes varied significantly with the identity of the customer (old, regular customers, of course, being favored because of their presumed large potential), the builder's estimate of the likelihood that a bid would result in an award, and the condition of business (how large the backlog was, and how hard it was to get orders). In principle, however, engineering to develop a bid was very limited in most cases.

The proliferation of bids also had an important effect on the ability of builders to adhere to promised delivery dates. Original delivery promises must rest on the assumption that only a small proportion of bids would result in engineering and shop commit-

ments.   They also rested on the assumption that the percentage
of acceptances would remain the same from month to month.
When an unexpectedly high proportion of bids was translated
into orders, either for a short period of a month or two, or longer
during a cyclical boom, deliveries were bound to go seriously
awry.   Furthermore, with the layouts oversimplified, the amount
of engineering sometimes ran significantly over or under that estimated in the bid.   And, of course, the amount of the need for
special (as distinct from standard) parts, which developed when
the layouts were detailed, directly affected the shop loads.   Indeed, one builder frankly stated that precise schedules could not
be determined until all engineering work had been done.   In
this case, the builder did not schedule parts into his shop until
after he had received customer approval of the detailed prints.

We must add to this background of the builder's situation the
fact that builders are small companies, and not a few operate
with scheduling systems less advanced in concept and in operation than might be desirable.   We should also note that since
technical skill in the design phase and in the shop are often
spread quite thin, they may be bottlenecks, with the result that
missing one delivery because of unforeseen problems almost inevitably sets back several following orders.

It is no wonder that deliveries by builders are more often late
than in accordance with quotations.   One builder frankly admitted that he delivered late about two-thirds of the time.   He
hastened to add the valid point, however, that a large part of this
delay was the fault not of the builder, but of the buyer — parts
departing from specifications, changes in part or equipment specifications after the order had been placed, delay in returning bids
and blueprints sent to the customer for approval, and similar
items.   For what it was worth, we report that he estimated that
working with a reasonably alert and capable buyer, the responsibility for delays was likely to be divided evenly between builder
and buyer.   Perhaps more important than responsibility for delays is the fact that a goodly portion are inevitable, granting the
context in which the author found the builders to be operating
and the fact that a context like this cannot easily be changed by
one buyer or one builder.   Another important premise which

emerges from the usual builder's context and method of operation
is the small likelihood of any profound engineering work being
done on an "invitation to bid" basis. In particular, builders
would rarely explore many alternative approaches to designing
equipment. For this reason a moderate amount of preliminary
engineering analysis by the buyer's project engineer, before asking for bids, is likely to yield attractive dividends over the whole
term of a project. Possible benefits, for instance, include getting
a superior design, getting bids with no or minimum contingency
factors and, getting earlier delivery of trouble-free equipment
as the result of avoiding some trouble spots in design.[2]

Builders' Suggestions to Buyers

What actions did the builders recommend that a buyer take to
aid in getting top-notch performance from builders on special
automatic equipment? Each builder interviewed was asked this
question. Careful pre-award planning, especially carefully
worked out specifications, led all other suggestions; it was a suggestion advanced by every builder interviewed. In particular,
four of the builders suggested making greater use of mock-ups
and other feasibility checks to define the equipment's specifications clearly before builders were asked to bid on projects. The
suggestions on this point also included using development contracts to verify the workability of proposed fixtures and tooling
mock-ups and to perform other experimental work beyond what
might reasonably be expected from a builder in preparing a proposal that might or might not result in an order for him. Another
step frequently advocated was an increase in the number of plant
visits by a buyer's representatives. The builders pointed out that
not merely does this acquaint the buyer's personnel with the way
in which a particular builder operates, but in more than one instance the builders indicated that visits before a contract was
let often led to the project's receiving more than ordinary consideration. Such a visit could be used as a way of drawing the
attention of a builder's engineers to potential trouble spots, and

---

[2] For interesting parallel problems in preparing bids in the military
products (electronics) industry, see R. W. Johnson, "Technical Proposals
— Their Uses and Abuses," *Advanced Management,* November 1956, pp.
19–24.

of discussing alternative approaches to handling them. The up-shot was likely to be a better designed piece of equipment than would otherwise be the case.

One builder advocated the alternative of the buyer's asking for visits from builders. Before any bids were requested, he suggested asking five or six builders to send a man to visit the buyer's plant, to discuss the project, to inspect current operations on the part, and to analyze possible approaches. This builder stated that he assumed that before calling anyone into the plant, the buyer's personnel would have done a thorough analysis of the project on their own. After this round of discussions with five or six builders' representatives, the builder continued, the buyer should make up his mind on the characteristics he wanted, set forth in detail his specifications, and ask for bids. This builder saw no reason why the buyer should not be in a position to include in the invitation to bid at least a rough schematic layout and a precise statement of operations contemplated at each station. He also obviously expected that each of the five or six vendors seen initially would be asked for a bid, and that no others would be included in the invitation. The author is inclined to believe that instead of asking for a representative to call at the buyer's plant, visits to vendors' plants are likely to make available more and higher quality engineering advice. Furthermore, the number of builders whom it is worth consulting on a particular project, as well as the number of builders who are likely to be interested, is clearly a function of its expected dollar cost. Our informant above, for instance, was probably thinking of a project involving a piece of equipment worth between $25,-000 and $50,000; for a less expensive piece of equipment, bringing in as many as five or six suppliers would not usually be justified. One need not accept his suggestion that the invitation to bid include a specific layout to find merit in the essential idea of closer builder-buyer liaison during the important formative period of a project.

The following list of the recommendations of one builder, the Albert Corporation, serves fairly well to indicate the general tenor of suppliers' comments on the steps which would aid in getting optimum performance from special automatic equipment vendors:

1. Furnish complete data — specifications and operating experience — to the builder with your original inquiry.
2. Place your order as soon as possible after receiving bids.
3. Expedite approval of drawings sent to you for approval during the design stage.
4. Minimize the design changes you make in the finished part or specifications after you have placed your order.
5. Advise the vendor promptly of any changes in specifications of workpieces.
6. Place primary responsibility for liaison on one man (a key man if possible) in your organization and try to avoid changing his assignment over the term of the contract.

Personal feelings also play a part in determining the cooperation obtained. One builder, in particular, was very frank in stating that personal feelings affect the quality of performance a builder gives his customer. He pointed out that almost all builders are one-man enterprises, and that it is not uncommon for the principal in them to be earning much more than most of the people they deal with in buyers' organizations, more often than not by a very wide margin. He commented further that a strong personal relation will cause a builder to lean over backwards, and to go to great lengths to satisfy a buyer's requirements, whereas the lack of such a feeling can lead pretty quickly to a routine performance. One builder stressed the desirability of a buyer's getting to know a builder personally, and two other builders mentioned the desirability of dealing frankly with builders, and of evidencing faith in their ability when an order has been placed. Perhaps these comments merely signify that buying special automatic equipment is a cooperative affair like numerous other cooperative activities which pervade our industrial civilization. They certainly should remind us that while following sound procurement procedures may be necessary to do a good job of acquiring special automatic equipment, just following sound procedures may not be sufficient to obtain the optimum performance from builders.

Summary

From this welter of builders' comments, there is clearly discernible the strategic importance of the communication process in trying to create an optimum relationship between buyer and builder: difficulties of communicaton underlay so many of the problems described. Efficient flow of information from buyer to builder was essential in establishing the specifications for the equipment desired, in supplying pertinent background to the builder and answering his questions, and in effecting necessary changes in product and equipment specifications. The reverse flow of information, from builder to buyer, so that the buyer would understand the fundamentals of the builder's operations, was likewise vital, especially in avoiding unreasonable or impossible demands as well as perhaps establishing a foundation upon which useful personal relations may develop.

Equally important, however, is the strong confirmation found in the builders' comments of the fundamental importance of doing a thorough job of initial analysis and pre-award planning, including development of adequate specifications before asking builders to quote. It seems to be clearly established that a builder can rarely, if at all, afford to do any significant detailed design work as the basis for his bids and that therefore any feasibility checks of processes or fixtures must be the buyer's responsibility. The benefits of a thorough development job which reduces uncertainties to a minimum at the very beginning of a project are bound to be realized throughout the entire procurement cycle.

Another important conclusion which the author believes may be drawn is the desirability of the project approach, whenever it can be arranged. This means making one or more projects the primary responsibility of a project leader, a project engineer, or whatever job title such an individual may be given. The importance of skilled personnel, able to deal effectively with builders on technical grounds, has also been underscored several times, explicitly and implicitly. This is a factor which most buyers will be able to control only in the long run because of the general shortage of this type of skilled person. Likewise, the builders' comments underscore the potential injury which may develop from project leader turnover.

Over all, the comments of the builders seem to reinforce the usefulness of the concept of temporary or periodic partnership that we suggested in the preceding chapter. What we intend to suggest by the comparison, of course, is simply a close affiliation of organizations, extending even beyond the terms of one contract in many instances, in contrast to the "buyer beware" concept of a vendor-vendee relationship. To the degree that the partnership comparison is a fair one, then it suggests that a buyer needs to choose builders selectively after appraising their ability, their honesty, and, in some degree at least, the degree of mutual compatibility which may evolve. The data we have examined in this and in the preceding chapters indicates without a doubt that a top-notch job of buying special automatic equipment from builders constitutes an administrative task of no little difficulty, one perhaps not much, if any, less difficult than organizing and operating one's own equipment building group.

CHAPTER VII

The Coordination of Product Design and Special Automatic Equipment

THE ADVENT of special automatic equipment has not changed any of the well-recognized relations between product design and the manufacturing process, but it has added another, the relation of equipment design to product design. This new relation has developed mainly because of the handling and positioning problems involved in the automatic manufacture of discrete workpieces and assemblies. Because the design of the product determines what has to be done and places restrictions on how it can be done, product specifications vitally affect the ease and economy with which special automatic equipment may be employed. Control over changes in product design therefore assumes substantially greater importance when special automatic equipment is introduced in any quantity into a plant.

The essence of the coordination problem is twofold. The first aspect is to design the parts comprising the product so that, as a minimum, automatic manufacture will be feasible and, as an optimum, it will be as economical as possible. The second aspect of the problem is to design and later redesign the product in such a manner that in the long run the obsolescence costs of special automatic equipment are optimum though not necessarily, or even likely, minimum. An important companion effort which will help attain this second objective is to design the special automatic equipment itself in such a manner as to make possible its re-use after changes in product design, again seeking an optimum which is not necessarily achieved by maximizing the re-use of such equipment.

The efficient resolution of this coordination is not a matter solely of engineering, manufacturing, or marketing, but is essentially an over-all business decision. It is a matter to be decided from the point of view of the business as a whole. The task is to optimize the rate, timing, and nature of changes in product design in the long run by taking into account marketing (demand), engineering (technical), and manufacturing (cost) factors.

Different Types of Product Design Situations Encountered

While the essential need for coordinating product design and production engineering was the same for all the special equipment projects investigated, differences in the nature of the product and its newness significantly affected the kind of problems individual plants faced. Three different types of situations with respect to product design activities were found.

First, there were firms which had a model of product in production, the design of which had been well proven by at least one or two years' production (often, of course, it was much more) and which was not expected to change significantly for many years to come. Primarily, these companies looked upon special automatic equipment as a cost-reduction device which would follow the initial tooling for producing the item. In these plants there was a tendency to consider the problem of coordinating automatic equipment and product design to be fairly simple, primarily devoted to adapting present parts, with as few changes as possible, in ways which would facilitate the use of special automatic equipment. Parts and sometimes assemblies were considered individually, and the possibility of a basic redesign of the whole model or family of models was not explored.

A second type of situation was one in which the product(s) involved had historically been subject to frequent, periodic, and complete redesign. These were likely to be consumer products such as automotive, electronic, and electrical appliances. Another smaller, but still important, group falling into this second type of classification comprised plants making military products. And there were also similar instances involving industrial products which were changing significantly and rapidly in design because of rapid technological advances. "Rapid" typically is intended to indicate cases in which there were major design changes taking place every one to four years. In instances like these, special automatic equipment was more often an integral part of the original tooling for the model than a product of cost-reduction programs subsequent to the initial production runs. In some cases of this type the model life was so short that the plant was, in effect, frozen to the equipment and methods initially adopted because the remaining life of the design was too short to justify a second major investment in equipment, even if it turned out that the original choice was by no means optimal. In this second type of situation it was clearly desirable to seek close coordination between product design and production engineers quite early in the design cycle, not because later minor design changes could not be made to facilitate the use of special automatic equipment but because economically the opportunities to do so would be more limited.

A third type of situation encountered was one in which a plant was being newly constructed or retooled to manufacture a product not made by the company before and sometimes not made anywhere else before. After its initial run of a year or two, of course, the product, if successful, would fall into one or the other of the first two categories. But at first from the standpoint of developing special automatic equipment it presented a significantly different problem. The problems of getting the "bugs" out of both the product design and plant processes were accentuated by the greater inexperience of the personnel. Furthermore, the demand for the product was usually much more uncertain than in either of the first two types cited above. Some of these firms planned a two-cycle approach to organizing the production processes. The first cycle was designed to provide capacity to fulfill reasonably expected product requirements only for, say, the first year. There was the expectation, however, that by the end of the first year another, more accurate estimate of demand could be made, perhaps for the following three or four years, and that the production processes would be completely revamped in the light of both the revised forecast of demand and the initial year's production experience. These revisions were expected to go well beyond just duplicating present equipment to obtain increased capacity. In one of these cases, for instance, for the second cycle of production it was planned to move operations to another location and build a brand new plant as well as to develop new production methods and special automatic equipment. Such instances created the necessity and the opportunity for two cycles in coordinating product design and production. It was possible to plan to have certain operations, which eventually might be handled automatically, set up the first time on the basis of full manual operation until any bugs in the product design had been cured and until there was a better basis for forecasting market demand. This kind of solution was not always the best, however, and it was important to identify the operations for which the procurement of special automatic equipment could not, or should not, be postponed until the second round. It was also important to decide how long to continue production using the methods of the first cycle.

It is true that a piecemeal approach to the coordination of product design and production sometimes was moderately successful. Nevertheless, optimum results in all three types of situations seem likely to require a program of broad-scale coordination in the basic approach to the product's design.

Facilitating Automatic Production

It is often necessary to make minor changes in product design in order to utilize special automatic equipment. This was the only kind of coordination of product design and production engineering which was observed in many of the plants visited, and one or more examples of this kind of coordination were found in all of these plants. Sometimes the solution was as simple as providing a small protrusion or a small hole or slot, which might be used to orient a part in a feeding mechanism, or as changing the sequence of operations slightly. Others were more difficult, such as changing the location of flash on a forging from the edge of a workpiece to its flat face, in order to effect a change in the method of processing, or spacing all holes in an automobile engine a minimum of $1\frac{7}{8}$ inches apart to allow for husky spindles on processing equipment.[1] The more complex modifications encountered involved changes in shape, in function, and sometimes

---

[1] George De Groat, "Plymouth Puts 'Forward Look' Into V-8 Production," *American Machinist*, August 15, 1955, pp. 88D.

in material, changes which significantly altered the nature of a mechanism. Sometimes the changes were made in order to avoid requiring assembly operations which were not feasible at all with automatic machinery.[2] Occasionally tolerances on the finished workpiece would be relaxed to accommodate the special automatic equipment, and often, perhaps even more often, the tolerances on incoming materials or parts were tightened to try to insure more uniform workpieces for automatic processing, whether they were rough castings or forgings[3] or finished stampings or machined parts ready for assembly.

In most instances an equipment project leader accepted the design of the part or parts involved and asked for changes only as a last resort. Said one special automatic equipment supervisor, "We pretty well leave product design alone and do the best we can, taking the design as is." This was a typical attitude, it seemed, in quite a few of the companies visited — the product designer was "king," and his decisions were not questioned. But by far most of the parts had not been designed with automatic production in mind, with the result that while in many cases a

---

[2] David H. Esperson has described how the design of a choke coil, manufactured for use in TV receivers, was radically redesigned to facilitate automatic fabrication. One major change was the use of larger wire (.026 inch in diameter as compared with the original .005 inch); furthermore, the larger wire was cellulose acetate wrapped, and permitted winding without a coil form which had previously been required. It also eliminated an operation, cementing the finished leads. The use of fishpaper tape backing, on which the finished coils were mounted, and which provided accurately located pilot holes actuating automatic feed and indexing, was also a radical change from the dummy resistor on which the coil was formerly wound. See "Redesign Permits Automatic Assembly," *Automation*, March 1957, pp. 139–142.

Another project which produced radical design changes in order to facilitate automatic production was the Bell Telephone System's wire spring relay project. The old style relay, for instance, used fifty-four individual parts which had to be assembled by hand to produce the "contact assembly"; for the new relay, two automatically molded subassemblies of wire springs accomplish the same purpose. The new relay used eleven standard parts, regardless of application; less frequently required variations are obtained by adding parts to the standard relay. See H. M. Knapp, "Designing for Automatic Production," *Automation*, September 1954, p. 51–56.

[3] Closer tolerance castings and forgings were reported to have been an important factor in the operation of the Plymouth V-8 engine plant in 1955. See George De Groat, "Plymouth Puts 'Forward Look' Into V-8 Production," p. 88E.

part *could* be processed automatically as designed, an alternative design might be processed more easily and cheaply.

From the standpoint of product design, the difference between a workable design and one which provides for economical processing may be small. K. O. Tech, Engineering Vice President of Cross Company, builders of special automatic equipment, has compiled some data on examples which can be used to illustrate the difference.[4] One of his examples concerns an intake manifold for an automobile engine which had been designed in such a way that it had to be clamped on a pallet to provide the means of guiding it and locating it through the machining operations performed by a transfer machine. Tech pointed out that since each piece had to have a pallet, it was necessary to have a large inventory of pallets and also a pallet return mechanism, neither of which would be required if the piece were designed to be self-guiding and self-locating. He compared two specific instances; the first was a piece of special automatic equipment for an automobile engine manifold of the first type (pallets necessary) while the second was a piece of equipment for another design of manifold which needed no pallets but which was self-guiding and self-locating. He reported that the first machine cost 28% more than the second.

Tech referred to a second example which involved another automotive part, a bearing cap assembly. One design, designated "A," provided for a single protrusion, along the center of one side, which permitted very easy handling of the part. A second design, "B," however, had a large circular head which made it impossible to provide a simple guide, and therefore required a considerably more complex transfer mechanism than did design "A." Reported Tech:

> The cost of the equipment to manufacture 110 "B" Bearing Caps per hour was 45% greater than the cost of the equipment to manufacture 180 "A" Bearing Caps per hour. Much of this additional cost can be attributed to the design of Bearing Cap "B."

[4] Unpublished manuscript of a speech delivered at the 1957 Design Engineering Conference of the American Society of Mechanical Engineers titled "Designing for Easier Machining, Handling, and Assembly." This is abstracted in considerable detail in "Designing for Automation," *Tool Engineer,* July 1957, pp. 193–196.

In all these cases the part could be processed automatically, but features of each product's design made a considerable difference in the cost of equipment.[5]

Sometimes the material of which a part is made limits the special automatic equipment designer. One instance encountered in the field work was a glass part, which created problems in automatic handling and feeding because it was so easily broken. Another such instance has been reported [6] in connection with a transfer machine comprising many stations, which was designed to machine a cast aluminum valve body. Because the material in this part was relatively soft, there was the danger that repeated clampings of the part at each station as it moved through the line might distort the locating surface. Even though it was more expensive construction, therefore, this equipment was designed to transport each part through the line clamped on a pallet, which would absorb the wear from clamping at each station.

The physical characteristics of a part and of the material of which it is made are often vitally related to the process specified for its manufacture by the product designer. Gears, for instance, can be made in many different ways; one author has listed ten different ways to do so (excluding secondary operations like shaving or lapping).[7] But from the standpoint of making production automatic, it certainly makes a considerable difference

---

[5] Again anticipating our later discussion of project analysis, we find that the financial implications of differences in the equipment costs of these magnitudes are significant. Assuming that we are dealing with a replacement situation in which a payback period of three years is involved and the estimated economic life is five years, a 28% increase in the investment required (as in the first example cited by Tech) will raise the payback period to nearly four years and drop the time-adjusted rate of return from 25% to a considerably lower 10%. In some cases the difference in capital investment may be the difference between doing and not doing a project, for a 10% rate of return may not be large enough to justify proposed equipment in comparison with the current method. If the difference in capital investment required were as great as 45% (as in Tech's second example), the rate of return would, of course, drop even more, to only about 5% — not a very attractive proposal.

[6] "Ford Sharonville: Proving Ground for New Ideas in Automation," *American Machinist,* December 1, 1958, p. 104.

[7] Louis D. Martin, "An Objective Look at the Field of Instrument Gearing," *Collected Papers 1956* (Detroit, American Society of Tool Engineers), Library Edition, Paper 24T23, p. 2.

in the kinds of problems likely to be encountered whether the process specified is hobbing, stamping, die casting, cold extrusion, or injection molding. In handling the raw material alone, of course, there would be major differences in the ease or difficulty of automatic gear manufacture using these several processes.

There may also be simple but important differences in die design which materially affect the ease or difficulty of automatically loading and unloading work. Richard H. Melvin has noted several kinds of cases in which a die designer's apparent lack of appreciation of the problems of automatic handling created problems.[8] One of these circumstances was what he described as "panel crossover," a situation in which "two panels which are fabricated on the right and left sides respectively in one double die, are reversed to left and right sides in the following die." If manual handling is involved, say between two presses, the fact that the right and left panels must be "crossed over" between the two operations may cause few or no problems, and under some circumstances may actually facilitate handling. But with mechanical handling, the same two sets of dies may require a more complex mechanical motion than would simply maintaining the left panel on the left and the right panel on the right for all operations.

One simple but usually important aspect of product design is the method used to fasten the parts of an assembly together. There are at least nine methods of fastening, for instance, which have been performed automatically:[9] coining, staking, riveting, spinning, screwdriving, stud-setting, nut-setting, welding, and special fasteners. While all these methods may be performed automatically, some are more easily made automatic than are others, and there are significant differences in the economy with which each may be performed. For instance, compare what are frequently alternatives: fastening pieces together with the conventional nut and bolt, which sometimes requires a lock washer, or staking a rivet. The first utilizes two or three parts while the

---

[8] "Press Unloaders and Die Design," *Automation*, January 1957, pp. 118, 120.

[9] Kenneth R. Treer, "Automated Assembly — 2," *Automation*, November 1956, pp. 64–67.

second uses only one part. Since all parts must be oriented and fed properly into the assembly equipment, the difference in the number of parts is important. We must also consider the intrinsic difficulty of the motions of starting and tightening the nut and bolt together with the simplicity of deforming the end of a rivet. These differences are important whether the method of assembly is manual or machine, but they are likely to become much more significant when machine methods are involved. It is also true that there are factors other than low-cost automatic assembly which may bear on making a design choice, such as the functional difference of being able to disassemble the nut and bolt easily. It is quite conceivable that, weighing all the relevant considerations pertaining to a particular operation, using a bolt and nut might be the preferred method of fastening for hand assembly but that a staked rivet would be the best choice for automatic assembly.

There are many advantages in appraising all product designs at their inception from the standpoint of ease of automatic assembly even though the immediate concern is simply ease of fabrication. For one thing, it may not be long before the problems of design for automatic assembly must be faced anyway. Once the fabricating operations have been mechanized, the principal area for lowering costs is likely to become assembly operations. Indeed, an executive of the Ford Motor Company has observed that in the group manufacturing parts and accessories, "only about 20% of the labor was involved in machining operations (where most of the recent efficiency gains have come), and most of the opportunity for gain now lies in assembly." [10] Still another reason is that a part or assembly designed for easy automatic assembly can almost always, if not always, also be easily handled in automatic fabricating operations; the sorting, orienting, and transportation problems are likely to be amenable to the same technical solutions in both cases.[11] Finally, while a design

---

[10] "SAE Production Meeting: Headliners — Machine Tools and Automation," *American Machinist*, March 28, 1955, p. 159.

[11] Kurt O. Tech, "Designing for Easier Machining, Handling and Assembly," cit., p. 12. See also Ralph E. Cross, "Automation Tomorrow," *Collected Papers, 1956* (Detroit, American Society of Tool Engineers), Library Edition, Paper 24T34, pp. 5–6. Cross works back from assembly

suitable for automatic assembly may be equally suitable for automatic fabrication, the reverse may not hold true. In fact, ease of automatic assembly may require a completely different design concept, a different process, a different material, or conceivably a combination of all three types of changes.

Standardization and Product Design

Leaving aside any other advantages which may be involved (such as economy of engineering effort and minimizing parts inventories), standardization has two important results with respect to special automatic equipment. First, it may have the effect of consolidating several short runs of parts, none long enough to justify special automatic equipment, into a longer run of one part, the size of which becomes adequate to justify this type of equipment. And second, standardization is one way to attempt to minimize the chances that special automatic equipment will become obsolete when a product is redesigned. Or, to put it another way, unless some consideration is given to standardizing parts design, special automatic equipment may become obsolete so quickly that it makes this kind of equipment uneconomical in the long run. At the present time, at least, it seems unrealistic to think of freezing many product designs for very long. There is the very real problem of style in consumer products, and the pressure of technological progress in all products, both forces which seem almost certain to require frequent modifications in design. Nevertheless, many minor parts and components may be carried forward from one design to the next and in some cases other parts may be radically altered but still be within the "geometric" capacity of processing and assembly equipment, and may employ a large number of the same operations. Redesign would then be in large part a recombination of basic modular elements designed to accommodate the new design to the old equipment with a minimum of obsolescence and retooling costs, yet still permitting an improved product from the standpoint of technical performance, or style, or both.

---

to processing to develop the conditions required for both machining and assembling an automobile engine intake manifold automatically.

The state of affairs in which existing equipment closely restricted product design had been reached in one plant visited during the field work. This plant was in the electrical manufacturing business and its basic production line comprised several million dollars' worth of special automatic equipment. The equipment had just been changed over to the manufacture of a new product design, and the plant manager noted that this most recent model had been designed so that it could be manufactured on the existing equipment. The "ground rule" that the redesign must be suitable for processing on the existing equipment had been established at the beginning of the product-design task. On the whole, however, most of the companies consulted in the field work had not reached the point where existing facilities had attained this kind of importance, primarily because their investment in special automatic equipment was largely of fairly recent vintage and in most cases still did not comprise a large proportion of the total plant investment.

At a less restricted level, however, a Westinghouse executive has reported a good example of the kind of standardization which seems to be evolving (the product in this case was room-sized air conditioning units):

> A manufacturing engineer works with the design engineer at the time of the inception of a design or a change in design. As an example, we redesigned compressors for room coolers. We eliminated lower horsepower units, and concentrated on ¾, 1, 1½, and 2 horsepower. That was done so that we could get volume production and get into automation to the fullest extent possible. We have practically the same compressor for all sizes, the same dimension crankshaft, connecting rods, and pistons. To get the different ratings, we will use Freon-12 and Freon-22. Or we may use one or two cylinders in our compressor. These cylinders are designed so that they are manufactured on the same machine, with only minor tool changes.[12]

A second project in which the basic design approach was standardized to permit the combining of requirements, so as to get one long run without the necessity for frequent setup changes, involved electric motors:

---

[12] J. R. Weaver, "Six Approaches to Effective Cost Control," *Production,* August 1957, pp. 72–73.

By keeping the same material thickness, we can use the same dies for blanking out our laminations and fastening them to stacks. We also maintain the same ID and OD dimensions, and we give the engineers the mass variation they require by making different stack lengths.[13]

Another good example of standardization to make possible the long runs needed to make special automatic equipment most economical has been described in connection with the machining of diesel engine parts. The engines in the line cover a range of 20 to 1650 horsepower. They are based on three progressively larger sized cylinders; have 2, 3, 4, 6, 8, and 12 cylinders; and are made in both V and in-line models.

Manufacturing is simplified and interchangeability is improved because many components in the engines have been standardized. Bores are spaced in the same amount on 3-cylinder in-line and V-6 engines, so the same heads can be applied to both. Hole spacing for fly-wheel housings is identical for V and in-line units, and pan-rail hole spacing is the same. Pistons, gear trains, and other components are the same, so the processing equipment is much simplified.[14]

Thus far we have examined the part standardization of product design can play and sometimes must play in helping to accomplish special automatic equipment projects. A standardization program may aid in attaining this objective and at the same time reduce the risk of obsolescence to which such equipment is prone. It played this role in the electronics firms visited in the field studies (as well as permitting the consolidation of relatively short runs for processing over one common type of equipment). The electronic industry has had perhaps more reason than most to be sensitive to the problem of coordinating product design and production engineering to avoid equipment obsolescence because the industry has been subject to a high rate of design change.[15]

---

[13] Raymond Sollohub and Robert Coen, "Simplified Setups For Job Shop Automation," *Collected Papers, 1958* (Detroit, American Society of Tool Engineers), Library Edition, Paper 131, p. 1.

[14] George H. De Groat, "Flexible Automation for Diesels: Cast-Iron and Aluminum A and Inline," *American Machinist,* January 12, 1959, p. 102.

[15] See John Markus, "Mechanized Production of Electronic Equipment," *Electronics,* September 1955, p. 160.

The most striking example encountered of a broadly based program was one found in an electronics manufacturer. This concerned the standardization of printed circuit board designs for the purpose of using automatic inserting machines to assemble components to the board in the assembly process. First was the problem of standardizing the dimensions of the boards to be used, especially the maximum and minimum length and width. These dimensions, and the maximum dimensions in particular, affected not only the design of the automatic inserting equipment, but also the capacity of other equipment, such as the capacity of a following dip-soldering operation, in which the bottom of the board was dipped in a liquid solder bath to solder the component leads to the circuits previously etched in the bottom of the boards. Of course, the range of sizes as well as the size of increments was important in the over-all design of the electronic product being manufactured; they became a basic and limited assortment of modules to which the product engineer would be restricted in building up his circuits.

There also arose another important standardization question, that of the increments of size for component spacing over the surface of the printed circuit board. Since each component was assembled to the board by inserting two leads through holes going through the board, it was necessary to adopt a standard grid, on which all circuits would be laid out, to maximize the usefulness of inserting equipment. The purpose of this grid was to define the ability of the equipment to bend leads of components to length and then insert them into the printed circuit board. One plant visited had adopted a grid standard based on increments of one quarter of an inch. This meant that the components on any board to be assembled using this equipment would have to be located by coordinates which were multiples of .25 inch, measuring from two of the four edges of the board to locate the mounting holes. In turn, of course, this implied that the leads of, say a resistor, could be bent to lengths which were multiples of .25 inch also and then be located in the assembly equipment by the same coordinates which designated the matching holes in the printed circuit board. Thus the grid standard imposed another design module on the product designer, limiting the number and arrangement of possible locations which could be used on each size of printed circuit board.

There was common agreement among all the electronic plants visited that such a grid standard was essential to automatic manufacture of this type of electronic product. There was considerable difference of opinion, however, as to what that standard should be. One plant adopted the .25 inch standard used as an illustration above. Another adopted .10 inch and another .50 inch. Another firm has published a still different specification, as follows: [16]

1. All holes in the board for mounting axial lead components will be on a 0.2-in. module.
2. Axial lead components will be mounted on standard insertion centers: 0.8-in., 1.0-in., 1.2-in., and 1.4-in.
3. All axial lead components on any one board must be mounted in the same direction and if possible should be placed in rows.

The smaller the grid increments, the more complex and more costly the special automatic assembly equipment would be. On the other hand, the smaller the grid increment, the greater the freedom allowed the circuit designer. Some designers, foreseeing an accelerated trend toward miniaturization of components, contended that the smaller grid increments were essential to provide flexibility to adapt to future changes. There were also the problems of developing and following an industry standard and coordination with military procurement agencies, since military procurement is so important in the electronics industry.[17] And superimposed on all this was the necessity for

---

[16] William M. Hancock and John C. Souter, "Mechanized Assembly of Carrier Equipment," *The Western Electric Engineer*, April 1957, p. 28. See also Edwin Suuronen, "Manufacturing Functions," *Automation*, March 1958, pp. 60–61, for a description of developing standards for electronic assembly in a General Electric plant. See also Alfred H. Johnson, "Developing the Hardware," *Automation*, April 1959, pp. 46–48, for a description of a design standardization program undertaken at an IBM plant to facilitate production of electronic products.

[17] Subsequently it was reported that the Electronic Industries Association had adopted a standard module for rectangular grid systems of 0.025 inch, with preferred multiples of one, two, and four times the basic standard of 0.025 inch. See Joseph Harrington, Jr., "Automation Standard Permits Design, Manufacturing Economies" (Abstract), *Automation*, March 1959, pp. 141–143.

using components — resistors and condensers, notably — which were standard not merely in their electrical characteristics but standard also in size and shape in ways and to degrees not important in hand assembly. Sometimes the position of wire leads on components needed to be modified in order to permit insertion into printed circuit boards. A similar and important problem arose in connection with feeding; sometimes components were attached to a tape, much like a machine gun belt, to facilitate automatic feeding; in other cases they were packed in a spring-loaded magazine for the same purpose. Thus the problems of mechanized assembly were gradually pushed back from the final assembly stages to component manufacture and the number of necessary design revisions was multiplied.

It is noteworthy that it has been in the electronics industry that a basic module design approach has been developed, although up to this time it has been largely on an experimental rather than a production basis. This development is the so-called "Project Tinkertoy," sponsored by the United States Bureau of Standards in contracts with various electronic manufacturers.[18] This system uses a standard sized ceramic wafer as the basic module to construct resistors and capacitors. The electrical characteristics of each resistor and capacitor are determined by the number of standard wafers comprising the component in question. Equipment has been developed to manufacture the wafers automatically as well as perform assembly operations, using printed circuit boards. Although this design system has not been very popular among manufacturers to date, it may play an important role in the future if it is developed further. It is mentioned here solely as a dramatic example of a highly developed standard approach to product design, fostered by the desire to maximize the use of special automatic equipment in one type of manufacturing operation.

One interesting development subsequent to the writer's field

---

[18] For a brief summary of this project, see L. K. Lee, "Automatic Production of Electronic Equipment," Eugene M. Grabbe, Editor, *Automation in Business and Industry* (New York, Wiley, 1957), pp. 409–415. For more detailed data, see R. L. Henry and H. H. Rosen, *Summary of Modular Design of Electronics and Mechanized Production of Electronics*, Vol. 1, PB–111275, Contract NBS 12.05–20–5532, National Bureau of Standards, Washington, 1954.

work has been the development by component manufacturers of packages of module components which constitute a circuit. The construction of these module circuit assemblies is based on some of the principles mentioned above.[19]

Planning and Controlling Design Changes

One of the first steps in planning a project to acquire a piece of special automatic equipment should be to determine the probable remaining life of the part, the related subassembly, and the product of which it is an element. Some of the factors which should be taken into account in making such an estimate are the history of past changes in the product (or similar products), the major trends in technology which are likely to cause changes or obsolescence, and the direction of development efforts being made by competitors. For a variety of reasons, the kind of forecasting required to weed out those projects which will not pay off before the equipment becomes obsolete is difficult, but it is essential to determine the best assumption which can be made about the estimated life for the part and product. At the same time, we must recognize that such estimates are only informed guesses and even the best of forecasts are inherently uncertain.

A more promising approach than simply forecasting the remaining life of a design is to try to explore the nature of possible changes, consider their impact, and then incorporate sufficient flexibility into the equipment to accommodate those most likely to materialize. If this can be done economically and then one misses the exact timing of a change, the cost of a bad forecast may still be small. If a possible change cannot be accommodated economically, then this fact and the risk it poses to the project must simply be weighed in judgment. A good example of the scope of an investigation which tried to identify areas of possible design changes and to perceive the directions which changes were likely to take has been outlined by Murray Braid, project leader for an equipment system which was to do all the machining on selected models of automotive valves:[20]

---

[19] Richard H. Anderson, "Preassembled Components Simplify Modular Electronic Assembly," *Automation*, September 1958, pp. 83–85.

[20] M. D. Braid, "Automation for Valves," *Automation*, April 1957, pp. 49–50.

To prevent the possibility of obsolescence of process (equipment), a thorough study of present requirements and an accurate analysis of future trends and demands is imperative. In the case of automotive exhaust valves, this analysis had to answer such questions as:

1. Will the valve remain a one-piece valve design or will the welding of a head and stem material be necessary?
2. Will the materials used in the next five to six years be forgeable, as they are today?
3. Will a cast valve be required?
4. Will the material be machinable?
5. What heat treatment is likely to be required?
6. Will the over-all physical dimensions change radically, i.e., head diameter, length of stem, stem diameter?
7. What tolerance and finishes will be required?
8. What type of retainer grooves will be used?
9. Will the stem have a carbon relief?
10. What identification markings are likely?

No doubt questions like these cannot be answered with absolute certainty, but it is likely that areas of probable change will be identified and something will be learned of the nature of the changes. It might also be worthwhile to estimate the probability that a particular change will take place at certain times (for example, "two chances in ten within two years"). Such estimates would be arbitrary and their validity could not be proved rigorously but they would probably describe the risks more precisely and efficiently than methods currently in use.

It is one thing to identify and appraise the risks of design changes and then adapt equipment design to accommodate forecasted changes. It is another thing to try to control, through product design planning, the direction which design changes take. The latter objective requires that the problem of changes be considered at the beginning of a product design project. Just what is involved in doing so can probably best be described by using an example. One product development project which took probable changes into account from the very beginning of the design process has been described in connection with the development of a new V-8 engine by the Chevrolet Division of General Motors Corporation.[21]

The statement of design objectives established at the start of this project is significant:

Adaptability to a broad range of displacement with a minimum number of different parts.

Over-all dimensions compatible with anticipated space limitations of passenger car design.

Adaptability to a broad range of compression ratios to match the octane trend of future fuels.

Provisions for mounting accessories required for both passenger cars and trucks.

Flexibility in the use of machine tools to accommodate future engine modifications.

The end product of the project was a basic design "W," known as the "Turbo-Thrust V-8" engine for the 1958 passenger cars, with a compression ratio of 9.5 to 1, and the "Workmaster V-8" engine for 2½ ton trucks, with a compression ratio of 8.0 to 1.

Not only was the one basic design used for engines with two different compression ratios, but it was structured to be modified to meet probable future requirements.

What is it that makes the W engine so new and different? In past years, the majority of V-8 engines introduced were designed to provide a specific displacement and compression ratio. When it became necessary to increase the displacement and compression ratio for the next model year, these engines required major redesigning and retooling. This was an expensive procedure. The W engine is different from the standpoint of being designed specifically to provide for future increases in displacement and compression ratios to meet yearly modification changes without the need for major redesign and the usual retooling required to provide the manufacturing equipment necessary to produce the engine.

Maximum bore diameter of the cylinders determined the over-all length of the engine, and this maximum took into account the

---

[21] The facts and quotations in this section are taken from John T. Rausch, Howard H. Kehrl, and Donald H. McPherson, "Development of the Chevrolet W Engine: A New Concept in V-8 Engine Design," *General Motors Engineering Journal,* July–August–September 1958, pp. 10–16.

bore necessary to provide adequate displacement for both truck and passenger car requirements, existing and in the future. In order to avoid retooling of both the foundry and cylinder head machining equipment, it was decided not to place the combustion chamber in the cylinder head but in the upper cylinder bore. Thus, whatever changes were made in the piston shape, stroke, or bore diameter, the flat bottom cylinder head would remain unchanged in design. Ultimately, a wedge-shaped combustion space was developed which allowed minor changes in compression ratios (within the range of 10.0 to 1 down to 8.0 to 1) to be achieved by changing the number and size of milled cut-outs in the combustion chamber, changes which could be accomplished simply by adding or removing cutters on the machining equipment.

Future increases in compression ratio beyond 10 to 1 can be accomplished by modifying the top of the piston. The manufacturing equipment to meet this eventuality has been designed and future changes can be made at a reasonable cost.

In this development work, the production engineering group also played a part, although a full description of its role is not available.

Thus the ultimate achievement in the coordination of product design and production engineering seems to be a combination of a broad standardization program and planning. As far as the product design group is concerned, these are the ways in which they can probably contribute most effectively toward achieving the objective of optimum control over special automatic equipment obsolescence losses. In a moment, we shall turn our attention to another major facet of coordination, namely, incorporating flexibility in special automatic equipment design. Before we do, however, we should note that standardization and planning in product design are not likely to be infallible. Some plans will turn out to be faulty, and some standards adopted will turn out to have been poor choices and require changing at some cost. Likewise, there will be costs for planning and standardization. But the costs, if planning and standardization are reasonably well executed, are likely to result in lower net costs than would otherwise be incurred.   Planning and standardization also expose a firm to another kind of risk, which might be described as the risk of design atrophy.   Too stringent controls through standardization and planning can stultify any creative efforts by designers which call for departure from existing standards or plans.   Certainly any standards or plans must be changed from time to time even though the changes result in the obsolescence of equipment, and failure to recognize this necessity may create a critical situation.   Alert management and skillful administration can combat the insidious influence that planning and standardization might have on design creativity.

Designing Flexibility into Special Automatic Equipment

Thus far we have been discussing ways of preventing obsolescence of equipment by establishing controls over the initial product design and subsequent revisions thereof.   Another approach which may be pursued either concurrently or independently emphasizes flexibility in the design of special automatic equipment.   Ability to adapt to substantial changes in product design (beyond the minor changes we referred to in our discussion above) can provide a kind of relief from obsolescence which control over product design alone cannot provide.   No matter how efficient the controls over product designs may be, there is always the risk of necessary product design changes, the nature of which cannot be predicted because they cannot be identified at the time the processing equipment is designed.   Especially where large and expensive equipment is concerned, therefore, one of the first steps taken to guard against this unpredictable kind of risk is to provide for space in the original equipment designs so that new processing stations can be added at regular intervals along the length of the machine.[22]

Two other examples provided for adaptation to a range of changes in one or more important respects.   In the design of a set of special lathes to machine automobile crankshafts, for instance, it was reported that no alterations were required to change over from production of one crankshaft to another with

[22] See "Ford Sharonville: Proving Ground for New Ideas in Automation," *American Machinist,* December 1, 1958, p. 104.   See also "New Plants, Tools, Cars," *Production,* January 1957, p. 73.

a longer or shorter throw.[23]   The clamping fixtures for the lathes had been designed so that the change could be accomplished by replacing the supporting blocks inserted in the fixture with other blocks of different size, an operation which, it was said, would take only a few minutes to complete.   Then, installation of a new set of cutting tools would complete the changeover to a new crankshaft.   Clearly, the usefulness of such flexibility is dependent upon an accurate forecast of the direction in which changes in product design are likely to develop.

A second instance which attempted to provide broader flexibility concerned a transfer machine, again for automotive parts.[24] All drill units were designed to be exactly the same size and capacity, each being equipped with three horsepower motors regardless of the number of drills assigned to each station when the line was initially designed.   Then, if a design change required an increase in the operations at any of several lightly loaded stations, the added capacity would already be available to make the change quite easily.   This policy was reported to have additional advantages through simplifying setup work and reducing the maintenance burden by minimizing the number of replacement parts stocked.

Examples of trying to provide even more general flexibility to accommodate changes have occasionally been reported.

A number of machines at the Aircraft Engine Division, Ford Motor Co., Chicago, are also designed to accommodate major revisions in part design — an occurrence expected frequently in the manufacture of modern aircraft.   Machine design is such that various heads can be rearranged around vertical cylindrical bases and installed on parallel or angular spacing blocks as needed to handle various machining conditions.[25]

One of these pieces of equipment, which had been made by a vendor, was also seen in the plant of another manufacturer during the author's field work.   Simple in concept, this one appeared to be a very flexible type of machine:

---

[23] T. W. Black, "Standard Machine Vs. Special Machine . . . A Case Study," *Tool Engineer,* January 1958, pp. 103–106.

[24] "Ford Sharonville: Proving Ground for New Ideas in Automation," p. 104.

[25] "Flexibility in Transfer Machines," *American Machinist,* August 26, 1957, p. 20.

There are two novel Hartford 3-spindle universal drilling machines in this plant, also constructed to simplify rearrangement in the event of product design changes. Columns supporting three drill spindles are adjustably located radially around a center column. The center column has a stack of index plates which permit quick changeover for automatically indexing any number of holes in a specified bolt circle.

The spindles can all be used for drilling, or they can be set up for a sequence of drilling, reaming, and counterboring or countersinking each hole in sequence. At present the machines produce 47 holes in a 48-hole bolt circle, leaving one hole position blank.[26]

Another step which may be viewed as the logical extension of the one suggested by the equipment in the preceding paragraph is to design special automatic equipment using module elements. Obsolescence would then be minimized because the equipment could be easily and economically salvaged, through its basic components being disassembled and recombined into a new layout, with such new elements as were required, and the storing or otherwise disposing of unneeded components.[27] The basic elements of one machine in many cases would be identical with some of the basic elements of another, although the need for a range of sizes means that in some cases elements would not be interchangeable except with another piece of equipment of the same size.

The chief executive of one vendor building assembly equipment has described[28] how his firm has developed designs for one standardized base, one standardized loading movement, and one standardized control circuit, equipment elements which

---

[26] Ibid., p. 121.

[27] Builders' advertisements calling attention to "building block" design features appear regularly in current issues of trade journals. Also, see comments on the practices of individual builders in "Modernization and Building-Block Design," *American Machinist*, March 9, 1959; in Ralph E. Cross, "Building-Block Designs Reduce Tooling Costs," *Tool Engineer*, December 1958, pp. 47–50; and in "Hartford Takes the Plunge from Specials to Building Blocks," *American Machinist*, April 7, 1958, p. 89.

[28] William C. Cummings, "Standardizing Assembly Machines," *Automation*, March 1959, p. 55. See also Robert Brehm, "Creating a Transfer Machine," *Automation*, February, 1959, p. 47. Brehm describes in some detail the practice of Snyder Corporation (of which he is Chief Engineer) and includes a table showing the major characteristics of each of the 19 standard way-type machining units Snyder uses in designing transfer machines.

can be combined in a variety of ways with custom-made parts to effect the assembly operations required.

One firm, the Delco-Remy Division of General Motors, which has pursued a make program with respect to special automatic equipment for many years, has also apparently gone a long way toward establishing standard machine components for the assembly equipment which it designs and builds in its own shop. According to its chief process engineer, it not only has developed a standard basic machine, with a standard indexing device, but it has also developed standard "ordinary" tooling to perform such common tasks as welding, riveting, and driving screws.[29]

The value of this kind of module equipment design depends upon the ability of a user to disassemble an obsolete piece of equipment and salvage many of its parts, except special tooling such as the parts feeding elements and the holding fixtures,[30] by re-using them in assembling a new piece of equipment for processing a redesigned or an entirely different part. For the user to do this would require that it have personnel in its organization who were able to design special automatic equipment, including the special tooling needed. Furthermore, the user would need to have a fairly sizable program of acquiring special automatic equipment to get enough use out of the inventories of machine elements which would undoubtedly accumulate. An-

---

[29] Statement attributed to George L. Weiser in James C. Keebler, "Art of In-Line Assembly," *Automation*, May 1959, p. 54.

[30] Actually, of course, it would be possible to design much of the tooling to standards in such a way that many of these components, too, could be salvaged. Henry M. Adams has recorded some interesting history in this connection:

"Standardization, some time before World War I, started with drill bushings, locating pins, standard clamps, etc. Then came the 'Manufacturer's Standard Manuals' which attempted to standardize everything from jig feet to almost complete clamping mechanisms. One auto firm had three sets of standards books, developed (in the late twenties) to such an extent that, for a jig or fixture design, it was possible to refer to the standard book for just about everything except the major castings. Jigs and fixtures parts listed in their standard books were kept in stock in their tool stores. About the only items which they had to purchase were the machined castings, and probably a few other parts which, by their nature, could not be standardized. All the rest of the parts could be taken off the shelf and assembled in their tool room." See "Automation — Its Effect on Jigs and Fixtures," *Collected Papers, 1956* (Detroit, American Society of Tool Engineers), Library Edition, Paper 24T31, p. 35.

other alternative would be to return the obsolete equipment to the builder and contract for the original builder to retool it. For any one special equipment builder, *machining* equipment is already likely to be standardized and therefore interchangeable to a considerable extent with other equipment manufactured by the same vendor.   Notwithstanding the two examples just cited, standardization of *assembly* equipment elements seems to be significantly less prevalent, in part the result of relatively low activity in this type of machine and in part the result of its being much more tailored to specific parts and dissimilar operations.

One comparison of the economies of reworking existing equipment designed, in part at least, using module elements has been described by a representative of Ford Motor Company:

> Through the cooperation of machine tool builders, some of the proposals we have discussed are now in use. . . .   Due to a recent design change in the crankshaft, it became necessary to change the machine tools. . . .   The builder supplied several new wing bases, columns, and other components and units. These machines were then converted . . . using the bases of the original machines.   Because it was possible to utilize the existing main bases, we avoided tearing down the machine foundations, and the basic hydraulic, pneumatic, coolant, and electrical services were undisturbed.   The total cost of converting three machines was slightly less than $300,000, whereas procurement and installation of new facilities would have cost more than $700,000.[31]

It is noteworthy that in this instance the original bases were undisturbed.   Thus, in a long-run program the typical savings may be proportionally smaller.   It will be impracticable if not impossible to re-use all salvaged machine elements, and there will also be situations in which it will cost less to build a new machine than it would to rebuild an old one.[32]   Despite these

---

[31] J. F. Randall, "Planning for Reduced Obsolescence," unpublished paper presented at the 21st Annual Machine Tool Electrification Forum, sponsored by the Westinghouse Electric Corporation, Buffalo, New York, April 24 and 25, 1957.

[32] Both limitations characterized Ford's experience in the fall of 1959 when it converted two existing V-8 engine machining lines to make a six-cylinder engine for its new "Falcon."   In this program there was extensive rebuilding, but expenditures made for all-new machines were about equal

limitations, however, the module approach seems to promise large economies.

In 1956 representatives of the Ford Motor Company tried to advance the building-block concept one step further by proposing that steps be taken to make the major machine elements of one manufacturer interchangeable with those of other vendors by standardizing major dimensions.[33] Ford was particularly concerned with the large in-line machining equipment, units of which typically cost several hundred thousand dollars each. At the same time, Ford took steps to contract for a piece of in-line equipment which was divided into sections, for easy expansion or contraction of the equipment by adding or removing one or more sections of the base, together with standard columns, drill heads, and other major assemblies, including separate hydraulic and electrical control systems for each machining unit. The term "unitization" has been applied to this design concept which divides the basic transfer equipment into self-contained sections. Such construction, although more expensive, would manifestly reduce the cost of rebuilding this kind of equipment.

A single user might seek to increase the economy of re-using special automatic equipment elements by requiring "unitized" design, even though industry cooperation might be necessary to achieve industry-wide interchangeability. Ford proceeded to take just such action, and within a few months had acquired a transfer machine from one builder that was designed on the building-block principle.[34] Ford was joined by other major automobile firms in an effort to achieve the objective of inter-

in amount to those for rebuilding. The rebuilding, however, saved Ford something like $1,000,000 in tooling costs and, equally impressive, made it possible to complete the project in only fourteen months compared with a normal span of two or three years. See George H. De Groat, "Rebuilding 'Building Block' Machines," *American Machinist*, October 5, 1959, pp. 81–83.

A nonautomotive project to rebuild a sixteen-station rotary machine is described in Richard Mueller, "Retooling a Dial Machine for Assembly and Inspection," *American Machinist*, March 23, 1957, pp. 130–131. A machine built originally to assemble part of a domestic thermostat was rebuilt to assemble and inspect a control transformer block.

[33] Rupert Le Grand, "Ford Says: 'Let's Have Building-Block Machine Tools,'" *American Machinist*, July 16, 1956, pp. 113–121, and J. F. Randall, op. cit.

[34] T. W. Black, "Trends," *Tool Engineer*, March 1957, p. 75.

changeability of major machine elements produced by various vendor-builders. At last report, representatives of both builders and users had reached limited agreement on certain basic specifications, and were presumably working toward additional refinements.[35]

In making use of module elements some European firms may be ahead of most United States practice. Use of modules is said to be employed extensively by the French automobile manufacturer Renault for both machining and assembly equipment. Renault employs up to 700 people in machine tool production, designing and building a large share of its own equipment, and this division has become the country's sixth largest builder of machine tools.[36] On a smaller scale the use of standard machine components in a "build-it-yourself" program has also been reported taking place in Austin Motor Company in England and in other European countries.[37]

In a large company, such as Ford Motor Company, it would seem that perhaps the opportunity to interchange the machine elements of only one builder would be sufficient to effect considerable economies through re-use of equipment. Possibly some limit to the number and identity of builders utilized would be desirable; if limiting the number of suppliers were not possible, then the concentration of a majority of purchases from a few sources might accomplish most of the objective of making this type of equipment re-usable. To maximize the ability to re-use obsolete equipment, it might also be necessary for a user to provide a central control unit which would disseminate in-

---

[35] "Machine Tool Builders and Big Automotive Users Agree on Building Block Concept," *American Machinist*, January 26, 1959, p. 95, and James C. Keebler, "Deferring Status Quo," *Automation*, September 1959, p. 39. The basic machine elements for which standards have been promulgated include the main base, wing base, feed units, horizontal angular adapter, angular column, wing base adapter (dial type machine) and vertical column. For a description of these standards, and comments thereon, as revised to August 5, 1959, see William E. Hoffman, "Industry Agrees on 'Building Block' Standards," *Tooling & Production*, July 1959 (Reprint).

[36] See "At France's Renault It's 'Vive l'automation,'" *American Machinist*, May 4, 1959, pp. 112–113.

[37] On the English experience, see John W. Greve, "Tool Engineering in Europe," *Collected Papers, 1958* (Detroit, American Society of Tool Engineers), Library Edition, Paper 113, pp. 1–2. For other European experience, see T. W. Black, "Automation in Europe," *Tool Engineer*, September 1957, pp. 74–75.

formation about module units available and which might even operate a storage warehouse. It is possible that such an organization might ultimately be expanded to provide equipment design and manufacturing services, in effect becoming another source for special automatic equipment. Another and perhaps more desirable alternative might be to increase the amount of contract reworking of such equipment done by the original builders. Indeed, a perhaps unintended effect of Ford's proposal might well be to create a much greater degree of receptivity and cooperation among builders to the reworking of obsolete equipment.[38]

Methods of Effecting Coordination with Product Design

Up to this point, our discussion has dealt largely with objectives to be sought and policies which would effect the coordination of product design and production engineering. It will also be worthwhile to consider now some of the methods for achieving coordination, whatever the nature of general policies.

From an organizational standpoint, one of the most frequently used coordinating devices was a committee. One type encountered was an *ad hoc* committee made up of the product designer(s) concerned with the part(s) being processed, the special automatic equipment project leader, his supervisor, and the foreman of the production department which would be concerned. At the opposite extreme was a committee including the vice presidents of production and of engineering (as well as other working level persons). The first committee was organized to facilitate the use of special automatic equipment with respect to a particular group of operations on a part for which the final design had been "frozen," and the committee's term expired when the project was terminated. The second committee was concerned with giving direction to and maintaining control over a major special automatic equipment program, one phase of which was to insure against early obsolescence of this type of equipment.

[38] Equipment rebuilding for the Falcon engine program was accomplished by contract builders, not by Ford personnel. In some cases the rebuilding was done by a competitor of the firm which had originally built the equipment. See George H. De Groat, "Rebuilding 'Building Block' Machines," pp. 81–83.

The principal function of the engineering representation was to give warning of impending design changes, especially those of a major nature, which might be contemplated.

It is probably worthwhile pointing out that a great deal of the kind of coordination of product design and production engineering we are talking about might well be effected through a committee primarily concerned with implementing a standards program. Provided there is representation from the production engineering function, it seems quite likely that the ease or difficulty of production will be considered. It would be important, of course, that the production engineering considerations taken into account include ease or difficulty of automatic production in particular, probably by means of a review of proposed standards by competent production engineers before a standard is adopted.

In one relatively large project, a somewhat different type of committee, a task force group, was organized, including representatives of product design and production engineering. The task force members were relieved of their regular duties and moved physically to a new large office in order to undertake preparations to manufacture a new product. The group worked together continuously until the new product went into production, when it was disbanded and the individuals returned to their permanent job assignments. Since the product design had been frozen before this group was formed, the extent of the coordination was more limited in scope than it might have been, but the members of this task force were most enthusiastic about the degree of coordination achieved and the ease with which it was obtained.

Another organizational device used to coordinate product design and special automatic equipment was to appoint liaison personnel, permanently assigned to one functional group but spending a large portion of their time with the other functional group. For instance, in one company a product design engineer was assigned full time to the special automatic equipment group to provide this liaison. He was expected to participate as an adviser on all types of product design problems, and to help on possible changes which might facilitate processing on all projects undertaken. He was not empowered to authorize specific changes but was helpful in suggesting changes which might be acceptable from the standpoint of product design, in commenting on alternative approaches to such changes as might be considered, and in serving as a means of communication between the product design group and the equipment group. (He was also absorbing a great deal about special automatic equipment which would be of great potential value when he returned, according to plan, to a permanent assignment within the product design group.)

In another company, the liaison assignment was given to production engineers to work with the product design engineers. About half way in the cycle of generating a new product design, one or more production engineers would be assigned to work full time, usually for between three and eight months, as members of the design engineering project team which was developing the new product. The production engineers were expected to examine the preliminary designs, part by part, and suggest changes which would facilitate their manufacture, automatically and otherwise. They were also expected to work on perfecting the application of any new processes which would be required in the making of the newly developed product.[39]

There is an important advantage in having production engineers work with the product design group when design work is in progress rather than after it has been finished. The number of feasible alternatives available is likely to be at its maximum at the time the initial thinking about the design or redesign of a product is going on. As time elapses, the design, and perhaps the designer, becomes less tractable. When many parts are to comprise a finished product, the design of any one is more easily changed in the initial stages than later simply because of the progressively large number of interrelations which may be built up as the features of the subassemblies and parts grow in detail. This matter of timing is likely to be important for relatively minor

---

[39] An apparently similar approach in another company has been described by D. J. Jomie as the standard procedure in connection with every new product or major design change. See "Manufacturing Team for Automation," *Automation,* August 1958, pp. 36–37.

facilitating changes as well as for major changes in the basic design.[40]

One company attempted to avoid the necessity of coordination by adopting a policy of selecting projects which would require little or no design changes. This was a temporary policy and was to be abandoned after a shortage of design engineering personnel had been overcome. In another firm, an informal practice was initiated by the product design engineers after a special automatic equipment program had been in effect for some time and the desirability of such coordination had become manifest. Rough sketches of new designs were submitted to production engineers for comments on how easily they might be manufactured automatically, and what changes might be considered which would enhance that ability. Such a practice is reported to have been formalized in one Westinghouse plant:

> A system requiring that all tracings receive a manufacturing engineer's initial approval has been established, thus insuring that a thorough review is made of each new design. This approval must occur before tracings can be released for manufacture.[41]

The most common practice of all was for production engineers to request specific changes and simply ask the product design personnel for approval. A somewhat greater effort of this general type was taken in one company which invited product design engineers concerned to join members of the special automatic equipment group during sessions in which the general and detailed approaches to a piece of equipment were presented by the project leader for comment and criticism.

One particular facet of the coordination problem, determining the risk of product obsolescence, was handled in one case by requiring the product design engineer to make an estimate of the expected remaining life of the product design; such an estimate

---

[40] This factor was given credit for much of the cooperation achieved in the Plymouth V-8 engine program. See R. A. McCarroll "Many Technological Improvements Made in Plymouth Engine Plant," *Tooling & Production,* October 1955, p. 17.

[41] J. A. Miller, "Product Design Meets Production Techniques," *Automation,* January 1956 (Abstract), p. 120.

was to accompany every appropriation request for special automatic equipment. A variation of this practice was developed in one company which established a product planning group to guide its product design effort; every appropriation request involving special automatic equipment was required to be routed to the product planning group for comment.

Perhaps the most elaborate procedure reported for effecting the coordination of product design and production engineering has been described as follows:

> . . . preliminary product designs are turned over to production engineering departments for review prior to development of final design drawings. The production engineering group then undertakes a detailed study to determine if the part can be revised to make it productible at minimum cost.
>
> The production engineering department has full authority to change the preliminary part drawings in any manner that does not affect the part function, and it develops a manufacturing drawing of the part. *A prototype is built in accordance with the manufacturing drawing and is returned to the design department for performance evaluation.* If the prototype meets functional requirements, the tooling program is begun.[42]

The procedure described in the last paragraph just quoted would certainly seem to provide fully for giving production engineers, including those concerned with ease of using special automatic equipment, an opportunity to be heard. As the author of the article describing these procedures points out, however, the chief drawbacks of such a practice are the added cost and the added lead time they require. Then, too, carried to the extreme, one suspects that they might well create friction between design and production engineers. It is conceivable that there will be times when elaborate and time-consuming procedures like these will be worthwhile, if not as a general rule then at least for selected parts or subassemblies. Under many circumstances, however, they may simply be too cumbersome and too expensive, and these attributes may explain why no such routines were found to be employed in any of the plants visited during our field work.

[42] Clyde Mooney, "How to Plan for Low-Cost Production," *Tool Engineer*, January 1957, pp. 73–74. (*Italics added*)

Another coordinating mechanism, encountered in only two firms, was job rotation, the experience of having worked in both product design engineering and in special automatic equipment development. Although the instances encountered were accidental and not planned, they suggested strongly the usefulness of planned job rotation. In one of these cases, two production engineers had later become product design engineers, a post of greater administrative responsibility in that particular company. In the second instance, the supervisor of a special automatic equipment group had originally entered the company's employ as a product design engineer and had spent several years in that function. One of his project leaders had also worked as a product design engineer formerly. There was evidence in all these instances that the experience in the related function had proved to be of considerable value.

Others who had no firsthand experience with such job rotation were asked for their opinions on its value as a general procedure. As might be expected, opinions covered the entire range possible. The author was particularly impressed, however, with the more than ordinarily thoughtful reply of one product development group head who not only replied that he thought the idea of job rotation had merit, but that he had, in fact, already had his eye on two or three of his company's production engineers who were well qualified and desirable candidates for product development project leader positions in his own organization. In his opinion, the production engineering experience was ideal background, assuming that the individual had the college training in engineering which he held to be essential to product development work. Reciprocal experience of this type should probably be considered in formal company training programs for young, newly hired engineers. Not only is there likely to be a worthwhile return in improved day-to-day operations within the two functions, but also when some of these individuals rise to managerial posts, as at least a portion of them undoubtedly will, there is bound to be a second return perhaps more valuable than the first.

Third, and finally, there was evidence that mere physical proximity of product design and production engineers, without any other organizational or procedural changes, was likely to have an important and beneficial result. Under these conditions, they could, and did, communicate with one another easily and frequently. The mutual understanding, both functionally and personally, acquired new depths which promoted cooperation to a surprising degree.[43]

All that has been said is not to deny the quite frequent influence of accidental factors in cases of good coordination between product design and production engineering. The play of these factors was noted earlier in the case of the benefits from unplanned job rotation. Likewise, compatible or incompatible personalities are another influential factor. In the short run, at least, of say three to five years, such things as these are not too susceptible to management control, whereas planning, standardization, organizational arrangements, procedures and physical locations are often within management's power to influence materially.

General Management Implications and Summary

One important implication of closer coordination of product design and production engineering is the increase in the number of engineering man-hours that will be needed. In the beginning and then quite possibly on a continuing basis, more engineers will have to be hired (assuming that a company does not already have any excess engineering manpower). And this, of course, means that overhead costs will be increased, however subtly and indirectly. Whether or not total costs will be increased, however, is quite a different matter — the answer here depends on the effectiveness with which such coordination is carried out and on how events would turn out in the absence of coordination. But there certainly seem to be reasonable opportunities for savings which will more than offset the additional cost of effecting coordination. Designs are likely to be developed which will permit lower capital investment in special automatic equipment than would otherwise be required. Designs

---

[43] In the case of the Plymouth V-8 engine plant, physical proximity even overcame a pre-existing image of design engineers as "a 'gang of butchers' anxious to cut down every suggestion or request for design change originating from the manufacturing people." See Carl J. Demrick, "The Plymouth Story," p. 9, and R. A. McCarroll, "Many Technological Advancements Made in Plymouth Engine Plant," p. 16.

which permit the use of the same standard parts in several models of product may mean savings through automatic processing which would not otherwise be possible. Designs will probably evolve which, because of their simplicity and standardization, enable the special automatic equipment personnel to save hours of time in design, construction, and debugging. And designs which lengthen the useful operating life of special automatic equipment, or which at least facilitate its retooling and salvage, will increase a company's profits. These are the kinds of returns a company can seek from coordination, and they may be attractive indeed.

In any attempt to effect a significant measure of coordination of product design and production engineering coordination, steps toward coordination should be taken early in the design process. There is evidence, not great in quantity but nevertheless persuasive, that the earlier in the product design process the coordination can take place, the greater will be its impact and the easier it will be to execute. If the coordination efforts are postponed until a piece of special automatic equipment is to be designed, there is likely to be little freedom of action with respect to changes. For one thing, the effect on mating or complementary parts will have to be considered; for another, there may be earlier processing of the workpiece which, at this point in time, may be difficult to change. In the field work the most radical changes made in the design of a product to attain manufacturing economies were cases in which coordination was effected at the time work was first begun on designing a new model.

There is another administrative problem of considerable long-run importance buried in this matter of coordination of product design and production engineering. Using a sociological term, it can be described as a "status" problem between product design engineers on one hand and production engineers on the other. There are bound to be exceptions, but time and time again the author found that product design engineers were the prima donnas in the company. In some cases, the members of the marketing group were highest in status company-wide, but whatever the hierarchy, the product design engineers almost invariably took precedence over the production engineers and the production personnel of all types. One explanation encountered for this state of affairs was tradition, and this was undoubtedly a factor of fundamental importance in many companies. But representatives of three companies advanced another, and apparently a more cogent explanation: the majority of production engineers do not have college degrees. In other words, "they are not truly engineers, they are just technicians," was the implication — with the occasional brilliant exception, of course, who could be called a self-educated engineer even though he held no college degree. A great many of the production engineering personnel encountered were apprentice-course graduates, and some had careers which began with the most modest of jobs on the production floor.

It is quite likely that this situation will change gradually by itself, with the increasing proportion of college graduates among those newly entering the labor force. It would seem prudent, however, for a company management to take steps to see that some of the graduate engineers hired start in production engineering and specifically in special automatic equipment groups, and that all of them do not gravitate to product design or other functions. A basic problem with college graduates, however, is that they are not likely to be able to bring to bear the intimate knowledge of machinery and production processes which the apprentice-course graduates have and use. Perhaps the balance between theory and practice simply needs to be redressed by increasing the proportion of college-trained engineers to the more capable of apprentice-course graduates. In the long run there may develop a problem at the other extreme of too few apprentice graduates, for the number of capable men who do not go to college has shrunk drastically, making it increasingly difficult to maintain the quality of apprentices. And at the same time, the relative magnitude of apprentice programs, whatever the quality of their enrollees, generally has been growing smaller and smaller. Or, perhaps some elements of the traditional apprentice program need to be reformed and incorporated into a company training program for newly hired college-trained engineers. Whatever the course or courses of action, it seems to the author that there is need for attracting a higher percentage of college-trained engineers to production engineering jobs, if for no other reason than to furnish a better basis for communication between product designers and production engineers in general and especially among those concerned with special automatic equipment.

Why is there any need for coordination in these matters? Why has the design engineer not simply taken into account, when he designs the parts, the ease of automatically producing them? For one thing the necessity to take into account the requirements for automatic processing has arisen only comparatively recently, and for another, to date there has appeared no way of developing the skill to do this save by continued exposure to a variety of problems — experience. In the opinion of some there is also the matter of the complexity of engineering today, which is so great as to elude the grasp of one man, at least as a general thing. Kurt O. Tech has stated this point of view as follows:

> There are three strong influences on the design of any product:
>   First, the engineering or functional design of the product.
>   Second, the appearance or styling of the product.
>   Third, the manufacturing of the product.
>
> It is my opinion that the manufacturing influence, taking into consideration the latest methods in manufacturing practice, has the least influence of the three. This has come about because of the difficulty of mechanical design engineers to be completely familiar with all of the possible variations in manufacturing practice. Those of us who are working daily on manufacturing problems and techniques have difficulty in keeping abreast. I could easily see where most product designers would have a job on their hands keeping up to date with the technological progress in their own fields.[44]

Perhaps another way of looking at the matter is to say that another major engineering function has evolved, the task of joining products and processes to obtain economical production. There is probably more difference in the point of view required than there is in the basic technical knowledge involved. The advent of automatic processing alone may not have been the sole cause or even the origin of this development, but it un-

---

[44] Kurt O. Tech, "Designing for Easier Machining, Handling, and Assembly," p. 13. R. A. McCarroll of the Plymouth Division of Chrysler Corporation has voiced the same general opinion. See R. A. McCarroll, "Many Technological Advancements Made in Plymouth Engine Plant," p. 16.

doubtedly has hastened, or perhaps is only in the process of hastening, its evolution.

Something can and should be done, however, to keep product designers aware of some of the demands of automatic manufacture, so that they will at least be more amenable to changes which facilitate automatic manufacture, and will accept ease of manufacturing as a major goal of design. Certainly frequent intercourse among product design engineers and production engineers is one method for accomplishing these results which should not be overlooked. Another which deserves to be mentioned is the device of special automatic equipment exhibitions, both public and private. While probably only large companies can interest special automatic equipment builders in setting up private exhibitions of some of their most recent machines (as was done by the International Harvester Company),[45] frequent public exhibitions are held and occasional visits to these by product design engineers could be used as one means of interesting and informing them of developments in automatic processing.

In summary, then, the degree of coordination of product design and production engineering which a company achieves is likely to control the degree to which special automatic equipment can be utilized economically. Ultimately, ease of using special automatic equipment for all processing through assembly and, in many cases, through final testing should be a fundamental objective from the very beginning of the product design process — from the time when the first rough sketches are made. This kind of coordination is a principal means not only of facilitating the use of special automatic equipment, but also of minimizing equipment obsolescence losses caused by product design changes. In this connection, the coordination of product design and production engineering should lead, not only to a carefully controlled standardization program for the product designer, but also to planning the major dimensions of product design changes and to incorporating such flexibility in equipment that both will be adaptable to probable major design modifications. For companies using large amounts of special automatic equipment, a

---

[45] "Harvester's Personal Machine Show," *American Machinist*, October 8, 1956, pp. 178–179.

parallel program of controlled standardization of machine assemblies seems to be indicated, though at the present time the goal of complete interchangeability of elements among all machines in the plant seems to be impractical under most circumstances. Such a goal, however, may be practicable and appropriate for a company which builds its own equipment.

The magnitude of the task of coordination will be a function of the magnitude and rapidity of product design changes, on the one hand, and the degree to which special automatic equipment is an appropriate means of production, on the other. In the companies visited the coordination problem was more fully appreciated in those companies making products for which designs were changing rapidly, for example, in some of the automobile and electronic plants. Even in companies in which product designs changed much more slowly, however, the same general type of problem gradually unfolded as time elapsed and more and more special automatic equipment was acquired.

Various organizational and procedural devices can be employed in an attempt to achieve suitable coordination. The most impressive results were obtained by task force or project approaches, in which one or more production engineers were assigned as members of a group working on all phases of a new product or a new model, including both the product design function and production engineering.

The stakes involved in product design-production engineering coordination are high in many companies now and are likely to become high in many others in the future. The rewards for effective coordination are likely to be large profits and the penalties for inadequate coordination are likely to be large losses in obsolete equipment.

CHAPTER VIII

The Analysis of Proposals for Acquiring Special Automatic Equipment

THE ACT OF evaluation takes place (or at least should take place) again and again throughout the cycle of every project to acquire special automatic equipment, from the time it is a vague idea in its sponsor's imagination to the time it either takes final form in a piece of shop equipment or is abandoned somewhere along the route.

In the case of each project, however, these evaluations probably reach their culmination at the time a formal request for funds is presented (usually to the company's board of directors) to design, construct, and debug a piece of equipment. Despite the importance of expenditures made in developing a sound proposal, only rarely will they be more than a small fraction of the request for funds required to design, build, and debug equipment. For another thing, this occasion, unlike earlier evaluations, is a sort of point of no return, since in most instances if the request is granted the company will be largely committed to see the project through to completion. It would be rather difficult to foresee occasions upon which it would be wise, for instance, to cut off expenditures with the equipment halfway constructed. In short, the evaluation which must be made on every project proposal at this stage is a grave one because of the sums involved and because it is one which is not likely to be revoked or modified easily once a commitment has been made.

The objective of proposal analysis, whether the proposals are for special automatic equipment or for conventional equipment, should be to select certain proposals to which the company's resources will be committed and to reject others, the general aim, of course, being to maximize the gain to the company. Errors can be made either by approving projects which should have been rejected or by rejecting projects which should have been approved. To provide a basis for approval or rejection, the technique of analysis should be the comparison of probable net benefits versus the likely net expenditures required, weighed in the light of the risks assumed and in relation to feasible alternatives. The alternatives, of course, include undertaking the project as proposed; undertaking the project with modifications, such as utilizing different equipment or different combinations of equipment; and completely rejecting the project proposal after considering several feasible methods by which it might be accomplished.

As has been demonstrated in preceding chapters, special automatic equipment projects are likely to vary significantly from conventional equipment proposals in several important dimensions which result in exposing the acquirer to greater risks. For instance, there is usually much more uncertainty associated with the amount of the estimated investment — the total of expenditures needed to acquire a piece of equipment. Furthermore, the primary service life of special automatic equipment is likely to be both shortened and rendered quite uncertain because of changes in the design of the product or a component thereof. In other words, the analysis of special equipment proposals needs not merely the application of sound theory and sound procedures, such as would also be appropriate for conventional equipment decisions, but in addition calls for some method of discriminating and appraising the several types of risks involved.

Despite the urgency of careful channeling of a company's resources into special automatic equipment, the author's field research disclosed only a few firms that were doing an adequate job of analysis of this type of project proposal. Some project engineers were found blindly applying rules of thumb which they did not fully understand, and top management, which was often (and to a degree inescapably) "in the dark" on any technical appraisal of the project, was itself found wanting in the skill to make an economic analysis. Both employed data of questionable validity or of wide limits of error without giving any apparent consideration to these conditions and their implication for analysis.

This criticism is not intended to imply that company personnel at any level were not conscious of their responsibilities. On the contrary, this step in the series involved in acquiring special automatic equipment was one in which top management, for instance, invariably showed great interest and wielded strong influence. Top management's policies, habits of thought, and procedures for analysis — broadly speaking, the general philosophy with which they approached the decision to approve or to reject capital investment proposals — became in turn the guide lines for succeeding analyses and largely determined the boundaries within which operating personnel directed their efforts. The questions top management repeatedly asked and the rules of thumb they used were applied to each embryo proposal by the operating people themselves *before* the item was written up on the standard appropriation form and submitted to higher management for review. Such a system of behavior is quite understandable and is not altogether undesirable, for it can be highly useful as a prescreening device to cut down on the number of unacceptable proposals made to top management. If rules of thumb rather than sound analytical thinking are followed blindly and rigidly, however, some quite worthwhile projects may be kept from seeing the light of day, and some undesirable projects may be undertaken. In any event, such a system of behavior redoubles the importance of top management's using a sound and thorough method of analysis as an example for project engineers and their supervisors, as well as for its own sake.

In the following sections, we shall first describe the analytical methods we found in general use and comment on their usefulness. Next we shall turn to the problems of applying sound theory to the peculiarities of special automatic equipment projects and deal with the estimation of "investment," "savings," "service life," and "salvage value." Most of the emphasis with respect to all these estimates will be on methods of dealing with the unusual kinds of risks which are associated with the acquisition of this type of equipment. Then we shall examine an important phase of proposal appraisals, the development and analysis of alternatives. Finally, before summarizing, we shall briefly comment on organizational arrangements for analyses of special automatic equipment.

The principal discussion will center about replacement decisions, in which the issue is whether a proposed piece of equipment should be acquired to replace a piece of equipment already in regular use in a company's plant. The major areas which should be considered, however, will be the same when a proposal is related to, say, a new plant. In particular, the section on alternatives will suggest the general way in which a similar type of analysis can be applied to decisions involving equipment for making new products (i.e., items not currently in production in a company's plant).

I

Methods of Analysis Found in Use

In analyzing proposals for special automatic equipment the determining criterion used in almost all companies visited was the pay-back period, or the investment required divided by the estimated annual savings. For example, if a $15,000 investment was required by a proposal that promised estimated savings of $5,000 per year, dividing $15,000 by $5,000 yielded three years as the period required to recover the investment.[1]

In only four of the eighteen corporations visited (i.e., corporate entities, not individual plants) was anything closely approximating a valid rate of return calculation made, and in no more than two of these did it appear that it was given anything more than lip service. The conventional pay-back calculation was also made in each of these four companies, and in discussion of individual projects, management representatives habitually used pay-back standards as the principal criterion for approval.

---

[1] In one company a so-called rate of return calculation was made which was the ratio of the annual savings before deducting any depreciation to the required investment. To illustrate, this calculation would be to divide the estimated $5,000 annual savings by the $15,000 investment to get a rate of return of 33%. What was called a rate of return calculation in this plant was actually just the reciprocal, expressed as a percentage, of the three-year pay-back period.

The pay-back method of analyzing proposals has long been relied upon for all types of equipment. Terborgh[2] summarizes early surveys of industry practice in this respect, and a 1956 survey by the Machinery and Allied Products Institute[3] showed that 60% of a sample of 205 companies used the pay-back method of analysis for equipment decisions. The same survey showed that for equipment with a service life of ten years or more, a large majority (74%) of the companies using the pay-back criterion had established maximum pay-back periods somewhere in the range of three to five years. Practice with respect to equipment with lives of less than ten years was not reported. A McGraw-Hill survey[4] taken in the spring of 1955 showed similar pay-back requirements, both for manufacturing firms generally and for those in the metalworking industries:

	1 to 2 years and less	2 to 3 years	3 to 4 years	5 years	6 years and over
All Manufacturing	17%	19%	18%	27%	19%
Machinery	23%	16%	15%	30%	16%
Electrical Machinery	0	37	11	31	21
Motor Vehicles and Transportation Equipment	16	16	24	24	20
Other Metalworking	20	12	28	28	12

Another McGraw-Hill survey in 1958 [5] showed some tendency toward slightly longer pay-back periods, but for metalworking companies as a class, 19% still required a pay-back of two years or less and 52% more required a pay-back of three to five years. In other words, 71% of the concerns surveyed demanded a pay-back in five years or less.

How do these general pay-back standards compare with those we discovered? The maximum pay-back period allowed by the companies visited varied from two to four years, with the majority between two and three years. In almost all instances, however, a project might occasionally be approved which fell outside the maximum standard. In other words, these clearly paralleled the

[2] George Terborgh, *Dynamic Equipment Policy* (New York, McGraw-Hill, 1959), p. 189 and pp. 191–192.

[3] *Equipment Replacement and Depreciation — Policies and Practices* (Washington, Allied Products Institute, 1956), pp. 7–8.

[4] Adapted from McGraw-Hill Publishing Company pamphlet, "Business Plans for New Plants and Equipment, 1955–1958" (New York), p. 11.

[5] "Plan '59," *American Machinist*, October 20, 1958, p. M5.

standards for general equipment proposals revealed by the surveys just cited.[6]

Even more interesting was the fact that in only one corporation of the sixteen visited was the longest pay-back allowable for automatic equipment any different from the longest pay-back allowable for conventional equipment. It seems fair to conclude, therefore, that among the companies visited not only was the pay-back estimate the determining (and usually the sole) criterion in analyzing special automatic equipment projects but also that, with one exception, special equipment proposals were basically measured against substantially the same standards as conventional equipment proposals.

The general use of the pay-back technique and the narrow range of the pay-back standard employed may give a completely misleading implication of uniformity of analysis that will be quickly dispelled when the underlying concepts of "investment" and "savings" are examined. There were wide variations among the companies visited in the definitions of the elements which went into the total figures they called "investment" and "savings," differences so great that either of these figures for a particular project could easily have been made 50% higher or 50% lower by using alternative definitions. We will postpone exploration of these differences, however, until we get to the later sections of this chapter which deal specifically with investment and savings.

Usefulness of These General Approaches

How well does the pay-back calculation help in deciding whether to undertake the acquisition of a specific piece of special automatic equipment? What alternative approaches may be better, and why? So far as general analytical procedures for capital equipment are concerned, others have already criticized the logic of the pay-back method of calculation.[7] Because special automatic equipment is likely to embrace so many short-lived pieces of equipment, however, the practical

---

[6] Apparently capital is rationed even more frugally in Russia, where in a recent report by two Soviet officials it was said that the capital outlay for automation had been recovered in periods ranging from eight months to a maximum of two years. (Described in the *New York Times,* April 27, 1958, p. 16.)

[7] See Terborgh, *Dynamic Equipment Policy,* pp. 187–201.

as well as the theoretical complications of using the pay-back calculation take on added significance.

The pay-back period calculation, it will be recalled, is made by dividing the total expenditures required by the estimated average annual savings before deducting any depreciation charges on the proposed equipment. It is a rough measure of comparative risk, because the further in the future savings estimates must be projected to recover the required investment, the more uncertain the estimated savings will become and, therefore, the greater the risk which must be attached to the project. On the other hand, it is by no means a sufficient measure of risk. Two projects may be estimated to have the same pay-back period, for instance, 3.2 years, but even though the utmost care has been exercised in both cases, the nature of one project is such that it unavoidably rests on quite shaky estimates of savings while the savings estimate of the other may be much more reliable. Or, a similar unavoidable difference may exist in the quality of the estimate of expenditures required to accomplish a project. The estimated expenditures required in one case may have a probability of nine chances out of ten of being within the range of ±10% of the best estimate if the project is undertaken. In another case with the same, or perhaps even a somewhat shorter, pay-back period, however, the chances that the best estimate will be within the tolerance of ±10% may be only five out of ten. In either of the two pairs of examples described, it is clear that identical pay-back figures alone by no means adequately describe the risks involved. There is no disputing the fact, however, that the length of time required to recoup equipment expenditures is one of the important dimensions of a thorough analysis of a proposal.

The chief drawback of the pay-back calculation is that it does not give the analyst a measure of potential profitability. To highlight the difference in this respect between the pay-back and the rate-of-return criterion, let us assume that we have two proposals, each requiring an investment of $10,000 and each estimated to yield savings (before any depreciation deductions) of $3,333 per year. The pay-back period is therefore three years in each case. But if the estimated lives of the two projects were four years and eight years, respectively, the rates of return (after deducting depreciation but without taking into account time ad-

ustment or income taxes) can be estimated roughly to be 17%
and 42%.[8] A better estimate (the type we typically will use here-
after) can be made by taking into account the fact that the present worth of the savings in the later years — say, the savings during the seventh and eighth years on the longer-lived project —
are not worth as much as are the savings in the early years. For
this example, such time-adjusted rates of return (also called the
discounted cash flow rates of return) then become 10% and 30%.[9]
Whatever the method of calculation, the rate of return criterion
establishes the difference in the profitability of the two projects,
a difference which is not disclosed by the pay-back calculation.[10]

The dangers in the use of a pay-back period criterion without
considering the rate of return can be summarized by an absurd
— but still perhaps illuminating — situation. Instead of assuming a four-year life for one of the two projects in the example
just used, let us assume only a three-year life, at the expiration of

---

[8] The formula used for this computation is:

$$\text{Rate of Return} = \frac{\text{Average Savings}}{\text{Average Investment}}$$

$$= \frac{(\text{Savings} - \text{Depreciation})}{\text{Investment} \div 2}$$

For instance: $17\% = \dfrac{\$5,000 - \dfrac{\$10,000}{4 \text{ years' life}}}{\$10,000 \div 2}$

Dividing the original investment by two is the same as assuming a $10,000
investment in the first year of life, zero investment after the last year
of life, and a straight-line write-off over the intervening years.

If we take into account the fact that net profits after deducting depreciation charges will probably be taxed at a rate of about 50%, we can obtain
estimated rates of return *after taxes* of 9% and 21%, respectively. Because
the pay-back calculation is usually made on a "before taxes" basis, however,
we shall continue to pursue our analysis in this section on a "before tax"
basis, a procedure which will not materially affect our argument.

[9] Using a table of the present value of $1/12 received monthly; in other
words, a table compounding monthly, rather than annually.

If we make the same "time-adjusted" calculation on an "after-taxes"
basis, the rates of return after taxes become 9% and 19%, respectively (the
longer period for depreciation recovery working to the disadvantage of the
longer-lived project).

[10] The method of making the calculations for time-adjusted rate of return
is explained in Robert N. Anthony, "Planning Capital Acquisitions," Chapter
18, of his *Management Accounting* (Homewood, Ill., Irwin, 1956). Table
C, p. 497, is a copy of the table mentioned above.

which we forecast a drastic model change which will make obsolete the equipment involved. The pay-off period for such a
project would still be three years — but the investment would
return no profit. Indeed, if we place any premium on money
today, as compared with money next year, the proposal clearly
would be a "loss proposition." We would be disbursing $10,000
at the beginning of the project to get back $10,000 — and no more
— in installments of $3,333 each over the next three years.

Are the deficiencies of the pay-back criterion any more serious
for special automatic equipment projects than they are for conventional equipment projects? They seem to be, principally because the economic life of special automatic equipment is likely
to be much shorter. To demonstrate, let us assume that a company management is considering ten projects, each needing an
investment of $10,000, for conventional equipment, numbered 1
through 10 and having the pay-back periods shown on Exhibit
14. There are five pairs of projects in this group of ten, each

EXHIBIT 14

RANKING OF LONG-LIVED HYPOTHETICAL EXAMPLES
BY PAY-BACK PERIOD AND BY RATE OF RETURN

Project Number	Estimated Pay-Back Period (years)	Estimated Life (years)	Estimated Rate of Return (Time Adjusted)	Rank, by Estimated Pay-Back Period	Rank, by Estimated Rate of Return
1	2.5	15	48% ⎱	1	1
2	2.5	10	46% ⎰		2
3	3.0	13	38+% ⎱	2	3
4	3.0	9	36% ⎰		4
5	3.5	15	32% ⎱	3	5
6	3.5	12	31% ⎰		6
7	3.67	14	30% ⎱	4	7
8	3.67	10	28% ⎰		8
9	3.85	16	29% ⎱	5	9
10	3.85	10	26% ⎰		10

NOTE: Taxes not considered.

pair having the same pay-back period. The estimated life of
each member of the pairs differs, however, and this difference in

estimated life causes some difference when the estimated rate of return is calculated. The ranking of projects, however, is not affected by substituting the rate of return standard for the pay-back criterion. Notice, too, that relatively great differences in estimated lives of the members of each pair seem to be accompanied by only nominal differences in the estimated rate of return. For instance, for the two projects having a pay-back period of 2.5 years, the difference is only 3%. In actual practice, such small differences are usually not significant because of the limits of error implicit and unavoidable in the underlying data (savings, investment, and useful life ·estimates).

What accounts for the close correlation in the rankings produced by using two different criteria? A piece of equipment with a life of 16 years will certainly accumulate savings for 6 years longer — 60% longer — than equipment with an estimated life of only 10 years. Because these additional savings, however, will not begin to be realized until 10 years hence, the concept of "time adjustment," or discounting, assigns them only a very small present value, and the further in the future savings are, the larger the "discount" factor applied in computing the time-adjusted rate of return. With longer-lived assets, then, even large savings in the distant future will have only a minor effect on the time-adjusted rate of return.

Consider now a similar group of ten $10,000 projects (Exhibit 15), half of which are for special automatic equipment with relatively short lives, varying from five to eight years. These shorter-lived projects have been substituted for the five even-numbered projects of the group in Exhibit 14, and have been designated with an A. The odd-numbered projects are the same as the odd-numbered projects in Exhibit 14. In contrast to the situation in which we were dealing only with longer-lived projects, the ranking by rate of return is significantly different. Assuming that a company management wanted to keep the total of expenditures to $60,000, the pay-back criterion would indicate approval of projects 1 through 6A. In contrast to the earlier case, however, these would not be the same projects as would be approved by the rate of return criterion. Specifically, application of the rate of return criterion *would not* approve projects 4A and 6A although the use of the pay-back criterion would; and the rate

EXHIBIT 15

RANKING OF LONG- AND SHORT-LIVED EXAMPLES
BY PAY-BACK PERIOD AND BY RATE OF RETURN

Project Number	Estimated Pay-Back Period (years)	Estimated Life (years)	Estimated Rate of Return (Time Adjusted)	Rank, by Estimated Pay-Back Period	Rank, by Estimated Rate of Return
1	2.5	15	48%	1	1
2A	2.6	5	34%	2	3
3	3.0	13	38%	3	2
4A	3.1	5	23%	4	7
5	3.5	15	32%	5	4
6A	3.6	5	15%	6	10
7	3.67	14	30%	7	5
8A	3.7	6	19%	8	9
9	3.85	16	29%	9	6
10A	3.9	8	22%	10	8

NOTE: Taxes not considered.

of return criterion *would* approve projects 7 and 9, which the pay-back criterion would not.[11]

Now let us briefly consider the two criteria as applied not to a group of long- and short-lived proposals but only to a group of proposals for special automatic equipment with short lives, i.e., the five projects marked A in Exhibit 15. According to the pay-back criterion, these five would be ranked: 2A, 4A, 6A, 8A and 10A. But according to the rate of return criterion, the ranking would be 2A, 4A, 10A, 8A, and 6A. Furthermore, the rates of return may be used to separate the projects into three groups between which differences are probably significant despite the unavoidable limitations in the accuracy of the underlying data used in practice. One group consists only of project 2A with an estimated rate of return of 34%; a second, and clearly less de-

---

[11] When the calculations of rate of return are made on an "after taxes" basis, there are only minor changes in the ranking; in the case of two pairs of projects, the ranks are reversed over that shown by the last column of Exhibit 15. For instance, project 2A drops from third to fourth ranking and project 5 rises from fourth to third place. The same reversal occurs with respect to projects 4A and 10A. In the case of both pairs, however, the difference in rates of return is less than one per cent, and the same projects would be selected for a $60,000 capital budget.

The Analysis of Proposals

sirable, group includes projects 4A, 10A, and 8A, with estimated rates of return between 19% and 23%; and a third and distinctly less desirable group is composed of project 6A with an estimated rate of return of only 15%.

There is one circumstance in which the pay-back calculation is an appropriate tool for ranking projects. This is when all projects being considered have the same estimated life. Such a condition is possible when the plant is a production line for the production of one product, and the obsolescence of the product, rather than wear and tear or technological advances in the process concerned, is expected to terminate the useful life of every piece of equipment. Even so, the pay-back calculation gives us no absolute measure of how profitable a project will be. If the estimated life of the production line were five years, for instance, we would be foolish to undertake projects related to it which promised a pay-back in five years or more.

Of course, one could work back from the minimum rate of return one wanted and from that determine a pay-back figure which would assure that rate of return. If the estimated life of a plant was five years and we want to obtain a rate of return of at least 10% net after taxes on any equipment project, we could set a maximum pay-back period (after taxes) of four years. All we have done by this is to establish our primary criterion — a 10% rate of return — and then for convenience or as a matter of personal preference, expressed it as a pay-back period rather than as a rate of return. In any such approach, we would need to guard against failing to identify projects which in fact did not have an estimated life of five years but instead probably would have shorter (or conceivably, longer) primary service lives; and for such exceptional projects we would need to revert to our basic rate of return calculation.

Let us summarize our conclusions on the methods of analysis of special equipment projects at this point. First, as a general rule, employing the pay-back calculation as the only method of analysis is likely to be decidedly inadequate. Second, the pay-back period is a measure of one kind of risk, but it may often inadequately summarize all the risks actually involved in a particular project. Third, the time-adjusted rate of return will generally provide a basis of much greater validity for assessing the over-all economic value of special automatic equipment projects, whether they are being compared one with another or with conventional projects.[12]

II

It is not sufficient, however, for us to say simply that a manager should analyze special equipment proposals in terms of estimated rate of return as well as perhaps in terms of pay-back. He also needs to have sound concepts of the basic components of these calculations: investment, savings, and primary service life. Furthermore, he needs to be aware of how in the case of special automatic equipment projects these concepts may embrace elements that are rarely, or at least not very often, encountered in analyzing conventional equipment proposals. If he is not careful on this score, he may be charging a conventional proposal with a full allocation of the investment it would require but be taking into account only part of the appropriate charges for a special automatic machine.

And he needs to find some way of more thoroughly appraising the higher risks which are more likely to be associated with special automatic than with conventional equipment. Even if he employs appropriate concepts of investment, savings, and primary service life, but fails to take into account that each of these estimates usually has wider limits of error for special automatic equipment, he may appraise special automatic equipment proposals much too favorably. In other words, he may be comparing the weight of an apple with the weight of an orange, without realizing that the weight comparison alone does not reflect the basic difference between the substances being weighed.

In the next three sections we will therefore discuss some of the problems involved in determining the numerical values to be

---

[12] For a discussion of other methods of analysis which take into account the time value of money, see Gordon Shillinglaw, "Managing Capital Expenditures: Appraisal of Specific Proposals," *The Engineering Economist,* Winter 1959. For a further general treatment of theory, see Joel Dean, *Capital Budgeting* (New York, Columbia University Press, 1951); George Terborgh, *Business Investment Policy* (Washington, Machinery and Allied Products Institute, 1958), and *Dynamic Equipment Policy,* and Eugene L. Grant, *Principles of Engineering Economy* (New York, Ronald, Third Edition, 1950).

assigned to the three principal factors in our analysis: investment, savings, and primary service life. As a second task we will assess the limitations implicit in these estimates and examine ways of adjusting them not only to permit special automatic equipment proposals to be compared fairly but also to permit at least a rough comparison between special automatic and conventional equipment proposals.

Determining the Estimated Investment

The estimated investment may or may not be equal to the total expenditures for a project. The first problem, nevertheless, is to determine what kinds of items should be added (or subtracted) to accumulate the estimate of "total expenditures" for a project. Having established the kinds and amounts of expenditures which will probably be required, we can proceed to quantify the investment figure.

The first component of total expenditures is, of course, the invoice cost of the equipment, or the equivalent in the case of manufacture by the user. The cost of spares, excise taxes, and freight-in are also germane, as are the costs of installation, foundations, wiring, and auxiliary equipment. In the companies interviewed there seemed in general to be no lack of appreciation of the relevance of these types of costs although at times some items were roughly approximated or even omitted because they were considered negligible.

Another kind of cost, however, was not so generally recognized; this was the cost of project engineering required. In only three of the companies surveyed was the cost of the time of the project engineer and his assistants estimated and included in the total expenditures figure. Significant expenditures for this type of manpower occur before delivery of equipment in selecting a project, working out the approach, and dealing with the designer and builder, and after delivery in debugging the equipment and bringing it up to an acceptable level of performance on the plant floor. In the debugging period, other types of costs may also be relevant, especially the labor of operators and technicians. A project engineer might sometimes spend as much as six man-months of effort on a piece of equipment carrying a vendor's invoice price of $20,000. The engineer's salary alone (without any supporting costs) would be $4,000 to $5,000 for such a period, an appreciable addition to the invoice cost of $20,000.

Another type of expenditure that is frequently overlooked but which should be included in the total in analyzing special equipment proposals is the cost of making changes in other operations. Such changes include replacing, retooling, or relocating existing equipment used in preceding or subsequent processing of the product. These types of changes may be fairly frequent in the case of special automatic equipment because, as we described at length in the preceding chapter, it is often necessary to make design changes in a part to make it easier to process on the special automatic equipment, or to reduce tolerances to facilitate automatic feeding of a part. For instance, if new dies have to be made for a preceding die-casting operation in order to produce a different shaped part for machining on special automatic equipment, the cost of the dies (less any salvage value for the dies replaced) is directly attributable to the proposed changeover. Some expenditures of this type may be difficult to handle, for example, when there are benefits other than just permitting processing by the special automatic equipment, or when the equipment for the preceding operation can work on additional products *not* later processed by the special automatic equipment being considered.

Another expenditure to be considered is the cost of a product engineer's time in redesigning the product to facilitate use of special automatic equipment. Under some circumstances these product design costs will be too insignificant to bother with for the purpose of equipment analysis. Under other circumstances, the engineering costs may be substantial but the improvement in the product from a competitive or marketing standpoint may completely justify the costs, leaving nothing to be allocated to the changeover to special automatic equipment. In still other instances, however, the costs may be large and solely attributable to the proposed special equipment, and such costs should be added in determining the total expenditure figure. One example is based on the experience of the management of the Rice Company, which was considering the acquisition of an automatic assembly machine. In order to facilitate assembly by machine, it was proposed that the design of a press part be changed, a change which would mean scrapping a one-year-old set of dies for the press (without recovering any salvage value) and replacing them with another set costing $7,500. No product improvement was involved. If the costs of redesigning the part or of running tests to determine its acceptability had been significant, they too should have been added, along with $7,500 for the new press dies, in determining the total expenditures for analytical purposes.

Changes in Required Investment in Inventories

Special automatic equipment often necessitates inventory investment. There is likely to be a drastic reduction in the in-process inventory required at the operation concerned when processing by special automatic equipment as compared with processing by conventional equipment. In some situations, however, optimistic estimates have been made of ability to operate without in-process banks of parts, particularly with conveyor-linked equipment made up of 10 to 20 or more stations, in sequence. The effect on preceding in-process inventories, on raw material inventories, and, especially, on finished goods inventories is often overlooked. For instance, if a machine processes workpieces of more than one design or more than one size, the installation of a special automatic machine may lead to a policy of carrying a stock of finished parts produced by that equipment when none had been carried before; or, if there were such inventories before, then larger average inventories than had previously been stocked.[13] Changes in total inventory investment may or may not be sufficiently large to warrant taking it into account, depending on the individual circumstances. Because the usual bias is toward considering only the immediate in-process inventory at the site of the equipment and because one's first impulse is to conclude that inventories will be much smaller when the operations are to be performed on the special automatic equipment, there

---

[13] Martin Richmond has noted how the installation of special automatic equipment in a TV manufacturer's plant resulted not only in increasing in-process inventories but also in requiring more storage capacity for raw materials. See "How Automation Hits a Plant," *Factory Management and Maintenance*, November 1955, p. 140.

should be a careful analysis to determine whether any inventories — raw materials (workpieces) and in-process and finished goods — change upward or downward.[14]

It is difficult to determine how to take into account changes in the average inventory investment required. Such investment ties up capital just as much as buying a piece of equipment. Therefore, it can be argued that if there is a reduction in capital requirements for carrying inventory, it should be subtracted from the investment otherwise required for a piece of proposed capital equipment. For example, if the investment otherwise required for a proposed project would total $100,000 and that project would permit a $30,000 net reduction in total inventory, the incremental investment needed would be only $70,000. Such a procedure involves the difficulty, however, that investment in inventories generally and in in-process inventories in particular is by no means likely to carry the same risks of loss as investment in special automatic equipment, either from the standpoint of the probable occurrence of a loss or, in many cases, its magnitude — i.e., the loss as a percentage of original outlay — if there is a loss. In-process inventories can often be completed and sold, even though it may be necessary to sell them for less than a normal profit; furthermore, under some circumstances if they have not been extensively processed, their value simply as scrap metal may be an appreciable proportion of their original cost.

For these reasons, although there may be exceptional circumstances in which the risk and extent of possible losses related to inventory investment is high, the author believes that the better course usually would be to convert the reduced inventory investment into an income item, equivalent to interest saved on the sum involved, and add it to the other estimated savings to be achieved by the proposal. This method of disposition can only be accomplished by establishing a "demanded rate of return," or cut-off rate, for the investment in inventories. This may be established by reference to the cut-off rate for equipment expenditures; i.e., if the minimum acceptable rate of return for equipment expenditures is 25% before taxes, then one company's management might fix 18% as the comparable rate of return demanded for the less risky inventory investment. Such a figure might vary de-

---

[14] On the effect on inventories, see also Bright, pp. 135–136.

pending on the nature of the inventory involved, but in any case it would unavoidably incorporate a large element of judgment. In the case of exceptional projects, there should remain the possibility of reflecting inventory reductions (or increases) in the calculation of investment rather than savings.

Other Factors Affecting the Amount of Investment

Federal corporate income taxes should also be considered in adjusting the total expenditure figures to arrive at the investment figure for a project proposal. This tax adjustment is likely to be much more important for special automatic equipment projects because of the larger proportion of expense items associated with them, such as large amounts of the project engineer's time, debugging expenses (including skilled labor and production trainees), and costs of product redesign.

To make such a tax adjustment the total expenditures must be separated into two classes of items, first, those which will be charged to expense immediately (in the current year) in making out the federal income tax return, and second, those which will be depreciated (or amortized) over more than one year. Since the items charged to current expense will reduce the company's net income by their total amount, federal income taxes will also be reduced. If the current tax rate applicable is 52% (1957 rate), then a $20,000 total for items currently charged to expense will be absorbed to the extent of $10,400 by reductions in the current year's taxes, leaving $9,600 to be recovered by savings over the life of the proposed project. If "nonexpense" expenditures total $35,000, then disregarding any other adjustments for the moment, the investment for purposes of analysis would be $35,000 plus $9,600 or $44,600. Clearly, when any significant proportions of total expenditures are to be listed as expenses in computing federal income tax, the analysis is importantly affected.

The calculation of investment is not complete until it has been decided what adjustments, if any, should be made for salvage values, first, for the equipment being replaced and, second, for any value remaining in the equipment proposed at the end of its estimated primary service life. Any salvage value of existing equipment which is being replaced should, of course, be deducted from the investment otherwise required, since release of such capital values is a function of acquiring the proposed new equipment. There then remains the problem of estimating the salvage value, if any, of the special automatic equipment at the end of its economic life. We shall treat the whole topic of this type of a "future" salvage value estimate in a later section, after we have discussed the determination of the economic life of the equipment. In examples used up to that point we shall assume that the proposed equipment, whether conventional or special, will have no salvage value, or a negligible one, at the end of its primary service life.

The failure of most companies contacted to take these kinds of expenditures into account was usually excused by pointing out that project engineering, design engineering, and debugging costs were charged to "general overhead" or "administrative expense." It is true that such items of expense may be usefully included under general overhead for the purpose of preparing cash budgets or in compiling profit and loss statements, but this does not preclude the use of estimates of these expenses in determining which equipment projects to undertake. If they are not considered, not only will the forecasted profitability to the company be unrealistically high, but there will also be bias in comparing one project with another — a project which will require large expenditures of such expense items will show up better than it should when the pay-back and the rate of return calculations are made. This kind of bias would be especially pronounced when special automatic equipment projects were compared with conventional equipment projects. Sometimes, of course, the expense components of a particular project are too small to be very important in an economic analysis.

One challenge which can be made is that the kinds of expenses involved would not be avoided if the project had not been undertaken; that is, they are sunk costs and need not be taken into account. It is true that a company will probably not discharge a production engineer or a design engineer to avoid paying his salary if a particular project were rejected rather than approved. But the alternative usually adopted is not to discharge the engineers, but to assign them to other projects. In other words, a company's management can regard such charges as variable, subject to this limitation: that there exist other projects on which these men could work if the one in hand is not approved. The best way to take cognizance of these facts is to add to the estimated cost given each proposal the best estimates which can be obtained of the cost of the engineering time which it will probably require. As an alternative, it may be proposed that a company's management should simply raise the minimum or cut-off rate of return on acceptable projects so as to provide a higher margin of savings on projects completed and thereby in the long run approximately cover the costs of engineering man-hours consumed in total. Since the purpose of project analysis is to choose some proposals from among many, however, it is essential that the expected project engineering costs be allocated to each proposal individually.

We shall conclude our discussion of the conceptual problems of estimating the investment figure by highlighting the principal differences between acquiring special automatic equipment and conventional equipment. Compared with conventional equipment proposals, special automatic equipment proposals are, by their very nature, almost certain to entail a significantly larger amount of production engineering time. They are also more likely to bring about changes in product design or in the equipment for preceding and subsequent operations. Failure to consider expenditures of this nature may significantly bias the total expenditures estimate on the low side, which will result in an erroneous over-all appraisal of special equipment proposals. The fact that many of the costs associated with special automatic equipment projects create current tax reductions, and often sizable ones, makes it important to compute the investment after taxes. Another difference is that special automatic equipment proposals are more likely to involve estimates of funds released or required by changes in inventories. Such estimates need careful scrutiny, first, to determine the validity of the amount of inventory change forecasted and, second, to ensure that estimates are comprehensive, going back to raw material stocks on one hand and going forward to stocks of finished goods on the other. Finally, the amount of the estimated investment is all the more important when the estimated service life is short, and a short life is characteristic of much special automatic equipment.

Uncertainty of the Estimated Investment

Even after we have compiled an estimate of the required investment which, conceptually, comprises all the appropriate elements, we are faced with the problem of taking into account the probability of significant error in the total estimate. We must be careful to take into account the likely degrees to which we may have underestimated or overestimated each of the elements we have provided for, and we must also provide adequately for contingencies we cannot now identify but which may become significant by the time the project has been completed. For conventional equipment proposals the probable range in estimates of total expenditures is narrow and tolerable, whereas for special automatic equipment projects the range is likely to be far wider and — unlike conventional equipment projects — significantly biased on the high side.

First let us look at some actual experiences. The data in Exhibit 16 comprise a collection of estimated and actual expenditures for conventional equipment projects. They were compiled from a random selection of projects completed during 1955 and 1956 by three firms: the Abbott Company (a manufacturer of consumer durable products); the Fisher Company (a manufacturer of an electromechanical product); and the Lester Company (also a manufacturer of electromechanical products). The costs include the cost of the equipment and all installation charges, including foundation construction, erecting, and wiring, as applicable in each instance. Each company provided for contingencies differently. Abbott included no contingency allowance, while Lester added a 10% contingency allowance only to items other than the invoice cost of the equipment. Items other than the invoice cost of the equipment usually were a small fraction of the total, making the contingency fund a relatively minor part of the total estimated expenditures. Fisher's practice was the most liberal, its contingency allowances varying between 8% and 10% of the total project cost estimate, including the invoice cost of the equipment.

For these conventional projects the differences between actual expenditures and estimated expenditures were rather narrow. If we use as our standard a range of ±10% of the original estimate

EXHIBIT 16

SAMPLES OF CONVENTIONAL EQUIPMENT PROJECTS COMPLETED IN 1955 AND 1956
ESTIMATED AND ACTUAL TOTAL EXPENDITURES

	Abbott Company				Fisher Company				Lester Company		
Proj. No.	Estimate	Actual	% Over or Under Estimate	Proj. No.	Estimate	Actual	% Over or Under Estimate	Proj. No.	Estimate	Actual	% Over or Under Estimate
1	$ 1,522	$ 1,741	+14%	1	$ 10,931	$ 9,977	−9%	1	$ 9,705	$ 8,559	−12%
2	7,463	7,063	−5	2	5,421	4,599	−15	2	30,730	30,154	−2
3	19,319	17,841	−8	3	3,378	3,849	−17	3	3,900	3,854	−1
4	4,239	4,247	0	4	96,381	91,557	−5	4	16,475	16,371	−1
5	4,243	4,143	−2	5	4,374	4,721	−8	5	33,764	34,327	+2
6	7,006	6,880	−2	6	5,223	5,387	−3	6	22,001	22,378	+2
7	8,096	8,114	0	7	28,937	28,319	−2	7	39,190	39,478	+1
8	898	917	+2	8	3,508	2,958	−15	8	13,989	18,405*	+31
9	13,575	13,161	+3	9	7,800	7,765	0	9	3,394	4,148	+22
10	15,208	16,465	+8	10	5,488	5,109	−7	10	1,453	1,562	+7
				11	3,458	3,202	−7	11	8,700	9,521	+9
				12	5,002	4,163	−17	12	1,669	1,426	−14
				13	3,121	3,031	−3				
Total	$81,569	$80,572	+1%		$183,022	$174,637	−4.6%		$184,970	$190,183	+2.8%
Number over ±10%	1				4				4		
Number within ±10%	9				9				8		

* Overage caused by decision made during installation to replace steam line.
SOURCE: Company records.

(a likely figure for conventional equipment), we find only about one-fourth, or 9 of the 35 projects, falling outside this standard. Moreover, if we look only at the cases in which total expenditures were more than the estimate, we find that in only 3 of the 35 cases, or less than 10%, did expenditures *exceed* the original estimates by more than 10%. Taking the projects for each company as a group, the over-all performances on these conventional equipment groups was very close to the sum of the original estimates; Fisher's is the largest deviation, and this is less than 5% in amount, and on the low side of the original estimates.

Turning to similar data for special automatic equipment projects, Exhibit 17 presents estimated and actual expenditures for the Fisher Company and for the Lester Company, both manufacturers of electromechanical devices, and for 16 projects completed by seven other companies engaged in a variety of manufacturing businesses. Since the concepts of expenditures in these companies were so different, the data can be more easily analyzed if each subset is considered in sequence. In the case of Fisher, expenditures were consistently greater than estimates, about half of the project having overages greater than 10%. For all projects as a group, Fisher's actual total expenditures were only 6% to 7% above the original estimates. The degree of overage is significantly understated, however, both for each individual project and for the total of all projects by the omission of a charge for the time of project engineers. The time spent by project engineers in total on projects completed proved to be something like twice that originally contemplated, and would have comprised about 40% of the total actual expenditures had they been included therein. If rough adjustments are made to include the cost of the project engineers, Fisher's total actual expenditures would be about 20% greater than the sum of the original estimates.

Lester Company's projects show a much greater deviation of actual from estimated costs. This was due in large to its policy of including the cost of project engineers' time in many instances. If we use ±10% as a standard, we find that 70% of Lester's 40 projects had actual costs falling outside that band, compared with less than 50% of Fisher's projects. Lester's deviations also extend over a wider range and — unlike Fisher's — include a significant number which fell below the original estimates. De-

EXHIBIT 17

SAMPLES OF SPECIAL EQUIPMENT PROJECTS COMPLETED IN
1955 AND 1956

ESTIMATED AND ACTUAL TOTAL EXPENDITURES

Over or Under Expenditures as % of Estimated Expenditures	Fisher Company	Lester Company	Seven Other Companies
−60 or more	—	—	—
−50 to −59	—	1	—
−40 to −49	—	—	—
−30 to −39	—	2	1
−20 to −29	—	4	—
−15 to −19	—	1	1
−10 to −14	—	2	—
−5 to −9	2	2	1
−4 to +4	3	10	6
+5 to +9	5	—	—
+10 to +14	5	3	2
+15 to +19	1	1	1
+20 to +29	1	1	2
+30 to +39	—	—	—
+40 to +49	—	1	—
+50 to +59	2	1	1
+60 to +69	—	2	—
+70 or more	—	9	1
Total Pieces of Equipment	19	40	16
Number under −10%	0	10	2
Number over +10%	9	18	7
% outside ±10% limits	47%	70%	56%
Typical Project (Interquartile range)	$3,000 to $15,000	$5,000 to $28,000	$14,000 to $130,000
Total Projects			
Estimated Expenditures	$185,000	$1,318,000	$1,645,000
Actual Expenditures	$197,000	$1,822,000	$2,014,000
Average over by	6.5%	38.2%	22.5%

SOURCE: Company records.

spite these differences, however, the general tendency of Lester's
projects, like that of Fisher's was to exceed the original estimates
by a significant margin.   While 10 of Lester's project expenditure
figures fell below our arbitrary standard of ±10% of the original
estimate, 18 were above that range.   Furthermore, in total,

Lester's expenditures on all 40 projects were about 38% over the estimates.

If the assembly machine projects from these two companies are considered separately, Fisher's 9 assembly machine projects show an average overage of slightly more than 7%, and Lester's 11 assembly equipment projects are over by 97%. While breakdowns of such sparse data are not statistically reliable, there is further support for the premise that the costs of special automatic assembly machines are likely to exceed estimated expenditures. One user with substantial experience in building assembly machines of this type observed that in comparison with special metalworking equipment, assembly equipment required more engineering man-hours to work out the basic approach, and was likely to involve a good many more unknowns which would not become apparent until work was well under way. In the absence of stronger support, however, we will not pursue any further special analysis of assembly equipment in this section.

The bases upon which expenditure estimates for the seven other companies were compiled varied considerably; specifically, some included project engineering time and some did not. In some cases, the only available estimates were actually revisions of initial estimates, and naturally these revisions were likely to be more closely in accord with actual expenditures than earlier estimates would have been. In at least one or two cases, additional debugging was performed after the project appropriation records had been closed, and the costs thereof were charged as a current production cost by the manufacturing department in which the equipment was located. Despite the fact that these data are in some ways less satisfactory, the "seven other companies" subset of data are in general accord with the Fisher and Lester subsets.[15]

The contrasts between conventional and special equipment

---

[15] Estimated and actual expenditures were available for one additional project but have not been included in the "seven companies" tabulation because it was completely out of proportion to the rest of projects shown; it involved expenditures of more than $3,000,000 and therefore would disproportionately affect any total figures in which it might be included. The scope of the project also included some product development activities as well as equipment development and therefore was not comparable with the others we have studied.

projects are marked. We noted earlier (Exhibit 16) that expenditures for about 75% of all 35 conventional projects fell within ±10% of the original estimates. For the 75 special equipment projects, however, only 39% fall within the ±10% limits. Also, the proportion of projects which ran over by more than 10% is 45% for special automatic equipment compared with only about 9% for conventional equipment projects, a ratio of 5:1.[16]

A policy of buying, rather than building, equipment does not wholly insulate the user from the uncertainties involved in the designing and building stages. One vendor has noted:

> We have seen cases where assembly machines have been ordered, designed, built, delivered, and paid for; and then other companies have been called in to try to make the equipment work. The inevitable answer is "salvage the hoppers [for orienting and feeding parts], scrap the rest, and start again." [17]

If such a project is abandoned, then the expenditures to date, which are likely to include a sizable payment to the vendor even if the equipment does not work, will be a complete loss. And if further sums are spent to complete the project successfully, the total expenditures will be much more than was contemplated at the time the original appropriation for the project was approved. In our field work we encountered several cases involving vendors in which the latter alternative was adopted, and the result was always a substantial overrun in total expenditures by the time the project was closed.

---

[16] Although the author did not investigate process plants, there is evidence of parallel risks in designing and building chemical plants. An article on estimating total plant costs gives the following rules of thumb for determining contingency allowances, expressed as a percentage of the estimated cost of total physical assets involved:

Low	Firm process	10% to 20%
Average	Subject to change	20% to 30%
High	Speculative process	30% to 50%

It is not difficult to equate the low category, including processes the workability of which has already been firmly established, with conventional equipment projects, and the average and high groups with special automatic equipment projects. (See Cecil A. Chilton, "Cost Data Correlated," *Chemical Engineering*, June 1949, p. 106.)

[17] William C. Cummings, "Standardizing Assembly Machines," *Automation*, March 1959, p. 48.

Most of both Fisher's and Lester's projects were buy rather than make projects. For the seven other company projects the proportions were about equal.

To summarize at this point, if the cost of the project engineers' time is included as an expenditure, as seems advisable, there is a strong likelihood that the original estimate of expenditures for special automatic equipment proposals will be materially exceeded in a high proportion of instances.[18]   Furthermore, it should be noted that in both Fisher and Lester a small proportion of projects ran over their estimates by 50% or more.   Such great differences are much less likely when a firm is dealing with conventional equipment projects.   The Fisher and Lester experiences indicate that special equipment projects present a high risk that expenditures will be significantly (say, of the order of magnitude of 20% to 30%) over estimates, and a small but clear risk that expenditures will be greatly (say, 50% or more) over estimates.   In addition, there is no evidence that estimates which prove too low are likely to be counterbalanced by estimates which prove too high, in sharp contrast to conventional equipment projects for which it seems more likely that high and low estimates will average out both in number and in amount.

Taking Investment Uncertainty into Account

Three approaches to cope with the uncertainty typically attached to the investment figure suggest themselves, each of which has its individual advantages and disadvantages.   One is to try to remove some of the uncertainty — to try to make our estimates more precise.   A second is to try to adjust the investment estimate to reflect the uncertainty attached to it.   And a third is simply to apply higher cut-off rates, either for the pay-back period or the rate of return, in deciding whether to approve a particular project proposal.   These approaches are not, of course, necessarily mutually exclusive; indeed, all three might be employed in one company depending upon the nature of the project and the amount of expenditures involved.

There seemed to be some improvement, for instance, in later projects undertaken by Lester and Fisher.   The personnel con-

---

[18] Unanticipated increases in the expenditures required was also noted in Bright's study, pp. 115–116.

cerned, through experience and perhaps some training, can learn to make more precise estimates. The magnitude of a single project, however, and the long cycle time — six months to two years or more from start to finish — means that the experience of a particular engineer develops slowly. In addition, because of turnover a significant proportion of "inexperienced" personnel are likely to be involved in any continuing program of special automatic equipment acquisition.

Another way to obtain improved estimates is to use pilot projects to prove out uncertain mechanisms before the company commits itself to the whole project.[19] This device was rarely used in the plants visited; its use was limited to experienced and efficient special automatic equipment groups. As one vendor has noted, a project may sometimes be planned to work out the potential problem areas first and still add little or no cost to the final total expenditures required:

> We have found that all functional methods usually can be demonstrated, and functional risk eliminated, for a cost between 10 to 20 per cent of the total cost of a developmental program, and without materially increasing the total program cost. . . .
>
> Moreover, the most critical function can probably be proved out within the first $5,000 to $10,000 (i.e., first 20% of expenditures).[20]

The success of such an approach depends on the ability to identify the likely problem areas in advance, and even experienced personnel are likely to be surprised on this score. Though their batting average is less than perfect, routine use of inexpensive pilot investigations to prove out a questionable area of large or hazardous projects still promises to be an economical procedure.

Some projects will not warrant the delay and expense associated with efforts to get more precise estimates of required expenditures. The savings promised may be so large as to make the project a desirable one even if wide limits of error are associated with the expenditures estimate. Or the project may be a relatively simple one, such as a dial-type drilling machine for a

---

[19] As we noted earlier, such a procedure may also result in an over-all reduction in outlay by reducing the cost of debugging required.

[20] Richard S. White, "Minimizing Risk and Debugging in Developing Unique Equipment," *Automation*, June 1959, pp. 50–51.

common type of workpiece, so that reasonable care in preparing estimates will yield a figure with close tolerances. Even in such cases, however, if there are new features, such as automatic feeding of workpieces, it may often be possible and prudent to build the new portion and test it before finally approving the project; failure or modification of the new mechanism may increase the appeal of an alternative approach to the design of the rest of the equipment.

The intrinsic uncertainty of investment figures for special automatic equipment suggests that unknown costs could be provided for by adding a contingency allowance. If Lester, for instance, had added 35% to the estimated expenditures required for each project, the resulting total of overages for all projects would certainly have been within tolerable limits. Likewise (ignoring for the moment the very important omissions in these particular investment estimates), by adding a 15% contingency allowance instead of the 5% allowance actually included, Fisher would have achieved similar results. An appropriate contingency allowance percentage should be developed on the basis of each individual company's experience and should be revised periodically.

Such a standard contingency factor is valid only when the mix of projects undertaken by the company remains relatively stable. If, for instance, a company had been purchasing only special machine tools and then began to acquire assembly machines, the old contingency allowance would probably turn out to be too low on assembly machine projects, even though it might continue to be quite appropriate for whatever special machine tools were required. It is also by no means certain that the percentage allowance appropriate for a single machine of 4 to 8 stations costing $20,000 would be appropriate for a machine system for 25 stations, costing $100,000. Likewise a single project involving a process unique in the plant (for example, automatic welding equipment in a plant equipped mainly with machine tools) would not fit the average as far as a percentage contingency allowance was concerned, especially if the plant personnel had no prior experience with that particular process. It is also desirable that the projects be reasonably homogeneous as far as size is concerned; even though the average excess over estimate is, say 25%, if for individual cases it may range at random from 10% to 35%, then the impact of one or two large projects in the course of a year's program may distort the average up or down. And if the larger projects are also the most difficult and the least familiar to the project engineers, the chances of having this occur will of course be much greater.

The use of an average contingency allowance for all projects also carries another kind of risk. Through its effect in lowering the rate of return and lengthening the pay-back period, it could result in the rejection of some desirable projects for which the additional investment cushion was not required. The larger the standard contingency percentage, the larger, obviously, the chances of rejecting some proposals unjustifiably.

An alternative to using a standard percentage for all projects is to establish a tailor-made contingency allowance for each project separately. In this event, the project engineer and his supervisor would apply their intuition, developed through their experience, and a preproposal investigation (restricted or extensive as it might be) to establish whether a particular project was likely to require a contingency allowance different from the average experience in the past and, if it did, to estimate by how much. A company's average experience in the recent past, such as the 38% overage of Lester Company, seems to be a good point of departure for applying judgment. The computation of a contingency allowance for a specific project should begin with the tentative assumption that the average of past experience applies, and then the project engineer should seek to justify modifying the standard to better fit the particular project being considered.

Our theoretically ideal adjustment for uncertainty might be most nearly approached if for each project we could obtain a "probability schedule," for the possible range of outlay required, from which we could calculate a "most probable" estimated investment, as follows:

Estimated Investment Between	Probability
$10,000 and $10,999	.3 (3 chances in 10)
11,000 and 11,999	.2
12,000 and 12,999	.2
13,000 and 13,999	.2
14,000 and 14,999	.1

Midpoint	*Probability*	
$10,500	.3	$3,150
11,500	.2	2,300
12,500	.2	2,500
13,500	.1	2,700
14,500	.1	1,450

Most Probable Estimated Investment $12,100

The difficulty with this procedure, of course, is to obtain probability estimates that are meaningful. Perhaps the best source is the project engineer assigned to the job, provided that he had had the experience of working on at least three or four special equipment projects. Quite likely his estimates could be refined by being reviewed by his supervisor, who would be expected to possess a broader experience even if it were not all firsthand but simply intimate acquaintance with the events of many projects carried out by others.

One simple routine for obtaining such probability estimates would be to require the project engineer not only to prepare a "best" estimate of the investment required but also to answer a standard question, as follows:

What, in your judgment, are the probabilities that your estimated investment figure will be exceeded by:

(a) 10% or more?	*Answer:* (8) chances in 10
(b) 20% or more?	*Answer:* (3) chances in 10
(c) 30% or more?	*Answer:* (2) chances in 10
(d) 40% or more?	*Answer:* (0) chances in 10
(e) 50% or more?	*Answer:* (0) chances in 10

Once the question has been answered, the likely deviation can then be calculated as shown in the following example:

Probability		*Increment*		
.8	×	10%	=	8%
.3	×	10% more	=	3%
.2	×	10% more again	=	2%
				+13%

If the particular best estimate involved was originally $10,000, based on this illustration, the most probable estimate would be

$11,300. Assuming that the project promised a 37% rate of return before taxes with the investment estimate at $10,000 (as in our previous examples), then if the investment in fact rises to $11,000, the rate of return will decline to 30%; if the investment amounts to $12,000, the rate of return will be only 25%; and if the investment amounts to $13,000, then the rate of return will fall to 20%. Since the most probable investment required would be $11,300 then our most probable forecast of the rate of return would be 28%.

In a project like this, the engineer's estimate of the probabilities of overruns may prove far too optimistic, and the investment actually required might turn out to be $15,000. It might on rare occasions be less than his best estimate. Nevertheless, a major advantage of using a procedure like this is that if it is incorporated into the appropriation request, it forces all concerned to recognize that the investment estimate is more properly conceived of as a range of figures rather than a single figure. Presentation of such data would also focus attention on those components of the total estimate which the project engineer considered most likely to vary, and thus bring about a thorough airing of the contingencies which might arise. Indeed, there may be much to say for incorporating two additional questions in the standard appropriation request form, one asking the sponsor to identify the factors which might make the total amount of the overage more than 10%, say, above the estimates used, the other asking whether there was any course of action which might be taken to reduce or eliminate the chance of an overage of more than 10%. Such questions would practically insure the consideration of any appropriate pilot studies, and, hopefully, tend also to insure a thorough analysis by the project leader and his supervisor before submitting appropriation requests.

There remains some question whether even such a relatively simple procedure is workable; that is, whether it would be practicable to accustom the persons concerned (project engineers, their supervisors and those involved in the review procedures) to think in the fashion required. And, assuming such a procedure or something like it would be workable, there is the question of whether there would be sufficient improvement in the results to justify the effort. It seems that the procedure outlined should involve only slight additional effort and that it would probably constitute a useful approach under at least two circumstances: when a substantial investment (that is, $50,000 or more) is involved; and when the degree of technical advance involved in a project is obviously large or the process involved is new to the project engineering group. It may also be a useful approach when a firm only occasionally acquires a piece of special automatic equipment and therefore cannot count very much on averaging out the risks involved.

Finally, instead of adjusting the original investment estimates a third method might be adopted, one which attempts to allow for the uncertainty connected with estimates of investment required by raising the minimum or cut-off criterion. If we were basing our decisions on the pay-back period only, raising the minimum would have the same result as the policy first discussed; that is, adding a contingency allowance of a predetermined percentage (for example, 20%) to every special equipment project. The following examples demonstrate this point:

Original Estimated Investment	Estimated Savings	Pay-back	Pay-back Plus 20%
$10,000	$2,000	5.00	6.00
10,000	3,000	3.33	4.00
10,000	4,000	2.50	3.00
10,000	5,000	2.00	2.40

Original Estimated Investment Plus 20%	Estimated Savings	Pay-back	
$12,000	$2,000	6.00	
12,000	3,000	4.00	
12,000	4,000	3.00	
12,000	5,000	2.40	

In other words, we get identical pay-back figures either by adding 20% to the pay-back period after it has been computed or by adding 20% to the investment figure before the pay-back period has been computed.

We have rejected the pay-back period, however, as the sole criterion to be employed, especially when we are dealing with special automatic equipment project proposals. As soon as we introduce the additional factors of estimated primary service life and time adjustment, we complicate the problem of using a cut-off rate of return. Using a time-adjusted rate of return as a cut-off, we no longer will be able to provide the same cushion for all projects unless a different cut-off rate of return is calculated for each service life — for five years, six years, and so on.

The use of a different rate of return for each service life could be avoided by grouping, that is, having one cut-off rate of return for projects with lives of from five to seven years; another for the group with lives of seven to ten years; and a third for the ten to fifteen years group. Taking into account the limits of accuracy of all the elements involved in the rate of return calculation, such an approach would really impose little or no inaccuracy, but two problems would remain. It would not be easy to compare two projects falling in different life-groups when their rates of return were well above the cut-off rate. Supplementary calculations would be needed; indeed, the easiest approach would be to add appropriate contingency allowances directly to the investment figures and then compare "expected" rates of return directly. A second problem would arise when it was desirable to provide a different amount of cushion than that factored into the table of adjusted cut-off rates of return. Special calculations would again have to be made, and it would be easier again to adjust estimated investment figures and compare the expected rate of return directly with a primary standard. Primarily because of its awkwardness in use, the adjusted cut-off rate of return seems to be less efficient than adjusted investment estimates as a device to take uncertainty into account.

The essence of the foregoing discussion of the uncertainty of investment estimates may be stated as follows. Since it is in the nature of special automatic equipment projects to involve uncertain investment estimates, it is desirable to try to establish an expected investment figure on a systematic basis, the degree of precision sought being a function of the size of the project and the degree of uncertainty involved. Two key elements in any sound procedure for this are the careful judgment of the project engineer (and his supervisor), and the continuing analysis of the company's previous history of actual investment versus estimated investment with respect to special automatic equipment projects. Close agreement between individual actual and estimated expenditures is not to be expected, but a closer correspondence should result. An added advantage will be gained if the procedures employed focus attention on the range of investment estimates and the reasons for them.

Our discussion thus far has dealt with investment estimates in an appropriation request for funds to design and build equipment. Certainly most companies should and do conduct one or more earlier, preliminary rounds of analysis. At these earlier stages, less precise estimates are likely to serve the purpose, since increased precision usually increases the costs incurred in doing the job.[21] Even so, much of the philosophy evident in our treatment of "appropriation grade" estimates can be made useful in earlier rounds of analysis.

In dealing with the uncertainty related to the investment estimates for special automatic equipment projects, we must constantly guard against the danger of being overzealous lest we pass the point of diminishing returns. On the basis of the observations reported here, however, there seems to be room for considerable improvement in the typical level of current practice before there will be much danger on this account.

---

[21] W. T. Nichols of Monsanto Chemical Company has made the point that in any company a systematic classification of types of estimates, based on the procedures used to compile them, is a useful way of obtaining common understanding about the degree of precision of investment estimates. Although his comments deal with the chemical industry and not with the metalworking group, many of his observations seem to be appropriate to other situations as well. As in the case of special automatic equipment, for instance, the quality of the estimate is greatly influenced by the degree of detail employed in making up the estimate. The highest quality estimates in both cases, therefore — and the most costly — are to be obtained only by first doing much of the design work, which would be valueless if ultimately the project was not undertaken. (See "Capital Cost Estimating," *Industrial and Engineering Chemistry,* October 1951, pp. 2295–2298.)

For a way of getting estimates without a machine layout, see Robert G. Dexter, "Estimating Special Equipment Costs," *Automation,* May 1958, pp. 53–54. Dexter's approach is based on the analysis of operations to be performed on the special automatic equipment being considered, and takes into account the following factors: number of operations, the degree to which they are "experimental" or "routine"; the nature of the product; the speed of operations; the degree of adjustability of each operation; and the size of the parts involved. It is necessary to have a record of acquiring several pieces of equipment to use Dexter's method, for his factors essentially are a method of comparing a proposed piece of equipment with comparable equipment acquired earlier (or pricing by comparison).

III

The amount of estimated annual average savings is as important in proposal evaluation as the amount of the estimated expenditures. The general questions in computing savings are "What costs will be affected?" and "By how much will they change?" There are two aspects of the savings computation in cases of special automatic equipment, however, which typically seemed to be different enough in nature or in effect to warrant special attention. The first is the increased importance in the total savings estimate of types of costs other than labor costs, that is, material costs and so-called overhead costs. The second distinctive aspect is the added importance which is attached to the volume estimate — the average rate at which production is expected to take place over the life of the equipment.

Types of Costs Affecting the Estimate of Annual Average Savings

There seemed to be a tendency in many of the companies visited to justify special automatic equipment by comparing present direct labor costs (sometimes including an allocation of fringe benefits) with estimated direct labor costs using the proposed equipment. It was always assumed implicitly that nonlabor costs would remain the same as under present hand methods. This procedure ignores the possibility that nonlabor costs may quite significantly increase (or decrease) and reduce (or increase) net savings. There is in fact a high probability that nonlabor costs will change quite significantly in the kind of situation in which special automatic equipment is proposed. Almost without exception, it seemed that the pre-existing manufacturing operations involved were highly developed and were utilizing the labor involved with a high degree of efficiency. Under these circumstances, labor costs were already surprisingly low compared with material costs or with the sum of the overhead costs directly related to the operation. Therefore, there were opportunities for nonlabor costs to vary enough to wipe out labor savings or to augment them materially.

The experience of the Orlando Company with one of its special automatic equipment projects is a striking illustration of the potential importance of nonlabor costs — in this case, of material

costs only. The project involved a part currently being manufactured on several automatic screw machines, and the proposal
was to replace them with special automatic cold-heading machines. The existing direct labor costs were $1.12 per thousand
units of parts produced and the estimated direct labor costs
using the proposed special equipment were $.97 per thousand.
Since the annual production was well below 80 million, estimated
direct labor savings would be less than $12,000 per year, and
would hardly justify the investment expenditures proposed, which
were over $150,000. But the proposed material costs would be
only $2.07 per thousand compared with the existing $3.71 per
thousand. Not only was there a savings in material equal to
about 40% of current physical consumption (pounds of metal
per thousand parts), but a slightly cheaper type of raw material
could be used. In this instance the savings in material costs
were large enough to permit a substantial increase in direct labor
costs if necessary to adopt the new process.

It is possible for nonlabor costs to vary in the other direction
and significantly offset direct labor savings. The essential point
to be grasped is that, in estimating savings, the probable effects
on all costs — not just on direct labor costs — need to be considered, particularly when labor costs are often likely to comprise
only a small part of the total for the operation or operations involved.

In the absence of a fundamental change in process the odds
seem to favor increases rather than decreases in nonlabor costs
as a result of introducing special automatic equipment. The
principal opportunities for increased material costs seemed to lie
in two areas: higher input material costs and higher scrap costs.
The costs of the material input often increased with the introduction of special automatic equipment because of the "higher
quality" requirements for proper automatic handling and feeding.
For example, the Slocum Company acquired a piece of automatic equipment using coils of strip steel as its input. During
the debugging period on the new equipment it was discovered
that the feeding mechanism required thickness tolerances closer
than commercial standards. As a result, raw material intended
for this particular equipment was checked by hand for thickness,
and material exceeding the machine's tolerance was culled out.

It happened that the same stock was required for other purposes in the plant and oversize stock could be fully utilized elsewhere. The added cost of inspection and sorting, however, in effect raised the raw material costs significantly for the special automatic equipment.

In another instance, the Palmer Company acquired a piece of special automatic equipment, the input of which was several parts purchased from outside suppliers. For the equipment to function efficiently, however, it proved necessary to rewrite Palmer's specifications for all the parts used, both to change the physical configuration and to tighten the tolerances allowable for certain key dimensions. Again, these changes resulted in requirements for a part different from commercial standards, and therefore in a higher price from the supplier.[22]

A permanently higher scrap cost at the end of the debugging period seemed to be a somewhat rarer phenomenon than permanently higher material input cost, but it was by no means unknown. In the Morley Company, a portion of the parts fed into a new piece of special automatic equipment were regularly damaged beyond repair by the feeding mechanism employed. While a method was developed to prevent damaged parts from entering the first operation on the equipment, no economical way was discovered to prevent the damage in the first place and the higher scrap loss simply reduced the net savings, fortunately by a small percentage — but still in this instance by an annual sum equal to a luxurious pension for most company executives.[23]

Raw material costs of the two types we have been discussing here often appeared as a transitory condition during the debugging period and in the end were reduced to pre-existing levels. In many instances, however, such results were accomplished only by making greater investment expenditures, either for additional equipment or for more engineering time, or for both. For example, in the case cited above in which it became necessary

---

[22] Others have emphasized the point that special automatic equipment often requires higher quality input material. See, for example, practitioner Kenneth R. Treer, "Automated Assembly — 1," *Automation,* October 1956, p. 53. See also Robert L. Kessler, "How Special Machinery Is Developed," p. 53.

[23] Robert L. Kessler notes a similar experience in "How Special Machinery Is Developed."

to sort strip steel, the company began by using hand micrometers to sort raw material but it subsequently developed an electronic machine for that purpose. The cost of inspection was reduced, but not eliminated, by making an additional investment. In the other cases cited, however, the higher costs of raw material could not be avoided, even by making additional investment expenditures.

It is likely to be more difficult to determine overhead costs than material costs. Since overhead rates of from 200% to 400% of direct labor costs are common in many plants, it was surprising to find how often overhead items were inadequately considered. In three companies all costs other than direct labor costs were ignored, and in six other companies overhead was dealt with quite inappropriately by simply applying the full current overhead rate of 250% to the direct labor costs involved. Only one company approached the analysis of probable changes in overhead at the working level with anything like full sophistication.

Appropriate consideration of overhead costs requires a careful identification of those elements of overhead which will change as a result of the installation of the special automatic equipment being proposed. Elements most likely to be affected significantly include tool costs and tool grinding costs, material handling costs, and inspection costs. Tool costs may be greater because of closer tolerances required for the machine to function properly, because of a speeding up of tools at bottleneck operations so as to achieve the over-all output desired at the expense of faster tool wear, or because of the use of special tools, say, in order to combine several operations at one station on the equipment. The special tooling required is not only more costly to procure initially; it may also require considerable maintenance or replacement several times over the expected life of the equipment proper. Since special automatic equipment usually combines two or more operations previously separate, the immediate in-process material handling costs are likely to be significantly lower. There are exceptions, however, as in the case where a company found it necessary to construct special tote boxes in which to transport parts to be fed into an automatic machine because the former method of handling them damaged some parts so that the automatic equipment jammed. Likewise, some equipment may require that parts be assembled into a magazine before they can be fed into the equipment, adding a handling operation.

There are other types of overhead costs that may be of equal importance, such as property taxes, insurance, and power costs. Because of the relatively high capital costs of special automatic equipment and the fact that typically this kind of machine utilizes many electrical devices, there is little justification for ignoring these items, especially when they can be so simply and quickly calculated.

Occupancy expenses (usually prorated in cost accounting systems according to the floor space occupied) may also constitute an element of distinctive importance for special automatic equipment, but this expense element is especially difficult to evaluate since its value is a function of alternative uses of the space freed by the proposed equipment. Although the space released is sometimes as much as one-third, or one-half, or even two-thirds, of that formerly needed, it cannot always be utilized to produce other income, cut costs, or avoid expenditures which otherwise would have been required.

A monetary value should be placed on floor space released when a replacement decision is involved only if (a) the company has a well-merited expectation of growing production requirements which is almost certain to create demands for more space than is now available; (b) the company is planning a continuing series of equipment projects involving a substantial proportion of operations now physically near one another; and (c) the company has established a procedure to coordinate new equipment installation in a manner which will result in a new layout in the portion of the plant affected by the program and will consolidate floor space released. Even then, the value per square foot probably should be different from the cost accounting department's current assessment. If the company is growing so fast that the real alternative, if the space is not saved, is to construct another building, then the value of the occupancy cost elements (building depreciation, fire insurance, real estate taxes, etc.) should be based not upon the actual current costs for the structure occupied, but upon the current, and probably higher, costs of a new building.

If the equipment project involves establishing all new facilities, including a new building, any significant amount of floor space saved should be fairly easily and accurately translatable into reduced occupancy costs.

Because of the difficulties involved in putting a value on floor space saved, in all but exceptional situations the most suitable procedure is simply to compute the square feet of space which will be made available and then to take this into account as a nonquantitative factor. For instance, the management of Vaughn Company, one of the companies interviewed, had adopted a policy of postponing the construction of additional buildings despite the fact that in its main plant it was already cramped for space. They therefore required data on floor space saved (or additional floor space required) to accompany every equipment proposal, and they favored those which saved space over those which did not, even though the basic criteria in their decisions were pay-back and time-adjusted rate of return.

Another type of overhead cost may develop and may turn out to be most important. This is the cost of downtime, or periods when the equipment is not producing salable goods because it is down for adjustments or repairs. In practice, this factor can be taken into account (and almost invariably is) in setting the original performance specifications for the equipment. In other words, if we want an output of 400 pieces per shift and we expect the equipment to be down only 5% of the shift, on the average, then we can set our specifications at 420 pieces per shift. If the equipment meets our specifications when it is operating 95% or more of the shift, production will be at least 400 pieces.[24] Under these circumstances, the cost of up to 5% downtime has been capitalized in our investment estimate. An additional cost arises, however, whenever downtime exceeds our estimate, particularly when it is at overtime rates. Since the

---

[24] To make our point here as simply as possible, we have ignored any other cause of downtime than malfunction or breakdown. Under many circumstances, additional allowances may have to be made (for example, for rest periods) in order to achieve the actual shift output required.

prospects of additional downtime costs are contingent, these potential costs should be considered risks rather than costs. These risks do, however, add an important element of uncertainty to savings estimates for special automatic equipment projects.

Very closely related to downtime are the expected maintenance costs for the equipment. Downtime means a cost in two ways: first in lost production (or, for a given output obtained, increased charges for idle men and equipment); and second in cost for repair of the equipment (parts and labor of skilled personnel). Probably because maintenance costs are difficult to estimate, in only one of the projects surveyed was an estimate of increased maintenance made. This was simply a "guesstimate," based on an estimate of the complexity of the equipment, without any underlying quantitative data. In the absence of quantitative data, until a history of experience has been accumulated and analyzed, the estimate of experienced personnel is much superior to nothing at all.

The largest relevant overhead item, of course, is likely to be the depreciation charge for the special automatic equipment itself. If the total investment figure has been properly determined, the key factor in amortizing the estimated investment becomes the estimate of the useful life of the equipment involved. Because of its importance, we shall shortly devote an entire, separate section to the problem of estimating the useful life of special automatic equipment.

In all the preceding discussion of costs we have ignored the question of whether our estimates of cost should be, explicitly or implicitly, at current prices for materials and labor or whether we should attempt to forecast the average level of prices which will obtain over the estimated primary service life of the equipment. One firm was found in the author's survey which did project future labor rates for pricing man-hours saved, year by year. In this case, the firm had a three-year labor contract which largely insured the prediction three years ahead, but the projection went further and showed increasing wages for five years and then a leveling off. In no other firm was such a practice uncovered, and even in this one, the practice was limited to labor costs. One machine tool manufacturer[25] has advocated a policy of forecasting not only labor but also material costs in estimating savings. The same source advocates taking into account the estimated increase in the cost of the equipment being considered, if the decision were to be deferred, for instance, for five years.

In the present economic context, all such efforts are as a practical matter aimed at taking inflation into account. While there is no question that as a theoretical matter, any changes in the price level will affect the savings actually achieved, it is quite another matter to say that one can project the direction and magnitude of labor, material, and equipment costs for, say five or more years ahead. If one is willing to assume that inflation will continue, then it is quite clear that, all other things being equal, it is much better to undertake a special automatic equipment project (or any investment opportunity) today rather than to wait until next year. Thus it seems preferable to use the relatively much simpler concepts of current costs and to assume that inflation will affect all costs proportionately. It seems better to accept the risk that inflation will not deal with all costs proportionately than to accept the risks of an erroneous forecast of long-run price trends and the quite considerable complications which such an approach implies for practical project analysis.

Importance of Volume Estimate to Savings Estimate

The volume estimate, or the estimate of the average operating rate over the expected life of the equipment,[26] is likely to take on added significance for special automatic equipment. Perhaps the easiest way to demonstrate this is to use an example. Exhibit 18 shows the difference in effect of various degrees of error in the volume estimates for two projects. One is a conventional equipment project with a ten-year life and the other is a special automatic equipment project with but a five-year life. Let us assume that at a forecasted operating rate of 2,000 hours per year, each project is expected to earn a rate of return of 37%, and

---

[25] Jones & Lamson Machine Company. See "Delayed Replacement Wastes Profit," *American Machinist,* April 20, 1959, pp. 130–132.

[26] We are concerned here with the problem of forecasting average utilization, and not with the problem of determining machine capacity. Almost always the maximum output obtainable from special automatic equipment will be significantly greater than the average output actually expected from it.

that all the relevant costs are variable except amortization of the investment (depreciation). If the activity rate turns out to be only 50% of that forecasted, the conventional equipment project would still realize a rate of return of 12%, whereas the special automatic equipment project would yield no return at all. If the forecast error is low but by only 25%, the conventional equipment should earn nearly 25%, compared with 19% for the special automatic equipment. The effects of errors of other magnitudes and directions are tabulated in Exhibit 18 and are presented graphically in Exhibit 19. If the rate of return as based upon

EXHIBIT 18

EFFECT OF CHANGES IN THE VOLUME ESTIMATE
ON THE RATE OF RETURN:
CONVENTIONAL VS. SPECIAL AUTOMATIC EQUIPMENT

	Average Activity Level (Hours per year)	Conventional (10-year life)			Special Automatic (5-year life)		
		Savings	Pay Back	Time Adjusted Rate of Return	Savings	Pay Back	Time Adjusted Rate of Return
+20%	2400	$4,000	2.5	47%	$4,800	2.08	Over 50%
+10%	2200	3,667	2.72	42	4,400	2.275	45
Forecast	2000	3,333	3.0	37	4,000	2.5	37
−10%	1800	3,000	3.33	32	3,600	2.78	30
−20%	1600	2,667	3.75	27	3,200	3.16	22
−30%	1400	2,333	4.29	22	2,800	3.57	15
−40%	1200	2,000	5.00	17	2,400	4.175	8
−50%	1000	1,667	6.00	12	2,000	5.00	0

the original forecast were greater, the difference in effect of any volume forecast error would be more pronounced; and vice versa, if the expected rate of return were lower, the effect of any error in the volume forecast would be more nearly the same.[27]

---

[27] Consideration of taxes in this instance does not affect our conclusions. Although similar calculations on an after-taxes basis show a smaller absolute change in the rate of return for any given percentage error in the forecast of savings, for special equipment the time-adjusted rate of return is affected more than it is in the case of the conventional one, and relatively by just as much more as in the before-taxes calculation.

EXHIBIT 19

EFFECT OF VARIATION IN AVERAGE ACTIVITY RATE ON
THE TIME-ADJUSTED RATE OF RETURN:
CONVENTIONAL VS. SPECIAL AUTOMATIC EQUIPMENT

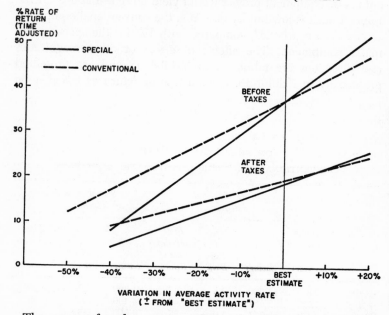

VARIATION IN AVERAGE ACTIVITY RATE
(± FROM "BEST ESTIMATE")

The reason for the greater effect of volume errors on the special automatic equipment project lies in the assumed shorter life — 5 years compared with 10. Since each project involves an investment of $10,000, the annual depreciation figures (on a straight-line basis) would be $2,000 and $1,000 respectively. These charges are fixed, meaning that they will not be changed in total if the actual volume turns out to be either greater or less than the forecast. In both cases the effect on savings will be more than proportional to the volume change, but it will be greater in the case of the shorter-lived equipment because the depreciation charges are higher in proportion to the savings: $2,000 depreciation and $4,000 savings (before depreciation), or a ratio of 50%; compared with $1,000 depreciation and $3,333 savings, or a ratio of 33%. The higher proportion of fixed cost associated with the special automatic equipment serves to increase the loss if the forecast proves to be too high and also to increase the profit if the forecast proves to be too low.

We have assumed that the other costs from which the savings figure is calculated were all variable (that is, that they rise or fall in direct proportion to the volume of activity). In fact, some of the components, especially any overhead elements in the savings (such as taxes and insurance), may be fixed, too, and therefore affect the estimate of total savings in a similar way. We shall not argue here whether such other fixed costs are more likely to accompany special automatic than conventional equipment, but simply observe that it would seem wise to determine them, at least approximately, for each individual project.

It must be admitted that some special automatic equipment projects may involve relatively long-lived equipment. When that is true, there is no longer any special (as distinct from general) relevance of the volume estimate. When the life of the special equipment is short, however, as in a high proportion of such projects, the acquirer should at least be fully conscious of the magnitude of the new depreciation charges which must be absorbed and the probability that actual savings will be much more sensitive to volume changes.

With a few exceptions, the field work disclosed little general appreciation of the importance of the volume estimate used. Indeed, the practice was widespread of using the plant's current operating rate as, or instead of, a forecast. A typical pattern in computing direct labor savings was to estimate the work force required by the proposed equipment, to price the cost of this labor on an annual basis, explicitly or implicitly assuming current production rates, and to compute savings by comparing the resulting cost with the current payroll for the method currently employed. The estimated direct labor savings so calculated were simply those which might be achieved at the current rate of output if the proposed process of manufacturing were used instead of the existing method. The relevant estimate of direct labor savings should be the savings which are likely to be achieved annually, on the average, over the expected primary service life of the equipment.

In periods of generally good business conditions, the effect of using the current production rate instead of a forecast is likely to be to predict savings estimates more favorable than are justified. Conversely, when general business conditions are poor, savings estimates are likely to be too low. Furthermore, the uncritical use of the current production rate may also mean that no consideration is being given to the very important question of probable obsolescence of the product design. Only in an unusual combination of circumstances would the current production rate be the same as a true forecast which took these factors into account.[28]

A large risk must inevitably accompany any estimate of future volume, but two correctives can and should be applied. First, make the forecast, as reliably as possible, over the whole period of primary service life; and second, consider the probable limits of error and their implication for each project. Each project can be analyzed using not only a "best estimate" of average volume, but also a "high" estimate and a "low" estimate. Explicit, standard definitions of these terms should be drawn up for each product the plant makes. As in our analysis of the probable range of the estimated investment figure, one may employ probability estimates for varying activity levels to compute a single "most probable" volume estimate. Using such a single estimate has the merit of simplicity, and avoids the risk of many figures obscuring important factors. It is therefore a preferable although less discriminating analytical device.

If the expected primary service life is very short, it may be prudent to begin with a forecast of volume year by year because the cyclical fluctuations may not average out over the life of the equipment. If the variations are quite significant, then savings can be estimated year by year; otherwise, the results of the year-by-year forecast should be averaged to get a "best estimate." The separate treatment for each year complicates the

---

[28] A serious consequence of using the current production rate as a forecast may be that it leads to a pronounced fluctuation in the number of projects originated. It will clearly be much easier to justify projects when the current operating rate is high, and difficult to justify many when the current operating rate is a low one. And such fluctuations in turn may generate overexpansion of the special automatic equipment group, followed by substantial cut-backs which in part will be shortsighted. This sequence of events is almost precisely what happened in one company visited during the research for this study.

time-adjusted rate of return calculation[29] and should be avoided as a general rule. For large projects, involving, say, $100,000 or more, the additional effort may well be justified when unusual variations in volume from year to year are forecast.

IV

The total savings which a project may realize are a function not only of its average annual savings but also of the number of years over which such annual average savings are realized. This section will be devoted to the problems raised by the necessity for estimating this time span, or primary service life. It will also deal with the topic of salvage values at the end of the primary service life, values which may be applicable for some special automatic equipment projects now and perhaps for more such projects in the future.

Estimated Primary Service Life

A principal characteristic of special automatic equipment is its relatively short primary service life. We have already described how this fact increases the degree of precision we need to achieve in making estimates of total investment and probable annual savings. In addition, there is considerable uncertainty attached to determining when its primary service life will end.

The cause for most of that uncertainty (as well as for the short life) is related to the fact that the equipment has been tailored to the characteristics of one or more parts of a single subassembly, and when the design of that part or assembly is changed, the processing equipment may become obsolete. In Chapter VII we sought to find ways of minimizing the impact of such changes and concluded that useful steps included standardizing product designs, exploring for some flexibility in the design of special automatic equipment so that it might well be adapted to minor design changes inexpensively, and adopting module components so that most of the machine elements could be economically

---

[29] For examples in which yearly figures differ significantly from the annual average, see John G. McLean, "How to Evaluate New Capital Investments," *Harvard Business Review*, November–December 1958, pp. 65–68. For detailed explanation and illustrations of the calculations involved, see Ray I. Reul, "Profitability Index for Investments," *Harvard Business Review*, July–August 1957, pp. 116–132.

re-used after a major product change made the equipment obsolete.

Such actions will reduce the impact of product design changes a great deal, but even after they have done so there probably will remain considerable risk of obsolescence due to unpredictable product design changes.[30]   There are a variety of forces at work generating frequent and not always predictable product design changes in many firms and especially in those plants that have enough sales volume of one product to merit their considering special automatic equipment in place of conventional equipment. A part, an assembly, or the whole end-item may be changed to correct defects discovered in a new model.   Or, any of these types of design changes may be made to reduce the over-all cost of the end-item.   Again, a design change may be desirable simply to improve the technical performance of the end-item with the objective of catching up with, or getting ahead of, one's competitors.   Finally, a design change may be one of styling, originated, as in the familiar case of automobile bodies, primarily to stimulate consumer demand and to meet or surpass competition.   To the extent that consumer products are involved, radical redesign of the end-item "package" and at least a substantial proportion of its component assemblies seems to be becoming more frequent, say, every two to eight years, rather than every twelve to twenty years.[31]   Indeed, the trend seems to be toward steadily shorter

[30] For an example in which such forecasting failed to identify an important type of change in the design of a product, see Bright, p. 213.

[31] One company visited during the field work for this research, the Trumbull Company, manufactured a domestic electrical appliance which had the following record of model changes. A completely redesigned end-item was introduced in 1948. In 1951 this model was "face-lifted," and a dozen or more parts were significantly changed in design.   Within a year thereafter, Trumbull made a few additional changes in this design.   At the time of our visit in 1956 a completely new model (not simply a "face-lifting" operation) was again under way.   A second product manufactured by Trumbull underwent major design changes in 1947, 1953, and 1955 (the last substantially a "face-lifting" undertaking).   In each case, the primary impetus for making model changes was stimulation of consumer demand and keeping up with competitors.

The automotive industry has furnished many examples of rapid design changes in recent years, many of which were not forecast.   One source has estimated that over a recent three-year period, presumably 1954–1956, product design changes in that industry required the expenditure of $240,-000,000 to rework facilities and purchase new machines.   See J. F. Randall, "Planning For Reduced Obsolescence."

product design lives under the pressure of both marketing factors (such as demand stimulation or competition) and technological advances. And this trend seems to be more and more evident for many industrial products, as well.

The same kinds of product design changes are likely to have a much smaller effect on conventional equipment. If the product is reasonably complex and one drilling operation is suddenly no longer required, there are likely to exist, or to materialize shortly, some other drilling operations which that conventional drill press could perform efficiently, without incurring many adaptation costs. Likewise, a hand-type power screwdriver for assembly work can easily be used elsewhere in the assembly department if the operation on which it has been used is eliminated. If within a given plant there is no long-run demand for idle conventional equipment, it is likely to have a wide range of alternative uses in other plants and therefore to have a relatively high resale value. Because of the greater likelihood of alternative uses of the equipment, either within a given plant or in many other plants, conventional equipment is much less likely to be rendered obsolete by a change in product design.

It is true that some special automatic equipment observed had a history of relatively long service life. In a few plants visited, special automatic equipment well over 10 years old was observed operating at capacity. Without digressing too far, it might be observed that some of these cases seemed to be related to having involved a relatively simple product (end-item) composed of, say, 10 parts or less; in others it represented the effect of a policy decision that made equipment adaptability a criterion for introducing a design change; and in a few it seemed to reflect simply a lack of effort to introduce changes which should have been made. In any event, our concern here is not to argue that there are no exceptions — for there may be a goodly number of them — but to establish the proposition that product design changes, some of which will be of sufficient proportions to cause obsolescence of special automatic equipment, are very likely to occur often and at uncertain times.

When the equipment's estimated primary service life is short, uncertainty takes on added significance, especially as to the impact of premature obsolescence. Consider the difference in effect of premature obsolescence on two projects with projected service lives of five years and ten years, respectively, each of which originally promised to yield a time-adjusted rate of return of 37%. If the actual life in each case turns out to be, say 20% *less* than the best estimate — that is, four years for the one and eight years for the other — the rate of return of the long-lived equipment would drop from 37% to 35%. The rate of return for the short-lived equipment, however, would drop from 37% to 28%, or a decline of 9% rather than 2%.

Of special note is the fact that the decline would be proportionately greater as the expected rate of return grows smaller. For instance, in the cases of two similar projects promising only 20% rates of return, the short-lived project's rate of return would fall from 20% to 11% while that of the long-lived equipment would decline only from 20% to 17%. When we take into account income taxes, both short- and long-lived projects decline somewhat less precipitously but the short-lived project still loses attractiveness at a much more rapid rate than the long-lived equipment as the primary service life is foreshortened. Exhibit 20 presents graphically the data on the 37% best estimate examples.

Overages cannot be counted on to balance shortages in the long run, even with several projects of similar lives and sizes. As long as we say (as we do in time-adjusted calculations) that the present worth of a dollar of cash flow to be realized in the near future is larger than the present worth of a dollar of cash flow to be realized several years later, each dollar of forecasted savings which does not materialize because of foreshortened life will weigh more heavily than each dollar of savings which accrues because of an unexpectedly long-lived project. Averaging could only be expected if service life estimates were deliberately understated to assure that there would be a majority of cases in which the actual service life exceeded the estimate.

The analytical process should therefore incorporate some method of taking into account the special risks which uncertainty of primary service life poses for special automatic equipment projects. Once more, there is a possibility of using probability estimates of various lives (which was suggested first in the case of the estimated investment figure). To do this, a separate probability schedule for each project would be needed, and it presumably would be based on historical experience, when available, and on subjective appraisal by informed engineers.

Exhibit 21 applies such an approach to the same two examples we have used before. This procedure is clumsy, however, and under many circumstances the final adjustment in the rate of

EXHIBIT 20

EFFECT OF DEVIATION FROM ESTIMATED LIFE ON
THE PERCENTAGE RATE OF RETURN:
CONVENTIONAL VS. SPECIAL AUTOMATIC EQUIPMENT

("Best Estimate" of Rate of Return Before Taxes = 37%
in Both Cases)

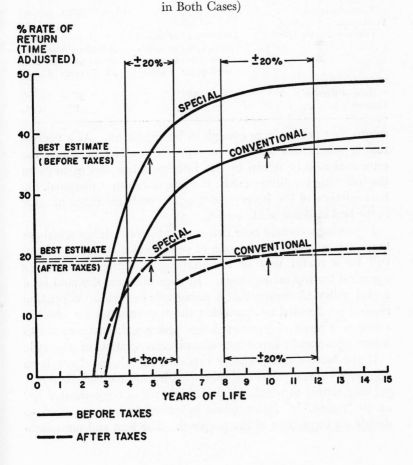

EXHIBIT 21

EFFECT OF UNCERTAINTY OF ESTIMATED PRIMARY SERVICE LIFE
ON THE RATE OF RETURN:
CONVENTIONAL VS. SPECIAL AUTOMATIC EQUIPMENT

	Special	*Conventional*
Investment	$10,000	$10,000
Annual Savings		
Before Depreciation	4,000	3,333
Primary Service Life—		
"Best Estimate"	5 years	10 years
Pay-back	2.5 years	3.0 years
Time Adjusted		
Rate of Return	37%	37%
Probability Estimate of		
Primary Service Life	1.0—4 years or more	1.0— 8 years or more
	.5—5 years or more	.8—10 years or more
	.1—6 years or more	.3—12 years or more
	.0—7 years or more	.0—13 years or more
"Risk-Weighted"		
Rate of Return	33%	37%
Change	−4%	0%

return may not be large enough to be significant. As a general rule it would not seem to be worth the effort to adjust the estimated rate of return in this fashion unless one or more of the following conditions exists: the rate of return is marginal, the best estimate of life is very short, or the probable range of error in the best estimate of life is wide.

In passing we might note that even if the probability schedules are not used to adjust the rate of return calculations, they may still be a useful way of summarizing the project engineer's appraisal for top management. In their absence, it would be a useful policy to require that a paragraph in each appropriation request be devoted to appraising the opportunities for obsolescence as a result of product design changes, in order to try to insure appropriate investigation and consideration of this risk.

If the facts about probable exposure to this risk have been adequately investigated and described by any method, then it is possible simply to weigh the probable error in the estimated life as an "intangible" factor when judgment is being applied to decide on disposition of the proposal. The best and most complete estimate of useful life, even one expressed in the form of probability estimates, is still far from being either precise or completely unbiased, and such direct application of pure judgment has the virtue of simplicity.

Finally, the risks associated with the obsolescence of product design can be recognized simply by using a higher cut-off figure for all special automatic equipment projects. For instance, the cut-off rate of return might be set arbitrarily, say, 5% higher, or at 30% when the criterion for conventional equipment stands at 25%. Additional refinements are possible, such as requiring a rate of return of 35% on all special equipment projects with an estimated life of, say, five years or less. Such modification of cut-off rates, while arbitrary and lacking the discrimination theoretically possible with a probability distribution, is an especially convenient device to make minor adjustments for one or more risks, each of which is not large enough to merit more refined analysis.

Salvage Value

In all our analyses, including the preceding treatment of estimated primary service life, we have assumed that the proposed equipment, whether it be special automatic or conventional, would (a) have no salvage value at the end of its primary service life and (b) decrease in value on a straight-line basis (that is to say, in equal annual amounts) over the span of its estimated life. Thus a $10,000 investment made initially to acquire a piece of special automatic equipment with a five-year life would decrease in value to $8,000 at the end of the first year of operation; then, to $6,000, to $4,000, to $2,000 and finally, at the end of its estimated primary service life of five years, to a zero value.

Whether a piece of equipment will have any appreciable salvage value in excess of the removal and disposition costs at the end of its primary service life depends upon the rate at which the equipment loses value, taking into account both physical depreciation and technological obsolescence, and how long the primary service application lasts. The uses to which much conventional equipment is put are so general that there is not a great chance of its being retired before it loses all or substantially all value. Thus, the assumption of a zero salvage value at the end of its long estimated life fits the situation so closely that taking discrepancies into account would bring about only negligible changes in most cases.

This assumption will often be appropriate, too, for much special automatic equipment irrespective of its age because such equipment has no appreciable value in the used machinery market even though it is by no means worn out. There was, at the time of our field work, only a negligible market in special equipment of this type among used machinery dealers. One source indicated that an occasional purchase of such equipment by a used machinery dealer was likely to be a speculative flyer entailing a high risk of never being able to sell the equipment. As a result, it was reported, only nominal prices could be realized by firms which wanted to dispose of such equipment. This condition could change. We noted in Chapter VII evidence of a recent trend toward more retooling for a second application, retooling both of equipment built of module components and of semistandard equipment manufactured by established builder-vendors. If large buyers of this kind of equipment continue to express an interest in rebuilding, or in having vendors rebuild, this kind of equipment, it is conceivable that a market will ultimately develop. Even if it does not, the opportunity for a second use internally of equipment designed of module components would make it desirable to recognize salvage values in analyzing some projects.

One way to recognize any significant salvage value which may remain after termination of the primary application is to deduct its present worth from the gross investment figure and to use the resulting net investment figure in subsequent analysis. To compute this present worth of the salvage value, some capitalization rate is required. Any figure suggested for this purpose will not be easy to defend, but the cut-off or minimum demanded rate of return for investment in equipment is at least a good first approximation.[32] As an illustration, let us assume that the

[32] Another way of looking at the matter avoids calculating a "present worth" for the salvage value, thereby resolving the problem of what capitalization rate to use, but it requires other assumptions to be made. This method considers the primary service life to extend over more than one ap-

conventional piece of equipment costing $10,000 which we have been using in other examples is expected to have a resale value of $2,500 at the end of its ten-year primary service life (after deducting removal and other related costs). If the company's cut-off rate of return were 25%, an adjusted investment figure for useful analysis could be computed in this way:

Net Investment (before salvage) $10,000

Less:
    Present Worth of Salvable
    Value at the End of Ten Years
    $2,500 × (.119)   298

Adjusted Net Investment for
    Analytical Purposes $ 9,702

The foregoing example demonstrates very well how little effect any residual value will have on a long-lived project when high cut-off rates are involved. On the net adjusted basis of an investment of $9,702, the rate of return rises only from 37% to 38%. Even if one-half of the original outlay were estimated to be salvable at the end of this project's ten-year life, the rate of return would rise only to 40%. When projects of this sort are involved, and granting the difficulty of even approximately forecasting salvage values that far in the future, it may be quite appropriate to ignore salvage values and assume they are always zero.

When short-lived projects are involved, however, as is likely to be the case with much special automatic equipment, the influence of remaining salvage values becomes greater. Taking our perennial special automatic equipment project with a five-year estimated life, for instance, a salvage value of $2,000 (that is, 20% of the original investment of $10,000) would raise the rate of return from 37% to 42%, and a salvage value of $4,000 would raise the rate of return from 37% to 45%. For a shorter-lived

---

plication, so that a zero salvage value becomes realistic, and calls for suitable assumptions to be made concerning the cost of retooling for the second application and the level of savings to be realized therefrom. For most cases such assumptions are likely to be difficult to make, and this approach is therefore likely to be much less generally applicable than the one described above.

project, the effect of salvage values is even more impressive. If we start with a project having only a three-year estimated life, but promising a 37% rate of return, we find that a salvage value of only 10% (that is, $1,000 of an original investment of $10,000) will raise the rate of return to 55%.

A relatively low salvage value has been assumed in the foregoing examples. This is considered appropriate because the engineering, controls, and special tools and fixtures required combine to make retooling rather costly. During my field work, I was given access to invoices for three machines, invoices which broke down the price of the equipment into the portion charged for standard elements, for special tools, and for electrical controls. The standard components, which are probably all one might expect to be able to re-use in most cases, ranged from 32% to 47% of the total invoice. A description has already been given of a recent rebuilding project costing about $300,000 which involved a transfer machine whose original cost was $750,000.[33] The salvage value, therefore, could be considered to be about 57% of the original cost. In this case, however, it had been possible to use the basic equipment at its old location, avoiding new foundation and installation costs. More important, perhaps, the rebuilding left the hydraulic, pneumatic, coolant, and electrical services undisturbed, conditions which could hardly be expected to obtain very often. Sometimes there may be no opportunity to use some basic equipment elements in a second application. Indeed, only a fairly large company with a relatively large, continuing program of acquiring special automatic equipment may expect to find a suitable second application. Furthermore, the nature and extent of the retooling required may vary significantly from project to project and, perhaps, from plant to plant.

To summarize, taking account of the salvage value will be important if:

(1) The expected primary service life is short, say five years or less;

(2) The remaining value is a significant fraction of the first investment (or creates a major reduction in the investment needed to effect a second application); and

---

[33] J. F. Randall, "Planning for Reduced Obsolescence."

(3) There is a high probability that a suitable second application will develop for the equipment at the end of its first term of service.

If there is an active market for used equipment of the type under consideration, then it is no longer necessary to foresee a second application in the plant concerned.

Let us examine now the way in which the equipment depreciates over its service life. The way depreciation is recorded is important in its effect on income taxes. We are concerned here, however, with the rate at which economic value disappears, which is almost always going to be different from the rate at which depreciation is accrued on the books. Any salvage value which can be recovered from time to time is important because it reduces the loss to which any investment in equipment will be exposed if the primary service life turns out to be unexpectedly short.

What would be most useful for analytical purposes is a schedule of salvage values at the end of every year during the estimated service life of the equipment. For special automatic equipment the salvage value is very likely to drop to zero, or close to it, the very day the equipment first operates, because it is likely to have no alternative use within the buyer's plant and it is likely to have no alternative use outside the buyer's plant.[34] Furthermore, the net expenditures for special automatic equipment, as we have seen, are likely to include a smaller proportion of hardware costs and a larger proportion of intangibles, such as project development and debugging costs. Nothing is likely to be salvaged from the intangibles if the primary service life is cut short, and it will cost money to adapt the hardware to another use, if, indeed, such adaptation is economical. Earlier we pointed out that conventional equipment is often likely to have

---

[34] One exception encountered in several cases during the writer's field work was the opportunity to utilize special automatic equipment, obsolete in terms of the competitive situation within the United States, in foreign manufacturing establishments, where they still possessed considerable economic value because of a different economic environment. In Japan, for instance, where the annual cost of an operator may be $1,200 compared with $4,500 in the United States, equipment like this might have material value, depending, of course, on the product involved and its suitability for foreign markets.

a secondary use within a given plant and, if not, then a high probability of having a resale value because it is suitable, without much adaptation cost, for use by other manufacturing establishments. Therefore, even if in a given situation the odds of becoming wholly obsolete in the early years of life were the same for both types of equipment, the amount of the loss, if the potential risk became an actuality, would usually be substantially greater for the special automatic equipment project than for the conventional equipment project.

EXHIBIT 22

POTENTIAL LOSS AT THE END OF EACH YEAR FROM
FORESHORTENED PROJECT LIFE:
CONVENTIONAL VS. SPECIAL AUTOMATIC EQUIPMENT

	Cumulative Savings (before deducting depreciation)	Estimated Salvage	Total Recovered by End of Each Year	Excess (Deficit) over Original $10,000 Investment, End of Each Year
	(in thousands of dollars)			
Conventional				
Year: 1	$ 3.3	$8.0	$11.3	$ 1.3
2	6.7	6.0	12.7	2.7
3	10.0	5.0	15.0	5.0
4	13.3	4.5	17.8	7.8
5	16.7	4.0	20.7	10.7
6	20.0	3.5	23.5	13.5
7	23.3	3.0	26.3	16.3
8	26.7	2.0	28.7	18.7
9	30.0	1.0	31.0	21.0
10	33.3	0.0	33.3	23.3
Special Automatic				
Year: 1	$ 4.0	$1.0	$ 5.0	$ (5.0)
2	8.0	0	8.0	(2.0)
3	12.0	0	12.0	2.0
4	16.0	0	16.0	6.0
5	20.0	0	20.0	10.0

Exhibit 22 illustrates the argument of the preceding paragraph quantitatively. It is based on our two familiar examples of special automatic and conventional equipment projects, each involving an investment of $10,000 and an estimated rate of return of 37% over the estimated lives of five and ten years, respectively. We have added one further set of arbitrary but reasonable assumptions, namely, estimated salvage values for the equipment for every year of its estimated life. If the service life of the equipment actually turns out to be drastically less than anticipated, it is evident that the special automatic equipment project would suffer much more than the other.

We have already suggested at the end of the section on estimated primary service life some analytical procedures for taking into account the additional risk of loss existing toward the end of the service life of special automatic equipment. In that section, it will be recalled that we were concerned with the risk that the service life might be only 80% of the original estimate. But what further provision, if any, should be made to take account of the additional risk that the equipment might have a primary service life of only 25% of the original estimate? In that event, there almost certainly will be a much more substantial loss than if conventional equipment were involved. If the known risk of obsolescence in the early years of an equipment's estimate of life is considerable, as it sometimes may be, most company managements will probably decide not to undertake the project at all. Even if the profit possibilities of the project were distinctly better than average, any other policy would be rational only if several independent projects of like size, involving similar risks of early loss and also chances of extra-high profits were also undertaken. Conditions permitting such a program, however, are likely to be quite rare. As a practical matter, then, this leaves only the problem of giving effect to a small risk of loss in the early years of estimated life. Instead of attempting to discriminate between individual projects — which is, in fact, not likely to be possible when we are dealing only with small degrees of risk — a sensible approach would seem to be to recognize the hazard on the average, by raising slightly our minimum cut-off criteria for special automatic equipment proposals.

V

Before concluding, it seems appropriate to comment on three related topics. The first, developing alternative methods of accomplishing a given project, is surely a key element in the long-run success of any program involving special automatic equipment. The other two are perhaps of lesser importance, but still important: the use of criteria other than rate of return on investment to select projects, and the fixing of organizational responsibility for analysis of project proposals.

Alternatives

It will be useful to distinguish two kinds of alternatives. The first comprises those alternatives which accomplish the single objective in question (that is, automatically forming a specific part or assembling a specific set of parts) by using a substantially different process from the original proposal. The second type of alternative involves relaxing the explicit or assumed objective of fully automatic processing in favor of some combination of manual and automatic processing.

EXHIBIT 23

ALTERNATIVE METHODS OF MANUFACTURING A MACHINE PART
COMPARATIVE COSTS, INVESTMENTS, AND SAVINGS
PORTER COMPANY

	Present Method	*Alternative Method A*	*Alternative Method B*
Direct Labor	$ .075	$ .041	$ .041
Material	1.366	1.340	1.270
Overhead	—	(no change)	(no change)
Total	$1.441	$1.381	$1.311

Estimated Life: 6 years   Annual Average Volume: 2,000,000 units

	Present Method	*Alternative Method A*	*Alternative Method B*
Average Annual Savings	—	$12,000	$26,000
Investment Required	—	$34,000	$65,000
Pay-off Period	—	2.83 years	2.50 years
Rate of Return	—	33%	40%
Incremental Savings	—	—	$14,000
Incremental Investment	—	—	$31,000
Pay-off Period, Incremental Investment	—	—	2.21 years
Incremental Rate of Return	—	—	50%

The following examples illustrate each type of alternative. The first example concerns the practice of the Porter Company, the only company encountered which fully and systematically developed cost and investment data for several alternative methods of accomplishing a single project objective. For one of Porter's projects, for instance, five alternative methods of manufacturing a machine part were developed, involving not only different manufacturing methods but also different product designs, all equally acceptable with respect to performance. Exhibit 23 sets forth the cost data and the analysis thereof made by Porter's personnel for another, simpler project. Compared with existing methods, Alternative Method A looks quite attractive. However, by developing Method B (which in this case involved the same basic processing equipment) the average rate of return was raised from 33% to 40%. Furthermore, the incremental analysis at the bottom of Exhibit 23 is a measure of the attractiveness of the incremental investment needed in this case to adopt Method B — the additional $31,000 of investment promises a rate of return of 50%.

Exhibit 24 shows another example, taken from published sources, of the range of alternatives which may be explored in connection with a single project. Each of the combination of machines shown apparently possesses at least the minimum capacity required, but they vary significantly in the total investment required as well as in the number of operators required. In this instance layout H would require as few operators (three) as any alternative, and at the same time it calls for the least investment. While a narrow financial analysis alone cannot be the basis for choosing among such alternatives as these, it certainly must weigh heavily in instances in which the nonquantitative factors — such as delivery promised, reliability of builder, reliability of equipment design, and flexibility of equipment in the event of re-use — are much the same.

The best alternative developed may in fact be the one requiring the least total investment, and the field work developed several cases in which this was so. At least as frequently, however, lower cost seemed to be accompanied by higher investment requirements. In such cases the marginal or incremental analysis set forth in Exhibit 23 is a useful device to insure that not only

EXHIBIT 24

Present Equipment Layout Compared with Eight Alternative Layouts

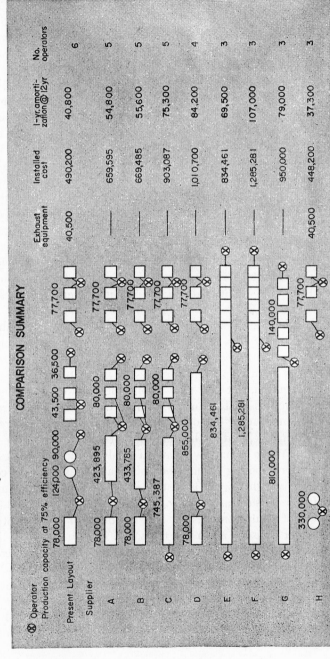

Source: W. C. Allen and T. Daly, "The Westinghouse Investment Program: Planned Facilities with Built-in Profits," *American Machinist*, December 16, 1957, p. 140. (Reproduced by permission; © McGraw-Hill Publishing Company, Inc.).

the total investment but also the incremental investment meets the minimum criteria established by a particular company. If the circumstances of Method B had been different, for instance, and the additional investment required promised an incremental rate of return of only 10% or 12%, it might well be difficult to justify its adoption.

To illustrate our second type of alternative, consider one project arising in the Zola Company. A proposal, which was estimated to need an investment of $1,450,000, was made to acquire an equipment system for processing a machine part successively through some 15 operations involving 12 machines. Savings were computed at $300,000 per year. Since the estimated life of the system was set at 10 years, the pay-back period was about 3 years and the estimated rate of return was about 18%. By acquiring only 3 of the 12 machines at an outlay of about $275,000, however, about $145,000 of the savings could be achieved, for a pay-back period of about 1.9 years and a rate of return of about 65%. The second stage would then involve an additional outlay of $1,175,000 to achieve additional savings of $155,000. For this incremental investment, the pay-back period would be 7.6 years, or about a 6% rate of return — hardly an attractive investment for most firms today.[35]

An even more striking alternative was developed in another firm, the Royce Company. This alternative took the form of buying a part from a vendor instead of manufacturing it on special automatic equipment. The Royce management began by considering buying as a temporary expediency when it developed that the special equipment involved could not be delivered soon enough to meet a pressing production deadline. Five special machine tool builders had presented proposals for the special automatic equipment involved. One of these proposals, to cost $240,000 (including tooling), had been selected and an order had been placed with the vendor who originated it. Producing the part involved several operations, which on this

---

[35] An almost identical situation is described in connection with manufacturing press parts by Raymond G. Rusing in "Will Automation Pay?", *Tool Engineer*, June 1957, pp. 109–115. By *not* providing automatic transfer facilities at one stage, estimated savings of $1,600 were lost, but an expenditure of nearly $55,000 was avoided.

special automatic equipment would cost $.97 per part. Because the best delivery quoted was three months late for Royce's requirements, Royce's management then obtained bids for making a three months' supply of the part from four job shops regularly doing this kind of work. As had been expected, all bids ranged upwards from $1.60 — with one exception, which was a bid for $.99 per piece plus $20,000 for special tools. The Royce management immediately investigated to make certain that no mistake was involved and found there had been none. The low bidder was a small shop, with low overhead and the advantage of being on a piece-rate basis. A principal element in the owner's ability to quote such a low price, however, was use of ingenious tooling of standard equipment for multiple cuts, yet still holding the close tolerances involved.[36] Royce's management tooled up a second source (quoting $1.67 each plus tooling) just for safety's sake, but from the start deliveries of the $.99 bidder were fully satisfactory in quality and quantity. Needless to say, the special equipment order was soon cancelled along with the contract with the second source.

One aspect of developing alternatives is finding appropriate combinations of hand and automatic elements for each technical approach. In doing a thorough job, it is worthwhile to consider carefully the relation of the operator to the design of the equipment. Whenever an operator is required to tend a piece of special automatic equipment full time, it is wise to reconsider the basic design of the machine from the standpoint of fully utilizing the operator's time by having him perform some operations, such as loading, which in his absence could be done automatically.[37] Perhaps his spare time can be utilized in lieu of certain expensive mechanisms or perhaps in lieu of mechanisms which are expected to be not too reliable; the resulting minimization of downtime may be the most profitable use of his time in some cases. We encountered one illustration of this kind of op-

---

[36] For an illustrated description of similar ingenuity, see John P. Wright, "Screw Machine Parts From a Drillpress? Yes!", *American Machinist,* April 7, 1958, pp. 92–97.

[37] On this point, see William Bayley, commenting in a letter on an article, *Mechanical Engineering,* February 1958, p. 112. To the same effect, see also comment by L. C. Lander in the same place, p. 113.

portunity in our field work. In this case, the principle was discovered to be applicable after the project was completed. The relevant part of this project concerned the development of a rather expensive automatic feed-back control mechanism for a grinding operation. In the end it was clear that an operator, who was required in any event, had more than enough time to check and adjust the grinding wheel periodically for wheel wear so that no real savings were derived from the feed-back control.

The whole matter of developing alternatives is an intriguing one and, in the author's opinion, a very crucial one. It is in this area in particular that the project engineer's creativeness may have the greatest payoff, greater even than in the technical machine design itself. There is no doubt that alternatives should be thoroughly explored before an investment choice is made final.[38] At the time and at the level at which prospect proposals are finally approved and disapproved, about all that can be done is to determine whether a thorough exploration of reasonable possibilities has preceded the final proposal. It is important, too, that personnel at the working level understand just what is expected of them in this respect. The real spade work must be done at the level of the project engineers and, in some degree, at the level of their supervisor.

Exhibits 25 and 26 show analytical forms used by one company which require both that alternatives be thoroughly explored and that the analysis of these alternatives (Exhibit 26) be made in terms of the incremental analysis we favor. These exhibits also provide for another element in a truly rigorous analysis of this kind of project: a calculation of savings in comparison with the cost picture which would obtain if the present method were made as efficient as possible, making relatively minor changes to accomplish this result.

In any event, a firm's objective should be the development of a process for most economically manufacturing a given part or product. This goal may be attained by acquiring special automatic equipment employing the process now in use, by acquiring

---

[38] On the development of alternatives on the part of the project engineer, see W. P. Smith, "Creative Production Engineering," *Automation,* February 1957, pp. 133–138.

EXHIBIT 25

Economic Comparison of Manufacturing Methods

Process Development Section

PRODUCTION DATA	
Net Hourly Production Requirement	1100
Shifts per day	2
Daily Production Requirement	17,600

Project __Adjustable Tie Rod Socket Assembly__ No. __5600__

Division __Motor Car__

Project Engineer __John Jones__ Date __June 1956__

Index Volume (Annual) __4,065,600__

Average Labor Cost __$2.40/Hour__

MANUFACTURING COST	Existing Method	*Best Manual Method	Alternate Plan 1	Alternate Plan 2	Alternate Plan 3	Alternate Plan 4	Alternate Plan 5
Net Hourly Production	950	1100	1100	1100	1100		
Direct Material (If affected)	—	—	—	—	—		
Direct Labor Operators	16	13	8	6	5		
Hours/Unit	.0168	.0118	.0073	.0055	.0045		
$/Unit	$.0403	$.0283	$.0175	$.0132	$.0108		
Manufacturing Expense †Indirect Labor Operators	—	—	—	—	—		
Hours/Unit							
$/Unit							
Maintenance Operators	—	—	1/2	1/2	1		
Hours/Unit			.00045	.00045	.0009		
$/Unit			$.0011	$.0011	$.0022		
‡———— Hours/Unit	—	—	—	—	—		
$/Unit							
Total Cost $ per Unit	$.0403	$.0283	$.0186	$.0143	$.0130		
Total Cost Index Volume	$163,844	$115,056	$75,620	$58,138	$52,853		
Annual Improvement Potential	← $48,788	Debit Existing Method	$39,436	$56,918	$62,203		

(Annual Improvement Potential is based on "Best" manual method

* "Best" manual method is the improvement that can be made with existing facilities.
† Labor not included on standard routing such as; inspection, material handling, tool setup, etc.
‡ Add items that affect the cost comparison such as; scrap, expense tools, operating supplies, etc.

EXHIBIT 25 (CONTINUED)

ESTIMATED IMPROVE-MENT COST	Best Manual Method	Alternate Plan 1	Alternate Plan 2	Alternate Plan 3	Alternate Plan 4	Alternate Plan 5
Capital Expenditure (Details not affected by model change)		176,000	299,000	356,000		
Special Tooling Expenditure (Details affected by model change)		22,000	19,000	33,000		
Installation Cost		4,000	6,000	9,000		
TOTAL IMPROVEMENT COST		202,000	324,000	398,000		

AMORTIZATION PERIOD

(Improvement Cost divided by Savings Potential)	—	5.1 yrs.	5.7 yrs.	6.4 yrs.		

IN-PROCESS INVENTORY

20,000	18,850	14,000	13,000	4,000	

	EFFECT ON:	PRODUCT OR QUALITY	MACHINE RELIABILITY– OR FLEXIBILITY	FLOOR SPACE
Flexibility		Good	Excel.	Good	Good	Poor	

SOURCE: General Motors Corporation.

special automatic equipment employing another process, or by acquiring equipment which is not fully automatic.[39]

The writer is impressed with the necessity for a broad-gauged approach to each individual project, and the likely benefits of a thorough analysis of costs and investments of reasonable alternatives before settling on one. We cannot expect, of course, to find the "one best method" on very many occasions but we may reasonably expect to hit close to it consistently. Expressed negatively, the goal is to avoid making a substantial investment in a piece of equipment only to discover it is not the third or fourth best alternative but the tenth or twelfth best.

Criteria Other Than Rate of Return

Up to this point we have predicated our discussion upon the proposition that the choice among possible projects will be

[39] For a succinct statement of this goal, see G. R. Fitzgerald, "Mechanical Assembly Equipment," The American Society of Mechanical Engineers, Paper No. 56-A-83, presented November 25–30, 1956, before the Management Division of the ASME.

EXHIBIT 26

ECONOMIC COMPARISON RECAP

Process Development Section

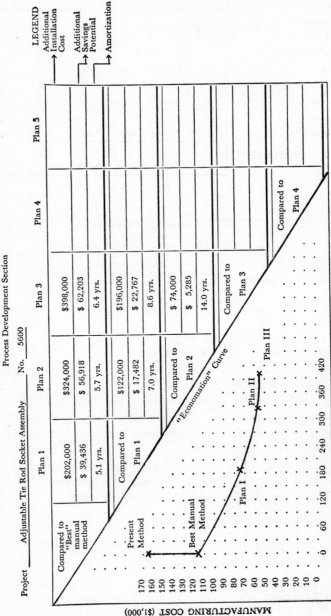

REMARKS Plan I is recommended for action. Plan II requires an additional investment of $122,000 which amortizes in 7.0 years and might be considered. However, Plan II includes a revision to part design which is questionable by Division. Plan III is considered uneconomical because of the long amortization period of the additional investment.

John Jones

made upon the basis of their probable rates of return. Such a use of the rate of return as the criterion for making decisions about prospective projects assumes that there will be more good projects than there will be investment funds, and by and large this will probably be true. In contrast with other types of capital investment, however, the execution of a project involving special automatic equipment requires certain unusual production engineering skills. When the project engineering skills are in short supply, as they are at present, they may in fact be a more limiting factor than are investment funds, despite the fact that investment funds may at the same time be difficult to obtain. Under these circumstances, it makes sense to maximize the profit per engineering hour required rather than the profit per dollar of investment required. Consider, for example, the following alternative projects, each of which has an estimated life of five years:

Project No.	Investment Required	Annual Savings	Time Adjusted Rate of Return	No. Engineering Hours Required
1	$10,000	$4,200	40%	1,000
2	10,000	3,900	35	1,000
3	10,000	3,600	30	667
4	10,000	3,300	25	667
5	10,000	3,100	20	667

If the company's engineering capacity is limited to one engineer, or 2,000 hours per year, two courses of action are open to it: undertake projects 1 and 2, and defer or abandon the others; or, undertake projects 3, 4, and 5, and abandon or postpone 1 and 2. The first choice maximizes the rate of return on investment (about 37% on an investment of $20,000, compared with about 25% on $30,000). But the second choice maximizes both the total annual profits, $10,000 per year compared with $8,100 per year, and the profit per engineering hour. The estimated savings per engineering hour are $4.20 and $3.90 for Projects 1 and 2, respectively, and $5.40, $4.95 and $4.65 for projects 3, 4 and 5, respectively. Given such a situation, in which engineering hours are more scarce than investment funds, the company would be better off following the second course of action. Of course we have assumed that a 20% rate is above the firm's cost of capital, and that all other things are equal for the purpose of simplifying our analysis here. In the actual situation, however, there may well be other intangible considerations, such as the

likes and dislikes of the personnel who have to carry out the
projects selected, the degree to which the projects involve ex-
posures to risk of failure, and the opportunities for additional
projects which may be opened up by successful completion of
one of those currently being reviewed.[40]

In spite of diligent questioning about this matter, we found
only one company in our field work which gave any consideration
to the matter of a shortage of engineering hours. The personnel
of many plants visited, however, complained of the shortage of
skilled project engineers and technicians. It should be noted
that the firm which had at times used the engineering man-hours
required as a decision criterion was one which had many years of
experience with this type of project, employed many engineers
in this type of work, and had a well-developed approach in
general to administrative routines.

Much the same kind of situation might exist with respect to
another factor required or affected by special automatic equipment projects. Floor space was a major consideration in two
plants visited; we mentioned one of these cases earlier in this
chapter. It is possible to take account of changes in the amount
of floor space required as part of the savings calculation, although
we have already noted the difficulties involved in doing so. But
in each of these cases it was not a matter of cost with which the
plants were concerned. For reasons we did not fully explore but
which we simply accepted, the managements of each of these
plants desired to avoid additional construction at that site, and
therefore gave preference to projects which reduced the amount
of floor space required, or, failing that, to projects which required the least amount of additional floor space. Both firms

---

[40] The second best alternative for each project should also be considered
to find out if there would be a significant reduction in the engineering man-
hours required. For example, let us assume that alternative 1A to project
1 could also be executed for an investment of $10,000 and would have an
estimated life of five years, but would require only 667 engineering man-
hours and would return annual savings of $3,700. Such an alternative
would yield a return of $5.55 per engineering man-hour, and the optimum
course of action would then be to undertake projects 1A, 3, and 4 in the
situation assumed.

It should also be noted that if the competitive projects have different
estimated service lives (as is likely to be the case) the stream of savings
from each must be reduced to a common basis, the present value thereof.
This can be done by using an appropriate discount rate, such as the cut-off
rate of return the company has set.

also employed the estimated rate of return as a major factor in deciding which projects to undertake. Since not one criterion but two criteria were employed, judgment was applied to reconcile divergent rankings when necessary. In a similar manner, one rapidly expanding company located in a small town which wished to avoid increasing its total employment figure gave preference to projects which reduced the manpower required. Its management considered this factor separately and apart from the dollar savings in labor costs which might be involved. Again, this was a supplementary criterion, employed along with payback and rate of return criteria.

The uses of floor space and personnel criteria are probably significant merely as exceptions to the typical situation, and perhaps exceptions not too frequently encountered. The use of the engineering hours criterion probably has somewhat more general relevance because of the widespread engineering shortage, because it will probably continue to exist for some time, and because even if additional engineers could be hired there may be a long breaking-in period before a shortage is remedied. It is therefore justified on an interim basis even though the preferable long-run solution would be to hire and/or train more project engineers.

Organizational Responsibility for Analysis

The whole object of our concern up to this point has been the procedures to be followed and the techniques to be employed in appraising a proposal for a piece of special automatic equipment. Who should be responsible for analyzing such a proposal, using the suggested procedures and techniques or modifications thereof?

One possibility is to delegate the analytical job to specialists in the accounting or industrial engineering organizations, a practice followed by seven of the companies studied. Another possibility is to centralize this responsibility in an analyst assigned to work with the production engineering group exclusively on projects involving special automatic equipment. A third is to place the primary responsibility upon each project leader. This would no doubt involve his working with other organizational elements in collecting data, such as the current direct labor costs per unit, the estimated demand for a given product, and the hourly wage rate for an in-process inspector. It would place primary responsibility on the project leader for determining which data were relevant and for collecting them, as well as for interpreting their significance.

The third course yields two major benefits. The first is the psychological effect on the project leader. Letting the project leader make his own estimates can give him a strong motive for living up to his own best estimates, especially his estimates of investment and savings (excluding the impact of volume). At the same time such a practice should give him the strongest of reasons to make a thorough and realistic analysis. The other, more indirect benefit which should accrue is the effect such a practice is likely to have on the direction and scope of the project engineer's efforts long before the formal project proposal is even typed up. The need for orientation toward getting the most economical performance for a given investment of time and money was stressed in connection with the topic of alternative projects. Making the project engineer responsible for an economic as well as a technical analysis should do much to create this kind of orientation during the formulation and analysis of possible alternatives.

No fault can be found with the proposal that a specialist be assigned to the special automatic equipment group to *assist* the project engineers in gathering and analyzing data, whether it be for the exploration of alternative approaches to a project or for the preparation of a formal proposal in the form of an appropriation request. Indeed, under many circumstances this could not help but achieve a better job of analysis. The danger to be avoided is that the specialist would not just assist project leaders but would in fact do the whole job and assume responsibility which should be the project leader's. If such a condition developed, the project leaders would be less likely, perhaps even unlikely, to develop the kind of economic appreciation essential to supplement the technical abilities they bring to bear on their projects. Therefore if the second arrangement is employed, the project leader should still be capable of performing any of the basic steps performed by the specialist assistant even though the project leader would lack the other's proficiency.

If it is desirable to have project engineers competent and responsible with respect to economic analysis of project proposals, it is even more desirable to have their immediate supervisor likewise competent and responsible. Indeed, in many situations it may well be that placing the primary responsibility for project analysis at the supervisory level initially (along with providing adequate training or assistance, or both, to the degree necessary) will be the means of developing familiarity with analytical objectives and techniques among project leaders.

VI

Summary

The foregoing analysis has been built around a contrast between a typical special automatic equipment project and a typical conventional equipment project. The discussion was aimed at justifying the contention that a special automatic equipment proposal is so significantly different from a conventional equipment project that it requires different analytical procedures and different approval criteria. The following factors underlie this conclusion: (1) the greater uncertainty of estimated net investment, primarily because of the need for sizable amounts of production engineering man-hours; (2) the substantially greater fixed costs usually involved, making the estimated annual savings calculation both more difficult and more critical; (3) the substantial product design obsolescence factor affecting estimates of primary service life of equipment; (4) the tendency in many instances toward shorter-lived equipment, making the estimated life a more critical element; and (5) the greatly different pattern of salvage value, which exposes special automatic equipment to potentially larger losses in the early years of its estimated service life.

The existence of these differences and the fact that the general tendency of each is to multiply the risks of investing in special automatic equipment leads the writer to make the following general conclusions:

(1) More precision and more detail are required to improve appraisals of the risks and potential gains. Failure to discriminate carefully has a proportionately greater effect on projects

for special, as contrasted with conventional, equipment, and dependence on offsetting errors to yield an acceptable average is a more tenuous policy. This comment applies particularly to accumulating the net investment figure, to the concepts and detailed calculation of costs involved in savings estimates, and to a systematic weighing of the several types of risks.

(2) Special equipment proposals need a broader-gauged appraisal, from the point of view not merely of the manufacturing operation but also of the enterprise as a whole. A clear appraisal of the interrelation between the manufacture of a part and its design, both as they exist and as they could be, and of the probability of many types of product design changes, is likely to be essential for the adequate appraisal of a special equipment proposal. A realistic appraisal of the impact on inventory policies, both permitted and required, is another element in the broad-gauged approach necessary to deal efficiently with this type of equipment proposal.

(3) The nature of the risks and the great uncertainty lead to a need for something more than one set of best estimates to describe the economic implications of special equipment proposals. The investment estimate seems to represent an opportunity for profitably employing crude probability estimates. At the least, systematic procedures should be established to develop tailor-made contingency allowances for expensive projects and standard allowances for lesser projects involving special automatic equipment. Volume forecasts so importantly affect an analysis that they need careful, rational determination, and for any sizable project a range of estimates ("Low," "Best Guess," and "High") will probably be needed to assure a good job of appraising the merits and risks of a proposal. The volume forecasts are probably better left to such organizational units as the marketing department or a centralized forecasting group serving all functional units, but they need to be available. The uncertainty associated with the estimated life of such equipment is probably best taken into account by raising the minimum or cut-off rate (whether pay-back period or rate-of-return) somewhat above that required for projects involving conventional equipment. Included in such an adjustment may be an element designed to reflect the small but added risks created by the low

salvage value in the early years of an application of special automatic equipment.

(4) The exploration of alternative approaches to performing an operation or a series of operations is likely to be particularly fruitful in acquiring special automatic equipment. The importance of this kind of investigation needs to be firmly established as basic philosophy and to be facilitated by using it as a standard operating procedure. Possible alternatives should be evaluated not only from a technical (machine design) standpoint but also from the standpoint of the economic consequences.

(5) The optimum results are likely to be produced by project leaders who, besides their technical competence, possess some facility at making a broad-gauged economic appraisal. This conclusion implies the necessity for up-grading the job specifications for a type of manpower already in short supply, but it nevertheless seems to be the best long-run objective for a company to establish, whatever interim action may be necessary as a stopgap.

(6) The nature of the risks we have analyzed and the range of probabilities which are likely to exist with respect to the results of any one project clearly place special equipment as a type of investment which requires steady, long-run effort to pay off. In this respect, acquisition of special equipment may be compared with product research. It should be a continuing activity over a long period of years, to allow the law of probability to even out failures and successes, large gains and small gains.

In conclusion, two points should be stressed. The first is that all special equipment projects are by no means likely to be as inflexible and as risky as we have implied in this chapter. A company's management must discriminate among special equipment projects in these respects, so as to optimize the investment of a company's capital and the expenditure of its production engineering talent. The management would also be wise to place special emphasis in each instance on seeking alternatives which will carry fewer risks but equal or almost equal gains.

The second point is that analysis, no matter how desirable it may loom in acquiring special automatic equipment, is just one link in a chain. It is necessary but not sufficient to get the best results. The payoff in acquiring special automatic equipment lies in well-selected projects successfully completed. Analytical procedures can be overemphasized, and criticism of proposals can be carried too far, so that the sources of suggested projects dry up. Care needs to be taken, therefore, that it does not exceed its proper role in getting the whole job done.

CHAPTER IX

Summary and Conclusions

IN THIS STUDY we began by briefly referring in Chapter I to the rapid growth in equipment expenditures generally and to the relatively recent trend toward the increasing use of special automatic equipment. We also cited two examples encountered in our field work to illustrate the almost fantastically good results which a program of special automatic equipment acquisition, successfully pursued over a decade or more, may achieve. These and other data clearly suggested that in the future, manufacturing would be much more influenced by the management of equipment than in the past. Our investigation also suggested that for many plants an increasing proportion of equipment might well be special automatic equipment, rather than conventional equipment.

On the basis of our appraisal of the current situation, we reasoned that the task of efficiently managing the acquisition of special automatic equipment should be a matter of interest and importance to many businessmen, from the project engineers and their supervisor, who are engaged directly in the process of acquiring equipment, to the company president and the other members of top management, who determine the scope of the firm's efforts in these directions and, formally or informally, set policies and procedures which are likely to affect significantly the degree of success attained.

Since so few companies had been active for long in acquiring this type of equipment, we proposed to examine some of their experiences in order to find out, first, whether a general description could be drawn up of what was involved in the acquisition process and, second, whether any insight could be gained into the important policies and procedures involved in executing this kind of program. Specifically, this study was a systematic exploration of the experience of a sample of companies from the metalworking group (including the electrical and electronic industries) to develop a general definition of the steps required, and then to identify the key problem areas. Finally, as our investigation progressed, we singled out certain steps for special attention, namely: debugging equipment; deciding whether to make or buy special automatic equipment; dealing effectively with vendors of this kind of equipment; coordinating the function of product design and the function of acquiring special automatic equipment; and the financial analysis of specific project proposals. In each area we sought further definition of the particular topic, examined its relation to the over-all goal of doing a good acquisition job, and sought to isolate policies and procedures which might be expected to aid in attaining such a goal.

The relatively small sample of companies visited (eighteen users and nine builders) and their restriction to metalworking companies necessarily qualifies many of the conclusions drawn. On the major questions of fact, however, there was considerable basic agreement among the sources consulted.

The Major Dimensions of the Acquisition Process

To the extent we were able, we presented factual data to describe some of the general characteristics of this kind of equipment. The data we gathered on 85 projects showed that for the middle half, expenditures ranged from $7,500 to $50,000, while the elapsed procurement time, once the initial planning had been completed and an appropriation request approved, ranged from 6 to 24 months. The dollar figures alone were not a good indicator of the level of difficulty of a project because some of the smaller projects involved a great deal of tailoring, proportionately much more than did many of the others involving double or even triple the expenditures.

In Chapter II we presented and considered our evidence on the nature of the major steps involved in the acquisition of special automatic equipment. We found that these steps comprise a complex administrative task as well as a complex and uncertain technical task. A businessman is perhaps used to uncertainty in connection with general business decisions, but here we found a decision area in which uncertain technical results are added to uncertain business factors and complicate the decisions which have to be made. In this respect, the subject appears to be much akin to the function of product research and development.

The supervisors interviewed considered the major problem areas in the acquisition process to lie in the debugging of equipment, in appraising project proposals, in the design of equipment, and in the determining of methods and equipment specifications. Of secondary importance as sources of problems were the steps of getting ideas and developing them into project proposals, and finding qualified vendors. With respect to relations between the special automatic equipment section and other organizational units, the supervisors classified as most critical the relations with the product design engineering department and with equipment contractors.

The Debugging Step

In Chapter III we took a closer look at the process step of debugging, a step which, with its wide, uncertain limits as to time and cost, comes close to epitomizing the activity of acquiring special automatic equipment. Debugging constituted a major expenditure for most of the projects in our sample, typically consuming about 40% of the elapsed calendar days in acquisition cycles, and probably constituting a little less than that proportion of total project expenditures. Many of the errors and omissions of prior steps in the acquisition process — such as poor design, poor workmanship, and faulty assumptions about parts, processes, and conditions of use — are likely to come home to roost in the debugging stage. Even if the preceding steps had all been executed as skillfully as possible, however, a significant task of debugging would remain to be done on most new and previously untried combinations of mechanisms. A parallel can be drawn between the debugging which goes on in the final phase of developing a new product and this step in designing a new piece of equipment. One important aspect of debugging is the fitting of the equipment to the product, or the part or parts of the product which are involved. We discovered that the kind of problem encountered is almost as likely to be related to attributes of the parts being processed as it is to the design of the equipment involved, and that problems with the processes themselves were usually a much less important source of problems in debugging.

In this chapter we also considered some policies and procedures which might lead to more efficient debugging activities, notably the systematic testing and recording of data, and the use of both simple and more complex statistical quality control techniques to trace defective performance to its roots. We also noted how the planning and careful execution of earlier steps in the acquisition process may lighten the debugging load, and how the responsibility for debugging needs to be placed firmly on the individual or organizational unit responsible for the other steps in the acquisition process in order to avoid buck passing at an important juncture.

Make or Buy

In Chapter IV we turned from a problem on the operating level to one on the policy level, the question of whether to make or to buy the type of equipment with which we are concerned. We focused on the instance in which the equipment to be acquired would be both designed and built by the same firm, either the vendor or the using company. It seemed clear that there were many advantages in requiring a vendor to design as well as build the equipment, notably to avoid buck passing at a critical juncture, and that the decisive questions were likely to lie in the design area and in the capacity of the vendor to do that portion of the job. Essentially, our conclusion was that no clearcut, simple answer will serve equally well in every situation, but that the appropriate choice depends on the nature and complexity of the equipment, the over-all size and duration of the user's special automatic equipment program, the special technical problems involved (or the absence of them) in a particular project, and administrative factors, notably the timing and urgency of the delivery date required and the distribution of the work load on the using company's organization. While price is certainly a theoretical factor to be considered, it actually seemed to play a minor role, directly, at least, in this kind of decision — and probably quite rightly so. If a user's program was large enough and was planned to be continued for several years (rather than as an intermittent activity), we saw many advantages in following a combination policy, one of both buying and making special automatic equipment, not only because different methods of procurement are likely to be best suited to different projects, but also because such a policy affords an opportunity to even the work load and stabilize the special automatic equipment organization, and because there are long-run values to be gained from exposing such an organization to the different stimuli and experiences.

Dealing with Special Automatic Equipment Vendors

In Chapters V and VI we turned again to the consideration of a problem on the operating level, that of dealing effectively with vendors. In Chapter V we concentrated on the evidence found in the experiences of the various users visited, while in Chapter VI we found general confirmation in the comments of a sample of vendors who designed and built special automatic equipment. In passing we should note that many of the problems we examined here also had important meaning for any program, whether the equipment was bought or made by the using firm. Since the purchase of such equipment should entail the evaluation of design activities as well as the supervision of equipment manufacturing, the discussions of each of these steps are relevant in considerable measure to the firm making its own equipment.

One of the most interesting as well as one of the most important conclusions which emerged from this consideration of dealing with vendors pertained to the benefits to be derived from pre-award planning and especially the value of working up soundly conceived specifications in considerable detail. Clearly, the effectiveness with which a user worked with vendors was very greatly affected by the quality of the performance in the earlier step of working up the project. Stated this bluntly, one wonders how it could be otherwise. Nevertheless, the study uncovered many cases of users and of vendors alike experiencing frequent and serious difficulties which had their origins in failure to perform adequate pre-award planning — as well as a few instances showing the benefits which flowed from outstanding performance of this initial step in the acquisition process. Often, a complementary deficiency was the buyer's superficial and sometimes incomplete understanding of the builder's role and method of operation, knowledge of which would undoubtedly have aided in obtaining superior performance.

We also examined ways of appraising potential vendors and considered the function of monitoring — expediting — developments as they took place after a builder had been awarded a contract. We noted the seeming neglect of a test run for the equipment just after it had been assembled on the builder's erecting floor, and noted too, the potential importance of this phase in serving not only as a criterion for acceptance of delivery from the builder, but also as a means of providing necessary information for further debugging. We pointed out that when the test procedures are worked out in detail and are communicated to the builder as the project starts, they are, in effect, helping to develop better initial specifications for the equipment.

A recurrent theme in our study of relations with vendors was the emphasis upon the importance of communications between representatives of the buyer and the builder in many ways: in communicating the builder's capabilities generally and for a specific project, in communicating requirements for a specific project initially through equipment specifications, and in communicating progress and problems during the design and build cycle. We noted the undesirable effects on buyer-builder relations of rotating project leader assignments during the cycle of acquisition and the value of liaison by the responsible project leaders rather than by other buyers' representatives.

Finally, we pointed out three interrelated basic policy questions: first, the issue of whether it would be preferable generally to deal with many or with just a few selected vendors in acquiring this type of equipment; second, the matter of the most useful general attitude, with a hands-off attitude at one extreme and a close-cooperation attitude at the other; and third, the nature of standards for the builder's debugging responsibility. While we noted that at times flexibility in these matters might be necessary, and that the simplicity or complexity of the project at hand might be a factor in the choice, in general we favored a combination of carefully selecting a relatively few builders, working with them in close cooperation at all times, and attempting to maintain strict but reasonable requirements for fixing the responsibility for debugging.

The main ground for these conclusions, of course, lies in the assumption that as a result of these policies, a builder will acquire a more intimate knowledge of the buyer's product and manufacturing operations. Mutual familiarity should make for better communication between the builder's and the buyer's representatives, and the builder should be discouraged from the temptation to cut corners, a temptation which may frequently be present if he does not expect awards beyond the current project. At the same time, limiting the number of builders of special automatic equipment may widen the opportunities for the re-use of principal equipment components, either by the user's own designing and building group or by the original builder under another contract. If these kinds of results in fact are likely to come about from following this set of policies, then in the author's opinion the buyer's program should be measurably more efficient in its execution and the resulting equipment should be more profitable in its operation. As we developed more fully in that chapter, this is not to deny the value of competition and of having several points of view on the general approach to take in a project. Rather, we believe that an attempt should be made to limit the suppliers of major types of equipment to a few and, at least in most cases, not to reduce them to just one.

Relations with Product Design Function

In Chapter VII we directed our attention to one of the most critical organizational relations of a program to acquire special automatic equipment, the relation with product design. Our inquiry led to the conclusion that effective coordination between these two functions — a kind of coordination which runs both ways — is fundamental to a successful, long-run program. Effective coordination affects the results of the special automatic equipment program in two major ways. First, it helps increase the number of potential applications of special automatic equipment, and second it helps avoid early obsolescence of this kind of equipment. The kind of coordination we discussed emphasized standardization and planning, both in the design of the product and in the design of special automatic equipment. On the one hand, standardization of parts and subassemblies used in the product was viewed both as a means of insuring designs which facilitated the current application of special automatic equipment and as a means of helping to minimize obsolescence of equipment resulting from parts changes when new models were designed. There is much to be said in favor of making a program of product standardization the first step in a program to acquire special automatic equipment. Standardizing the basic machine types and elements (using "building blocks," or module elements) also was viewed as a practical method of maximizing the opportunity to re-use a significant proportion of equipment subassemblies in instances in which product design changes made equipment revisions mandatory. There have been some recent reports of rebuilding standardized equipment, notably in the automotive industry, which suggest that we may see more of this type of activity in the future. At the same time, we observed how the planning of the major dimensions of product design changes can provide a basis in turn for planning equipment in a way that will facilitate its being retooled even more economically to accommodate minor product design changes falling within the ranges contemplated.

We noted the difficulty, if not the impossibility, of trying to reduce to dollar amounts the savings which might be realized by effective coordination of product design and production engineering. Such coordination is, nevertheless, a principal means of exercising control over the long-run costs of a special automatic equipment program. And we are convinced that the kinds of long-run costs involved are likely to comprise a major portion of the total long-run costs of using this kind of equipment. We concluded this section by noting various devices being used to obtain coordination, including committees, liaison assignments, and the "project" type of organization, the last being especially suited for situations involving new product development. Although it is desirable to keep product design engineers constantly aware of special automatic equipment applications, the development of such equipment is in fact becoming a new function (or at least a drastically revised and more important version of an old function) despite the shadows of a status problem with which it is currently afflicted in some companies.

Analyzing Special Automatic Equipment Proposals

Finally, in Chapter VIII we turned to the function of analyzing specific proposals for special automatic equipment. Our interest was drawn to this topic because we found that both the operating level — project leaders and their supervisors — and the executive level — top management — seemed to be doing a rather inadequate job, by and large. There was good evidence that they were using outmoded methods of analysis for the most part, applying rather arbitrary criteria in making decisions, and in general were failing to recognize the fundamental differences between proposals for conventional equipment and proposals for special automatic equipment. In particular, two key characteristics of special automatic equipment seemed to be almost universally ignored: the typically much shorter primary service life, and the uncertainty associated with the estimates of expenditures required to complete this kind of project successfully. The first of these characteristics logically follows from the high probability that when the design of the product becomes obsolete, equipment like this, which is tailored to perform specific operations on a specific product, will no longer be usable. The second of these characteristics also must often follow from the definition of special automatic equipment, namely, equipment which is in no inconsiderable degree unique, requiring an element of what might broadly be termed research and development effort.

We also noted deficiencies in the concepts of investment used by most firms. Appropriate calculation of the investment, we concluded, must include the cost of facilitating changes in other operations and, especially, the generally neglected cost of the project leader's time on the project and the cost of the time spent by technicians assigned to debugging. Since these production engineering costs usually comprise a significant proportion of the total expenditures, their omission is likely to cause material distortions in any analysis procedures. We also noted deficiencies in common procedures for making savings estimates, notably the tendency to fail to take into account some of the relevant cost factors, such as material costs (including spoilage and scrap) and variable overhead elements. We also noted the problem of salvage value in a project of this type, the handling of which can sometimes be "sticky" in a project with these characteristics.

In our analysis we concentrated on exploring the implications that these special characteristics may have for an analyst who is seeking to compare one special automatic equipment project with another or a special automatic equipment project with a conventional equipment project. We assumed that the objective of users would be making the most profitable use both of a company's capital investment funds and of its sometimes even scarcer resource, the capacity of its special automatic equipment group to complete projects of this type. To deal with the pronounced and multifaceted uncertainties arising out of the two characteristics noted above and from other factors as well, we considered four techniques: improving the reliability of the estimates, making contingency allowances, using probability estimates to compute "most probable" estimates, and raising the cut-off rate of return (or pay-back period) required. Unfortunately, no one of these techniques, or even a combination of them, was wholly satisfactory. Some of them seemed to be more useful in dealing with one or two factors than they were in dealing with others. These kinds of refinements in analysis may be unnecessary when the merits of a particular project are overwhelming. Particularly with a project involving, say $50,000 or more of expenditures, however, one or more of these techniques is likely to prove useful, and not the least useful result may well be the way they can be used to seek a more precise identification of those aspects of the project which may be responsible for a major part of the uncertainty. In any event, a program of periodically reviewing completed projects, individually and collectively, will help develop more complete and more precise standard "expectations," which will improve the selection and execution of projects. Such a review can also be an essential element in the over-all evaluation of the company's special automatic equipment program.

We then discussed the importance of considering a range of alternatives employing different methods and also the desirability of considering the economic effect of relaxing the goal of fully automatic operation. In this connection, we stressed the usefulness of the concept of incremental return on incremental investment as a method of establishing the economic justification for progressively more automatic operation. We also found the same concept useful in comparing alternatives generally, whether for replacement or for a completely new facility.

We concluded this section by advocating a policy of encouraging personnel at the working level (the project leaders and the group supervisor) to become proficient in the financial analysis of their own proposals, so that they might better perceive the economic goals toward which they should be striving.

Some Important Areas Not Included

No attempt was made to produce a comprehensive study of all the administrative problems related to special automatic equipment acquisition. We have simply attempted to present a generalized description of the function, to identify the principal trouble spots, and then to give more detailed consideration to certain selected aspects of that function and of its relationship to other functions. We have not examined at all some of the important problems which arise when a company embarks on a program of acquiring special automatic equipment, and we have only briefly referred to others which deserve considerably more attention. For instance, we have done no more than point out the question of the appropriate role for a headquarters group in a multiplant company. Can and should such a headquarters group undertake specific projects for individual plants? Or should its role be solely one of a consultant, with full responsibility vested in each plant? Another cluster of problems surround the introduction of special automatic equipment to full production status. How much voice, if any, should a foreman have in the decision transferring responsibility to the regular production organization? Should there be specific standards agreed upon, such as output equal to one week's production requirements during a regular work week, which the machine must meet before the production group will take over? What are effective ways of breaking the news to the hourly personnel who will be displaced by a specific piece of equipment?

There are also intriguing and important problems which we

have only briefly described in what might be termed the "personnel aspects" of the group engaged in the acquisition of this type of equipment. This term refers not to the impact such a group's efforts may have on the rest of the plant's organization (though this, too, is clearly an important topic) but rather to the selection, training, and development of project engineers for this kind of work. With the existing shortage of qualified personnel of this type, which makes hiring people like this difficult and expensive, one of the most pressing problems for many companies visited was selecting promising individuals already employed by the company but performing different work, and training them to become effective project leaders. But we have reluctantly had to forego anything more than a cursory observation of these and other problems in order to accomplish the research we have presented here.

Top Management Considerations

Throughout our study our frame of reference has been the enterprise as a whole and our viewpoint has been largely that of the person or group primarily responsible for the management of the enterprise, the top management. This orientation has probably been most clearly revealed in our discussion of the analysis of proposals for special automatic equipment. The author believes that it is essential to maintain this point of view in appraising any function like this, as it is easy to upgrade the function to such a degree that it begins to harm, rather than help, in attaining the primary objectives of the enterprise as a whole. In the case of special automatic equipment — *automation* — the emotional appeal has been strong and some projects, even some programs of considerable size, seem to have been started simply because this type of activity was considered a trademark of "progressive management." There are no doubt instances in which special automatic equipment can be justified primarily on noneconomic grounds, such as safety and ability to obtain more consistent and higher quality characteristics. But automation simply for the sake of having an automatic production process hardly qualifies as a sound business goal.

One of the traps into which their excessive enthusiasm led many of the organizations visited was adopting, implicitly or explicitly, a goal of complete mechanization, that is, having no operator but only a completely automatic piece of equipment. Such a goal sometimes has led to acquiring pieces of special automatic equipment which employed less than the optimum method of production, judged by the criterion of rate of return on investment. A proper statement of objectives should not consider complete mechanization a goal at all, but should define the goal with respect to its economic consequences. The objective in acquiring special automatic equipment should recognize that a piece of equipment is simply one method of several by which the means of production may be organized, and that the primary goal of organizing these means of production — or, the choice of the method of production to be adopted — should be the lowest cost, all cost elements considered, in the long run. Given this kind of objective, the optimum combination of methods is likely to include some special automatic equipment, some conventional equipment, and some semiautomatic equipment, with operators performing those tasks they can do more economically than special automatic equipment.

Conclusion

It is manifestly impossible to present an adequate digest of a research project like this, the essence of which lies in the multiplicity of details. Some of the most significant aspects of our findings, however, may be summarized as follows. First, the performance of this function, the acquisition of special automatic equipment, is not simple but complex, not easy but difficult. Second, it is risky, much more risky than is the acquisition of production facilities generally, even when the function is skillfully executed, and it therefore requires awareness of the likely sources of risk and careful risk management if it is to be engaged in profitably. Third, it requires careful analysis and planning, both to identify in detail and then to control the risks involved. It requires careful analysis and planning, too, to insure minimum total costs for the equipment acquired. Fourth, it necessitates a coordination, which is difficult to achieve, with other functions of the enterprise, notably with product design. Fifth and last, it requires management at the outset to take a long-term view — something of at least the order of magnitude of five years — to fix appropriately the basic role and scope for the function, to schedule projects efficiently, to minimize costly fluctuations in the size of the special automatic equipment group, and to accumulate enough data on the results of projects to permit an evaluation to be made of the success which the function may have attained. These are certainly formidable goals and may sound discouraging. But, as is often the case in business, there is evidence that the rewards for accepting these kinds of risks and performing this function well are often high and well worth the undertaking.

An appropriate way to conclude may be to try to relate the whole of what we have been discussing in this work to several characteristic trends of modern economic activity, trends which are of relatively recent vintage and trends which are quite likely to persist in the future. For instance, the complexities, not merely of this function itself, but also those that arise from its necessary and desirable relation to other departments of the business, reflect a growing, perhaps accelerating, trend in our evolving business complex. In this particular study, the discussion of the intimate relation of product design to the acquisition of special automatic equipment is especially noteworthy. Of particular interest are the organizational problems which this kind of condition creates and the way in which it complicates a fundamental task of top management, keeping all organizational units heading toward the same, coordinated objectives even though each function is treading a different path. Moreover, the study is one example of many which show modern technology having an increasing impact on the nature of business management. There is no doubt that managing the factory is becoming more and more a job of managing technology; whereas in the past, it was usually dominated by the need to manage large numbers of people effectively. The task of managing people, of course, remains as a fundamental job of every manager, since by definition he directs the efforts of others as a means of accomplishing his objectives. And he has also always had to manage ideas, but now they are more often likely to be technical ideas. It may not even be too far-fetched to describe a project manager or engineer, such as we have been concerned with, as a business manager of technical ideas.

Another way in which this study reinforces a trend is the way in which it imposes upon managers of manufacturing businesses using special automatic equipment the necessity of adopting a more distant horizon for efficient planning. We have already noted the similarity in many ways between this kind of activity and the function of product research. The necessity to think through a workable long-term plan, with a horizon five or more years ahead, is certainly one of the most important similarities from the standpoint of business managers.

The study likewise implies a continued specialization of the factory. The range of products which many plants produce has been steadily narrowing over the years. Even though there are still a host of general-purpose machine shops, for instance, they no longer account for the mass of metalworking production. Instead, relatively specialized plants, each producing a narrow line of products for the most part, are the backbone of consumer goods manufacturing and, indeed, of some industrial products, too. And with this increasing specialization has developed the increasingly close coordination between plant and product. It is probably this trend which in turn has brought about another trend, again exemplified by the substance of our research, whereby broader-gauged personnel are required at increasingly lower levels in the business organization. Indeed, the type of individual increasingly being demanded is the "broad-gauged specialist." The requirements we have suggested for the project engineer and his supervisor comprise a job description for this kind of person.

In short, the need to acquire special automatic equipment efficiently is one more reason why the future manager's task will be at once more demanding and more exciting.

APPENDICES

APPENDIX A

The Warren-King Company: The History of the Acquisition of a Piece of Special Automatic Equipment

THE WARREN-KING COMPANY was engaged in the manufacture of electromechanical converters[1] used in large volume as sub-assemblies by other manufacturers. Four customers took over three-quarters of Warren-King's annual production. Most of the converters were installed in consumer durable products. Although Warren-King technically controlled the design of the converters it manufactured, a substantial change in the design of a customer's end item almost invariably required a complete redesign of the converter or a competitor would get the order. In the past, the product had been redesigned every three to six years.

In January 1954 the Peterson Company, one of Warren-King's largest customers, asked for a quotation on supplying 300 converters a day under an annual contract. The converter would be of a new design. Mr. Dana, General Manager and Sales Manager of Warren-King, knew that at least three other potential sources of supply would be bidding against Warren-King on this contract. The contract would cover a period of a year, but would probably be renewed because no one else could match the initial manufacturer's price after it had had a year's production experience on the item. Deliveries were to begin by January 31, 1956, with delivery of 60 converters by that date, and

---
[1] A fictitious name has been used for the product.

the proposed delivery schedule increased from 60 a day in February and March to 300 a day beginning April 1, 1956.

The Chief Engineer, Plant Superintendent (Mr. Kruger), Manufacturing Engineer (Mr. Gary), and Industrial Engineer (Mr. Otis), drew up Warren-King's quotation, based on preliminary designs and tentative manufacturing methods developed primarily by the Manufacturing Engineer, Mr. Gary. (Exhibit A-1 shows a partial organization chart.) It quickly became the consensus of the group that substantial investment in special automatic equipment would be necessary to come within striking distance of the selling price range which the customer had indicated was necessary. Mr. Otis was to prepare economic analyses of projects and alternatives for any special automatic equipment Mr. Gary might suggest for recovering manufacturing cost. During the following year, detailed blueprints were developed, "make or buy" decisions on components were made, and a bid was submitted to the Peterson Company. Mr. Gary accumulated a list of manufacturing equipment which Warren-King would need and also developed the specifications for several items of special equipment.

In April 1955, after receiving an informal notice that Warren-King would be awarded the contract, Mr. Dana established a steering committee to guide the program for the Peterson converter, under the chairmanship of the Assistant General Manager. Other members included the Chief Engineer; Mr. Kruger, the Plant Superintendent; Mr. Gary, the Manufacturing Engineer; Mr. Otis, the Industrial Engineer; and the Quality Control Engineer. The committee was to decide matters of over-all policy and questions that involved two or more departments when the persons involved could not agree themselves. The committee was to approve each piece of special automatic equipment before it was ordered.

Mr. Gary spent two months contacting potential equipment suppliers and getting quotations. Locating suitable potential vendors proved to be a problem. Most of the larger special equipment builders already had large backlogs as a result of heavy programs originating with the major automotive manufacturers. To meet the initial delivery requirement of 60 by

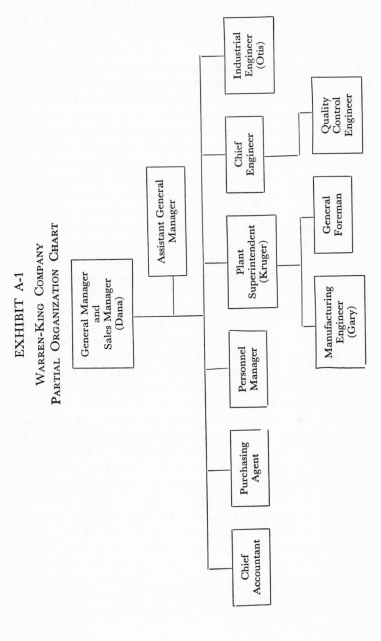

EXHIBIT A-1

WARREN-KING COMPANY

PARTIAL ORGANIZATION CHART

January 31, 1956, the steering committee believed that all equipment had to be received no later than December 1, 1955.

The Fairchild Grinder Project

One of the special machines which had been proposed for processing the Peterson converter was a grinder. The remainder of this discussion will be focused primarily upon the developments related to this particular piece of equipment, the "Fairchild grinder" as it came to be called by Warren-King personnel. The operations required were to finish-grind four diameters of a hardened steel shaft, plus two faces of a hub located in the center of the shaft. Each converter required two of these parts; in other words, to make 300 converters a day would require production of 600 of this particular part. Each end of the shaft had a slight taper, and each outside diameter carried a tolerance of ±.001 inch. The thickness of the hub in the center was critical, with a tolerance of ±.0005 inch. The specifications called also for a high surface finish of ten micro-inches, which is on the tight side.

Mr. Gary received only one quotation on this shaft-grinding job. The three other companies he approached said that in view of the specifications they would prefer not to quote. (All three were heavily loaded with work from the large automotive producers.) The sole quotation, from the Fairchild Company, a less prominent but nevertheless well-known builder of grinding equipment, would result in an expenditure of $53,763, after taking into account the cost of equipment, freight, and installation. No costs for debugging were included because in cases like this the equipment would typically be subject to a test run in Fairchild's plant. Fairchild stated that the equipment would be assembled in Fairchild's plant, would be ready for a test run by December 1, 1955, and would be shipped, if accepted by Warren-King, no later than December 15. The nominal capacity of the machine would be 65 pieces per hour. Mr. Gary estimated that the actual yield, after taking into account both machine efficiency and time allowances for the operator, would be about 60% of nominal capacity; therefore, two shifts of operation would yield 624 pieces, leaving an acceptable margin for error to obtain the 600 pieces which would have to pass inspection requirements each day.

Fairchild guaranteed to meet the specifications for production rate and quality on the condition that the workpiece specifications be modified. The Fairchild management proposed a reduction in the amount of stock to be removed from the four diameters. As originally planned, the shafts would be turned down on a lathe to the point where .008 inch remained to be removed from each diameter by grinding. Instead, Fairchild proposed that the turning operation leave no more than .004 inch. Mr. Gary felt that although the lathe operations would then be more difficult and take a trifle longer, the alternative of using conventional grinding equipment was so much more costly that he was inclined to accept Fairchild's modification.

As proposed, the machine would be hand loaded and tended by one operator per shift. The operator was also needed to touch up ("dress") the grinding wheels as required, using a special piece of dressing equipment which Fairchild was to procure and mount on the grinder.

In his presentation to the steering committee, Mr. Gary also set forth an economic analysis (Exhibit A-2) prepared by Mr. Otis. This compared the Fairchild proposal with the alternative of using standard equipment, that is, six plain grinders. Since Warren-King used the MAPI formula[2] in all of its equipment analysis, it had developed the form shown by Exhibit A-2. The analysis showed that nearly $58,000 per year would be saved by buying the Fairchild special grinder, and the outlay needed would be about $12,000 less than the conventional equipment would require. Computing a rate of return for this comparison was not feasible, since the proposal expected to be the less expensive in operation also required the lower estimated investment. On June 15, 1955, the steering committee approved the proposed acquisition of the Fairchild special grinder, and the equipment was ordered.

---

[2] George Terborgh, *Dynamic Equipment Policy*. For a later development of this approach to equipment analysis, see ibid., *Business Investment Policy*.

EXHIBIT A-2

ECONOMIC ANALYSIS OF FAIRCHILD GRINDER PROPOSAL

ENGINEERING ECONOMY STUDY

KLFC-1165			Study No.	25
Division		Works		Capital Exp. Project
Peterson Converter		Main Plant		100-71-423
Project Description				
Fairchild Special Grinder				
Department		Product		Est. Life of Job
SSC				10 Years

1–PROPOSED FACILITY		2–PROPOSED FACILITY	
a. Description Six Cincinnati Filmatic 4″ Center Type Plain Grinders		a. Description Fairchild Special Grinder	
Mod/Size	Prim. Serv. Life	Mod/Size	Prim. Serv. Life
4″ × 12″	10 Years	—	10 Years
b. Installed Cost	$66,000	b. Installed Cost	$53,763
c. Usage	16 Hrs./Day	c. Usage	16 Hrs./Day
d. Net Salvage Value	$9,900	d. Net Salvage Value	$5,376
e. Percent Salvage $\left(\frac{d}{b}\right)$	15%	e. Percent Salvage $\left(\frac{d}{b}\right)$	10%
f. Chart Percent	21.8%	f. Chart Percent	23.0%
(B) Next Year's Composite Cost (b × f)	$14,388	(B) Next Year's Composite Cost (b × f)	$12,365

Predelivery Developments Related to the Fairchild Grinder

Warren-King took no action on the special grinder from the date the order was placed, June 15, 1955, until August 14, 1955, when Mr. Kruger and Mr. Gary visited the Fairchild plant as part of a tour of all plants holding equipment orders for the Peterson converter project. When they found that no further work had been done on the design for the machine, they threatened to take the order away from Fairchild unless work began immediately. Fairchild design engineers pointed out that they

EXHIBIT A-2 (CONTINUED)

3–OPERATIONAL COMPARISON

Operating Costs	1–PROPOSED		2–PROPOSED	
Direct Labor...............	$ 54,270	$..........	9,888	$..........
Indirect Labor Mtl. Handling	1,317	....		....
Set-Up....................	219	....		....
Material...................		....		....
Maintenance..............		....		....
Tools/Exp. Items..........		....		....
Power Consumption........		....		....
Floor Space...............	308	....		....
Property Tax..............	1,168	....	952	....
Rework/Scrap.............		....		....
Downtime.................		....		....
Delete/Add. Oper..........		....		....
Fringe Benefits............	11,318	....	2,054	....
Sub-Contract Costs........		....		....
Others...................		....		....
Income Loss		....		....
(C) TOTALS	$ 68,600	$	(C) $ 12,894	$

TOTAL, (B) plus (C)	$ 82,988	$ 25,259
Proposal No. 1 Minus No. 2	$ 57,729	

Prepared By: R. E. Otis	Date: 6–1–56	Date:
Div. Ind. Eng.	Date:	Date:

had not received the sample workpieces that had been promised and that were needed for investigating the technical grinding problems, using a single-head grinder to simulate the operations to be performed. A month later Mr. Kruger and Mr. Gary returned to Fairchild's plant to see several of the sample workpieces being ground on a machine Fairchild was about to ship to another customer. This machine was similar but not identical to the Warren-King machine.

By this time it had become evident that an organized expediting program was needed, not merely for the Fairchild grinder but for all major equipment, and other members of the management group were assigned some of the responsibility for expediting. Mr. Otis, the Industrial Engineer, made the next visit to the Fairchild plant on October 28 and reported that Fairchild might not be ready for machine tryouts by December 1, but would probably have a completely assembled machine shortly after that date. He noted that Fairchild had ordered the wheel dresser from the Haynes Wheel Dresser Corporation and had been promised delivery on December 1, the date by which Fairchild was to have the machine ready for tryouts. He therefore suggested that Warren-King's Purchasing Agent try to work with Haynes to expedite delivery of the dresser to Fairchild before December 1, if possible. Mr. Otis found that parts ("hardware") for the machine were being fabricated. Fairchild had begun making the base, and it was to be finished in about ten days.

Mr. Otis's visit on October 28 also revealed a misunderstanding relating to the specifications. Fairchild's shop people were building a machine that failed to incorporate a change discussed more than a month before with a Fairchild sales engineer at the time Fairchild drawings had been submitted to Warren-King for approval. The change involved a spring-loaded center, which would support one end of the workpiece, and a stop which would locate the workpiece by reference to one particular hub face on the workpiece. After seeing Fairchild's layout drawings, the Chief Engineer, Mr. Gary, and Mr. Kruger had all agreed that such changes ought to be made to insure meeting the close tolerance on the hub thickness. When this discrepancy was reported, Mr. Gary began taking steps to make sure that the design change would be made, working through the sales engineer with whom he had originally placed the order. The ultimate result was that Fairchild agreed to make these changes but claimed additional compensation for making them, since the changes originated with Warren-King personnel and represented changes in the preliminary layout sketches in Fairchild's initial proposal upon which its bid had been based. In the final settlement, Warren-King paid Fairchild an additional $8,000 because of these changes, since considerable engineering work had to be redone by Fairchild to incorporate them.

Subsequently, Mr. Otis made several additional visits to the Fairchild plant to check Fairchild's actual progress against schedule. His experience on this project, incidentally, convinced him that expediting should be done early, regularly, and systematically. He believed that in future acquisitions of special automatic equipment it should start before the order was placed by obtaining a detailed schedule from the vendor, showing target completion dates for every major step: i.e., completion of layout prints; completion of detailed prints; manufacture of major parts; procurement of major items; start and completion of assembly operations; and start and completion of debugging.

It became increasingly clear that the Fairchild machine would not be ready in time to make parts for the January 1956 shipments of 60 converters, so Warren-King made provisions for the grinding operations on this workpiece to be done temporarily on standard equipment in its own general machine shop. This method required making several different setups to grind all the surfaces involved, and also resulted in considerable spoilage of workpieces. The temporary supply of parts obtained by this method was very much more expensive, but, under the circumstances, could not be avoided.

Debugging the Fairchild Grinder

On December 20, 1955, Fairchild notified Warren-King that the machine had been completely assembled and should be ready for a test run within a week. The production rate during the test, however, was well below that specified, and even more serious problems lay in the failure of the machine to produce work of satisfactory quality. It failed to obtain the necessary finish of ten micro-inches. It also tended to develop "checks" (fine, hair-like cracks) in grinding the parts. Such checks exposed shafts to grave dangers of failure in use, and were cause for rejecting a workpiece. Warren-King's engineers and shop personnel believed these checks might be caused by the fact that Fairchild had installed harder grinding wheels than had originally been contemplated. Softer wheels, however, would undoubtedly reduce output; they would need more frequent dressing and further impair the output rate. A third defect in the equipment was "flutter" in the grinding wheel, the workpiece holding device, or both. This phenomenon seemed to be substantially, if not wholly, the reason the machine produced a high percentage of parts outside the required tolerances (including one of ±.0005 inch). During January 1956 the checking was eliminated and the required surface finish obtained, but excessive wheel wear prevented much net improvement in the production rate.

Fairchild engineers protested that all these difficulties were caused by the grinding wheel, for which they were not responsible. They pointed out that their standard contract specifically provided that, in the absence of a special provision to the contrary, the vendor was not to be held responsible for problems relating to cutting tool wear. Mr. Kruger, to whom this protest was addressed, replied that no matter what the cause, the performance specifications of 65 good pieces per hour were not being met. Since Fairchild had specifically agreed to make a machine that would yield acceptable pieces at this rate, he held that it was up to them to go after the wheel manufacturer and solve the problem. The Fairchild engineers suggested that further debugging might proceed more efficiently in Warren-King's plant. Mr. Kruger, however, declined to approve this plan.

Toward the end of January the Peterson Company notified Warren-King that, because of a slump in consumer demand for its products, it would need only 60 converters a day for the foreseeable future. Warren-King's management still felt themselves under pressure to meet even this reduced delivery schedule. Two other special machines were so far behind schedule that Warren-King sent workpieces by air express to the equipment vendors' plants for processing on these pieces of special equipment, which also were assembled and operating but were not meeting the contractual performance guarantees.

By February there had been little improvement in the situation, and the difficulty of operating under existing conditions caused Mr. Kruger to propose to the other members of the steering committee that they accept delivery of all pieces of outstanding special equipment (including the Fairchild grinder) even though they still did not meet the original specifications. He argued that all except the Fairchild machine were close to performance specifications, and that delivery of the Fairchild equipment could be accepted on the condition that Fairchild agree to provide further assistance in debugging the machine after it had been installed in Warren-King's plant. With the equipment in the plant, he pointed out, Warren-King's production foremen, maintenance personnel, and quality control personnel could be called upon to assist in debugging and thereby speed up the process of "shaking down" the equipment. Besides, he pointed out, as long as delivery schedules remained at 60 a day, all equipment would operate sufficiently well to produce these quantities.

Mr. Otis and Mr. Gary opposed this suggestion, arguing that since the contract obligated Warren-King to pay the full contract price thirty days after delivery, the vendors would lose much, if not all, of their incentive to improve the equipment further. They stated that they believed it would be better to sweat out their present problems for a while longer and thereby avoid the expense to Warren-King of doing the debugging that, in their opinion, was the vendor's responsibility. Mr. Kruger's suggestion, they pointed out, also entailed the risk of accepting equipment that might not be capable of meeting production needs when Peterson's delivery schedule climbed to 300 converters a day.

The steering committee members were in such disagreement that they placed the issue before Mr. Dana. He decided that, in view of the high volume of Peterson's requirements for other Warren-King products and their importance as a source of business in the future, it would be unwise to run any avoidable risk of failing to meet the daily converter delivery schedule. As he believed that the geographically widespread fabrication of parts, involving air-express transportation and dependence on equipment vendors for processing of important parts, ran considerable risk of delays from many factors, he decided it would be best to take delivery of all three special machines outstanding.

Mr. Otis found that Fairchild would willingly ship the grinder and continue working on debugging in Warren-King's plant. The grinder was installed by the end of March. Some men from Fairchild immediately scraped the slides and installed a new locking mechanism. With the assistance of Warren-King's grinding department foreman and a representative of a grinding wheel manufacturer, the men from Fairchild experimented a great deal with different types and grades of grinding wheels. Their efforts then slacked off, and by the end of April all work on the machine was being instituted and performed wholly by Warren-King personnel.

When the Fairchild grinder was first operated in Warren-King's plant in April 1956, only 10 good pieces per hour were produced, as compared with the original specification of 65 per hour. Nevertheless, since only 120 pieces per day were needed to meet the schedule of 60 converters a day (two of these parts per converter), twelve hours of operation were enough to meet net current requirements. As successive bugs were diagnosed and as the operator learned more about the machine, production improved further. One year later in April 1957, however, the machine was producing at the rate of only 30 pieces per hour, or about one-half the original specification.

Efforts to improve the performance of this equipment slowed practically to a halt after September 1956 when Peterson informed Warren-King that it had current product development work under way which would more than double the power required from the converter unit. If, as seemed likely, this development work proved satisfactory, then Warren-King's current model of converter would be obsolete. There seemed to be only a very slim chance that parts for a new model converter could be processed on the existing special automatic equipment. Peterson estimated that it would need production of the current converter for only ten to fifteen months beyond September 1956, depending on the time required to complete its product development work. Thereafter, its requirements for this model converter would be confined to replacement demand for the repair of end items in the hands of consumers.

None of Warren-King's debugging costs was charged to the Fairchild grinder appropriation. The expenditures recorded on this project were $8,000 over the original estimate of $54,000 as a result of the additional payment made to Fairchild because of changes in the machine design, but probably much larger excesses were not compiled. Some measure of the cost of debugging is reflected in the delay in getting the equipment into production. The original timetable called for building and completely debugging the grinder in five and a half months. It was, in fact, nine and a half months until delivery, and even then Mr.

Gary and Mr. Kruger considered that the debugging period was by no means complete. Warren-King personnel and two of the vendor's employees worked on the machine for the best part of another month after it was delivered. And, despite all these efforts, the production rate ultimately achieved by the equipment was only about half that for which it was designed.

Summary of Costs, Fairchild Grinder vs. Standard Equipment

An analysis of comparative costs can be drawn up in the form of the original proposal for the Fairchild grinder. Referring to Exhibit A-2, the analysis of the proposal as it appeared before the event, we shall first take into account the reduction in volume from 300 per day to 60 per day and its effect on the operating costs involved for each machine. The costs for setup, floor space, and property taxes are fixed. They are so small, however, in proportion to the others (all of which were computed as a function of direct labor hours) that we shall assume the total operating costs were reduced in direct proportion to the reduction in volume. Operating costs per year then become about $13,720 ($60/300 \times \$68,600$) for the standard grinders ("Proposal No. 1"). If Peterson introduced its new model after taking only a year's production at this rate, as seemed quite likely, then the total costs on standard equipment would be $13,720 plus an appropriate share of depreciation. Assuming that Warren-King could convert standard equipment to other uses,[3] the charge of $14,388 shown in Exhibit A-2 for the first year's allocation still seems reasonable. The total cost using standard equipment to grind these workpieces would therefore equal about $28,000.

Taking into account the fact that the Fairchild grinder took about twice as long per piece as was originally contemplated, its total operating costs would be about $5,158 per year ($60/300 \times \$12,894 \times 2$). Practically no salvage value would remain, however, for the Fairchild grinder; an estimate of $10,000 seems lib-

---

[3] If there were no alternative uses, and the only course of action available were to sell the standard equipment as used machinery, the effective capital charges against "Proposal No. 1" would probably be somewhat higher, but it is unlikely that they would be enough higher to change the nature of the resulting total cost figures.

eral. On this assumption, total costs for a year's production on the Fairchild machine would be at least $57,000 ($53,763 + $8,000 additional + $5,158 − $10,000). In other words, the Fairchild machine would be at least twice as expensive. No account has been taken of the quite costly debugging which developed or of the costs of temporary supply when the equipment was not delivered as scheduled, because no quantitative data for these exist. Despite inability to quantify them, these costs were probably quite significant additions to the total extra cost.

If the deliveries continued at the rate of 60 per day for 24 months rather than for only 12 months, which would probably be an optimistic estimate in the light of Peterson Company's redesign activities, the total cost of conventional equipment might be twice the annual operating costs computed above ($13,720 × 2) plus, say, $25,000 depreciation over two years, or a total of about $52,000. The total of two-year costs for the Fairchild grinder, on the other hand, would then be about $62,000 ($57,000 + $5,158).

The comparison is probably even more unfavorable to the Fairchild grinder than the foregoing rough calculations suggest, not only because of the omitted but real debugging costs of the Fairchild equipment, but also because the costs computed allocate all the capital charges of the standard equipment to this grinding job. On the basis of two shifts, which was the level of normal operations for Warren-King, the six standard grinders would have provided grinding capacity of 24,000 machine hours per year. At 60 converters per day, the actual load would be only about 4,000 hours per year, leaving some 20,000 hours as potentially available for other work. On the other hand, the Fairchild machine had only a very slim chance of being utilized economically on other products, and in fact had but little spare time available (only four hours per day). The timing of events probably precluded the possibility of Fairchild's taking delivery on fewer than six standard grinders, had this alternative been adopted.

APPENDIX B

Total Expenditures and Time to Complete 85 Projects in the Sample Studied

THE GENERAL magnitudes which such projects may assume is indicated by the following frequency distribution of the figures on total expenditures for the 85 cases involved in the author's sample:

Total Expenditures	Number of Projects
Less than $7,500	23
$7,500 to $15,999	18
$16,000 to $24,999	10
$25,000 to $49,999	10
$50,000 to $99,999	6
$100,000 to $199,999	11
$200,000 and over	7
Total	85

The figures available undoubtedly understated the total expenditures required. Data were rarely available on the expenditures which in fact had been made in developing these projects prior to the time they were set down in proposal form. Also, the time of the project engineers during the designing, building, and debugging of the equipment was recorded in only a few cases, and in many instances the cost of mechanics and other technicians employed during debugging was not charged to the project accounts.

The dollar figures alone are not too satisfactory an indicator of the level of difficulty of a project, since a large project might (and sometimes did) involve a relatively small amount of tailoring, while some of the smaller projects might be substantially 100% special machines. Indeed, many of the projects in the under $7,500 class were to develop automatic loading, assembly, or testing equipment which was completely tailored to the needs of a particular set of operations.

Another important aspect of these projects was the time required for their completion. Not many data were available on the period when projects were being developed, but the total elapsed times beginning with authorization for designing and building activities and running through the end of the project were as follows:

Elapsed Time	*Number of Projects*
Less than 6 months	8
6 to 12 months	19
13 to 18 months	26
19 to 24 months	8
25 to 36 months	4
More than 36 months	9
	—
	74
Data not available	11
	—
Total	85

Unfortunately, in the instance of one company, the date for beginning 11 projects could not be determined accurately enough from the available records to warrant their inclusion. It should also be noted that in perhaps half of the projects which are shown to have been active for more than 36 months, progress was slowed or sometimes even halted for a time because of somewhat unusual circumstances, such as the pressure of other work, rather than because of difficulties being encountered with the project itself.

Selected Bibliography

General

A. Books

Bittel, Lester R., Melden, Morley G., and Rice, Robert S., *Practical Automation*, McGraw-Hill, New York, 1957. 376 pp.

Reprints from *Factory Management and Maintenance* magazine, a portion of which briefly describes specific installations of special automatic equipment. Many of the remaining articles fall in the general field of factory management.

Bright, James R., *Automation and Management*, Division of Research, Harvard Business School, Boston, 1958. 270 pp.

A pioneering survey analyzing broadly the potentialities, limitations, and implications to management of the automatic factory. It is composed of three major parts: the nature of automatic machinery; experiences with automation; and critical areas of automation. The second section, especially Chapters 7, 8, and 9 (pp. 88–123), contains much that is relevant to the acquisition process.

B. Other

Adiletta, Joseph G., "Comparing Machine Cost and Time Factors," *Automation*, May 1958.

Describes stages in acquisition process for a typical (hypothetical) piece of special automatic equipment. Analyzes elapsed time and cost of each stage.

American Machinist, "The Impact of Automation," Special Report No. 451, October 21, 1957.

A part of this survey is concerned with the extent of use of special automatic equipment, by industry and by size of plant.

American Machinist, "1574 Companies Report '56 Plans," August 29, 1955.

Parts of this survey analyze, on a less extensive scale, the extent of use of special automatic equipment in 1955.

Automation, "Survey Report and Automation Forecast," January 1959.

A report of a survey of the extent of use of automation equipment by 1,675 plants.

Bennett, Keith B., "Organizing The Attack," *Automation*, April 1959.

An engineer describes how a task force set about developing alternative basic approaches to a project at IBM's Endicott plant.

Brehm, Robert, "Creating a Transfer Machine," *Automation,* February 1959.

An excellent description of how a vendor goes about the job of designing and building this kind of equipment. Comments in detail on the standard subassemblies used by a vendor of special automatic equipment.

Brown, William W., "The Roll Label Project: A Case Study," in American Management Association, *Essentials of Machinery Procurement and Development* (Special Report No. 14), New York, 1956.

Narrates the essential elements in a Merck, Sharp & Dohme project to reduce labeling costs which involved a special automatic machine. Labels had to be redesigned; notes some debugging problems encountered.

Business Week, "It Doesn't Always Pay to Put All Your Chips on Automation," August 10, 1957.

The troubles which A. O. Smith encountered in establishing and operating a new automobile frame plant with much automatic equipment, in the face of a short, rigid deadline, are described in some detail.

DeGroat, George H., "Automatic Assembly," *American Machinist,* September 10, 1956.

Dumond, D. I., "Designing to Reduce Down Time," *Mechanical Engineering,* December 1958.

Dumond, D. I., "Improving Machine Dependability," *Automation,* June 1959.

Goeckle, William C., "Engineering Small-Plant Automation," *Tool Engineer,* November 1956.

A vendor's comments on the buyer whose needs for special automatic equipment are small.

Hawkinson, D. E., "How to Plan A Transfer Machine," *Collected Papers, 1954 Library Edition,* American Society of Tool Engineers, Detroit.

A vendor's sales vice president describes important considerations in acquiring a transfer machine.

Holmes, J. Q., "Standards for Manufacturing: What We Need," *American Machinist,* December 14, 1959.

Reviews the many various sources of standards for equipment and tools in industry, and the types of items covered thereby. Describes some additional standards now being developed and proposes others which should be developed.

Holmes, J. Q., "Conception and Development of JIC Standards," *Collected Papers, 1957 Silver Anniversary Edition,* American Society of Tool Engineers, Detroit.

History of JIC standards and how they were developed.

Kelly, John M., "Techniques for Safeguarding the Buyer," in American Management Association, *Essentials of Machinery Procurement and Development,* New York, 1956.

Kendall, George H., Sr., "How to Plan for Automatic Assembly," *Tool Engineer,* February 1957.

Kendall, George H., Sr., Host, Jerry A., and Kendall, George H., Jr., of Kenhos Corp., "What's Holding Back The Automatic Assembly Machine?" *American Machinist,* May 6, 1957.

Kendall, George H., Sr., and Host, Jerry A., "Planning for Automatic Assembly" (Parts 1, 2, and 3), *Automation,* May, June, and July 1955.

Kessler, Robert L., "How Special Machinery Is Developed," *Automotive Industries,* April 15, 1953.

The head of a special equipment group which has acquired more than 1,000 pieces of this equipment analyzes key steps in the acquisition process. Very specific.

Lahm, James J., "Organizing for Developing Automation Equipment," *Automation,* April 1957.

A Westinghouse equipment development engineer describes the acquisition process in general terms.

Lewis, Howard T., "Procurement of Major Equipment — New" (Chapter XV) in *Procurement — Principles and Cases* (Revised Edition), Irwin, Homewood, 1952. 823 pp.

McCarroll, Ray A., "Many Technological Improvements Made in Plymouth Engine Plant," *Tooling and Production,* October 1955.

A variety of useful comments about the experience McCarroll, then Master Mechanic, had in designing and building a new automobile engine plant, using vendors.

Roat, H. L., "Applying Creativity to Manufacturing Problems," *Tool Engineer,* October 1956.

Tells how "brainstorming" technique is used in developing the basic approach to a project.

Shaw, Walter P., "Wire Inserting Machine," *Automation,* December 1958.

Describes some of the problems encountered in developing a project in IBM to automatically assemble ferrite cores for electronic equipment, prior to settling on a basic approach for equipment.

Treer, Kenneth R., "Automated Assembly — 1, — 2, — 3," *Automation,* October, November, and December 1956.

A series of articles by a vendor dealing with the methods and problems of feeding small parts, and with general project procedures during the acquisition process.

Useful Statistical Techniques

American Standards Association, "Control Chart Method of Controlling Quality During Production," standard Z 1.3-1942, New York, 1942.

Bowman, Edward H., and Fetter, Robert B., "Statistical Control" (Chapter 6) in *Analysis for Production Management,* Irwin, Homewood, 1957. 503 pp.

Duncan, Acheson J., *Quality Control and Industrial Statistics* (Revised Edition), Irwin, Homewood, 1959.   946 pp.

A comprehensive treatment of these topics, including control charts, design of experiments, and analysis of variance.

Juran, J. M. (Editor), *Quality Control Handbook*, McGraw-Hill, New York, 1951.   800 pp.

Lewis, Wyatt H., "Inspection and Quality Control," Section 14 in Ireson, William G., and Grant, Eugene L. (Editors), *Handbook of Industrial Engineering and Management*, Prentice-Hall, Englewood Cliffs, 1955.   1203 pp.

Shainin, Dorian, "The Statistically Designed Experiment," *Harvard Business Review*, July–August, 1957.

Shewhart, W. A., *Economic Control of Quality of Manufactured Product*, Van Nostrand, New York, 1931.   501 pp.

Stephens, Kenneth S., "A Simplified Method of Analyzing Experimental Data," *Western Electric Engineer*, July 1958.

Product Design — Special Equipment Coordination

Adams, Henry M., "Automation — Its Effect on Jigs and Fixtures," *Collected Papers, 1956 Library Edition*, American Society of Tool Engineers, Detroit.

Anderson, Richard H., "Preassembled Components Simplify Modular Electronic Assembly," *Automation*, September 1958.

Black, T. W., "Standard Machine Vs. Special Machine . . . A Case Study," *Tool Engineer*, January 1958.

An example of flexibility being designed into special automatic equipment.

Braid., M. D., "Automation for Valves," *Automation*, April 1957.

An excellent outline of the major steps in a large project. The analysis of possible product design obsolescence is an especially useful example.

Cross, Ralph E., "Automation Tomorrow," *Collected Papers, 1956 Library Edition*, American Society of Tool Engineers, Detroit.

Comments on product design-special equipment coordination by the head of a large special equipment vendor.

Cummings, William C., "Standardizing Assembly Machines," *Automation*, March 1959.

A full presentation of the features and merits of a small vendor's design for equipment with standard elements.   Other useful comments on the pitfalls encountered in designing and building special automatic equipment.

DeGroat, George, "Plymouth Puts 'Forward Look' Into V-8 Production," *American Machinist*, August 15, 1955.

Esperson, David H., "Redesign Permits Automatic Assembly," *Automation*, March 1957.

Detailed examples of product designs chosen to facilitate automatic fabrication of electronic components.

Henry, R. L., and Rosen, H. H., *Summary of Modular Design of Electronics and Mechanized Production of Electronics,* Vol. 1, PB-111275, Contract NBS 12.05-20-5532, National Bureau of Standards, Washington, January 1954. 26 pp.

Johnson, Alfred H., "Developing the Hardware," *Automation,* April 1959.

Describes how design of electronic product was standardized to facilitate production.

Jomie, D. J., "Manufacturing Team for Automation," *Automation,* August 1958.

Describes how one company uses a product design-production engineering team to effect coordination at various stages of the cycle for a new product or major design change.

Knapp, H. M., "Designing for Automatic Production," *Automation,* September 1954.

Lee, L. K., "Automatic Production of Electronic Equipment" in Eugene M. Grabbe (Editor), *Automation in Business and Industry,* Wiley, New York, 1957. 611 pp.

Describes the principal features of several alternative approaches to automatic production of electronic products, including "Project Tinkertoy." Some data on costs and investment required. An excellent bibliography is included.

Melvin, Richard H., "Press Unloaders and Die Design," *Automation,* January 1957.

Mooney, Clyde, "How To Plan for Low-Cost Production," *Tool Engineer,* January 1957.

Randall, J. F., "Planning for Reduced Obsolescence," unpublished paper presented at the 21st Annual Machine Tool Electrification Forum, sponsored by the Westinghouse Electric Corporation, Buffalo, N. Y., April 24, 25, 1957.

Rausch, John T., Kehrl, Howard H., and McPherson, Donald H., "Development of the Chevrolet W Engine: A New Concept in V-8 Engine Design," *General Motors Engineering Journal,* July–August–September 1958.

Richards, Elmer A., and Wright, Arthur B., "The Relationship of Organizational Structure to Production Cost Reduction Activity," *General Motors Engineering Journal,* September–October 1953.

Argues the desirability of considering product design and manufacturing engineering in combination rather than separately, based upon a program generating 287 cost reduction proposals. (The program was not directed specifically toward special automatic equipment projects.)

Suuronen, Edwin, "Manufacturing Functions," *Automation,* March 1958.

Standardizing in the assembly of electronic components to achieve flexibility in automatic equipment.

Tech, Kurt O., "Designing for Easier Machining, Handling and Assembly," unpublished manuscript of a speech delivered at the 1957

Design Engineering Conference of the American Society of Mechanical Engineers. Abstracted in considerable detail in "Designing for Automation," *Tool Engineer,* July 1957.

Gives two detailed examples of the influence of product design on the ease of designing special automatic equipment.

Building Block Equipment Design

American Machinist, " 'Building Block' Concept — Machine Builders Speak Their Minds," January 13, 1958.

Comments from machine builders, *pro* and *con* at the time the first standards were in the developmental stages.

American Machinist, "Machine Tool Builders and Big Automotive Users Agree on Building Block Concept," January 26, 1959.

American Machinist, "Ford Sharonville: Proving Ground for New Ideas in Automation," December 1, 1958.

Cross, Ralph E., "Building-Block Designs Reduce Tooling Costs," *Tool Engineer,* December 1958.

DeGroat, George H., "Rebuilding 'Building Block' Machines," *American Machinist,* October 5, 1959.

Gives some features of the rebuilding of Ford's M-E-L engine plant to produce a new type of engine for the "Falcon."

Hoffman, William E., "Industry Agrees on 'Building Block' Standards," *Tooling and Production,* July 1959 (Reprint), 15 pp.

Describes and comments on the building block standards, as revised to August 5, 1959.

Le Grand, Rupert, "Ford Says: 'Let's Have Building-Block Machine Tools,' " *American Machinist,* July 16, 1956.

Analysis of Equipment Proposals

Allen, W. C., and Daly, T., "The Westinghouse Investment Program: Planned Facilities With Built-in Profits," *American Machinist,* December 16, 1957.

A general description of policies, procedures, and philosophy.

Anthony, Robert N., "Planning Capital Acquisitions" (Chapter 18) in *Management Accounting,* Irwin, Homewood, 1956. 511 pp.

Sets forth the fundamental techniques for equipment analysis. Table C, p. 497, was used to make all time adjusted calculations in this study.

Chilton, Cecil A., "Cost Data Correlated," *Chemical Engineering,* June 1959.

On the techniques of estimating total plant costs in the chemical industries.

Dean, Joel, *Capital Budgeting,* Columbia University Press, New York, 1951. 174 pp.

A basic work in the field. Develops the discounted rate of return technique we have used in our study, and fits it into an over-all scheme for investment planning.

Dexter, Robert G., "Estimating Special Equipment Costs," *Automation,* May 1958.

Presents the essentials of a short-cut approach to estimating bid prices.

Fitzgerald, G. R., "Mechanical Assembly Equipment," The American Society of Mechanical Engineers, Paper No. 56-A-83, presented November 25–30, 1956, before the Management Division of the American Society of Mechanical Engineers.

Emphasizes incremental cost analysis of alternatives, and comparison with present method made as efficient as possible.

Grant, Eugene L., *Principles of Engineering Economy* (3rd Edition), Ronald, New York, 1950. 623 pp.

Another basic work in the field. Includes treatment of a broad selection of engineering decisions.

Journal of Business, October 1955.

This entire issue (seven articles) is devoted to the topics of capital budgeting and proposal analysis.

Knight, Frank H., *Risk, Uncertainty and Profit,* Houghton Mifflin Co., Boston, 1921. 381 pp.

A classic treatment of this area. Basic concepts of risk and uncertainty are developed in Chapter VII (pp. 197–232), and methods of dealing with them, including grouping and specialized judgment, are discussed in Chapter VIII (pp. 232–263).

Lutz, Friedrich and Vera, "Treatment of Risk and Uncertainty" (Chapter XV), in *The Theory of Investment of the Firm,* Princeton University Press, Princeton, 1951. 253 pp.

Presents another discussion of methods dealing with this area.

Machinery and Allied Products Institute, *Equipment Replacement and Depreciation — Policies and Practices,* Washington, 1956. 30 pp.

Summarizes survey of 205 companies. Includes a bibliography on equipment analysis.

McLean, John G., "How To Evaluate New Capital Investments," *Harvard Business Review,* November–December 1958.

Presents examples of use of time-adjusted rate of return when the forecast of savings is not level, or when the investment required does not take place all at one time.

Nichols, W. T., "Capital Cost Estimating," *Industrial and Engineering Chemistry,* October 1951.

Suggests policies and procedures for estimating plant costs in chemical industry. Graphically portrays the probable limits of error of a cost estimate depending upon procedures utilized in making it.

Niland, Powell, "Investing in Special Automatic Equipment," *Harvard Business Review,* November–December 1957.

An earlier version of some of the basic ideas developed in Chapter VIII of this study.

Reul, Ray I., "Profitability Index for Investments," *Harvard Business Review*, July–August 1957.

Demonstrates the application of successive approximation to determine the time-adjusted rate of return for a project which has irregularities in the cash flows. Similar in general approach to McLean, op. cit.

Rusing, Raymond G., "Will Automation Pay?" *Tool Engineer*, June 1957.

A case study of press automation in which it proved uneconomical to fully mechanize the equipment.

Shillinglaw, Gordon, "Managing Capital Expenditures: Appraisal of Specific Proposals," *The Engineering Economist*, Winter 1959.

Discusses methods of analyzing individual projects. Advocates some method which makes time adjustment to cash flows. Compares three different methods of doing so: net present value of future cash flows, discounted cash flow rate of return, and uniform equivalent annuity, using one example.

Smith, W. P., "Creative Production Engineering," *Automation*, February 1957.

On the development of alternatives by the project engineer.

Terborgh, George, *Business Investment Policy*, Machinery and Allied Products Institute and Council for Technological Advancement, Washington, 1958.   260 pp.

Presents a revision of the original MAPI formula and examples of its application to various projects.

Terborgh, George, *Dynamic Equipment Policy*, McGraw-Hill, New York, 1949.   290 pp.

A basic treatment of economic analysis of equipment proposals. Presents the theory of the original MAPI formula.

Weaver, James B., "False and Multiple Solutions By the Discounted Cash Flow Method for Determining Interest Rate of Return," *The Engineering Economist*, Spring 1958.

Discusses specific types of situations in which the use of discounted cash flow methods encounter difficulties. Suggests corrective methods to use. A valuable appendix on analytical techniques and capital budgeting is included.

White, Richard S., "Minimizing Risk and Debugging in Developing Unique Equipment," *Automation*, June 1959.

Suggests minimizing risk by demonstrating the feasibility of doubtful elements before proceeding on any other phase of a project, and argues that this policy usually does not increase the final total costs.

Index

pilot projects,
  and developing specifications,
    101–102
  to improve estimated invest-
    ment, 229
  make or buy decision and, 88–89
  to reduce debugging, 51–52,
    65–66
  suggested by vendors, 159
  using vendors for, 88–89, 101
planning, 106, 293
planning and controlling design
  changes, 179–183
planning and scheduling debugging, value of, 67–68
plants studied, general characteristics of, 11
Plymouth Division, Chrysler Corporation, *see* Chrysler Corporation
point of view, freshness of vendor's, 78
pre-award evaluation of vendors,
  108–111
pre-award planning, 96–107
  benefits of, 106–159, 283–284
  cost of, 106
preliminary discussions with vendors, 142, 153, 160
present worth of salvage value,
  256–258
press work, 171, 216–217
printed circuits, 175–178
probability estimates,
  advantages of using, 233
  and estimated investment, 231–
    234
  and primary service life, 252–
    254
  and risk of product design
    changes, 180
  and volume estimates, 248
problem areas in the acquisition
  process, 4, 19–23, 33
  see also organizational units,
    relations with other

process, acquisition, *see* acquisition process
process capability tests, 64–66,
  109–110
process changes, pilot projects to
  test results of, 101
process knowledge,
  developing specifications and,
    102
  make or buy decision and, 85–
    86
processes employing special automatic equipment in plants
  studied, 16
processes, new, and debugging
  problems, 45–47
product design,
  basic types of situations affect-
    ing, 165–167
  benefits from job rotation, 195
  combining requirements
    through, 173–175
  forecasting life of, 179
  restricted by existing special
    automatic equipment, 174
  revised by production engi-
    neers, 194
  standardization of, 173–178,
    182–183, 285–286
  used to reduce equipment ob-
    solescence, 175–179
product design changes,
  adapting equipment to major,
    183–190
  to assist in feeding parts, 167
  cost as part of estimated invest-
    ment, 216–217
  effected through liaison per-
    sonnel, 191–192
  factors responsible for, 250–
    251, 297, 308
  limiting equipment projects
    undertaken, 193
  made while equipment was in
    process, 143–144
  minor types of, 167–169